INTEGRITY NOTARY JOURNAL™

A Single-Signing-View Logbook of Notarial Acts

INTEGRITY NOTARY JOURNAL™

A Single-Signing-View Logbook of Notarial Acts

ISBN: 978-0-9910947-1-4

Journal Owner and Contact Information

Name: _____

Address: _____

_____

Phone: _____

Email: _____

If this journal is found, please notify the notary public listed here immediately. If the notary public cannot be reached, please contact the Secretary of State for the state listed below.

Commission and Journal Information

State: _____ Number: _____ Expiration: _____

State: _____ Number: _____ Expiration: _____

Notary Public Signature: _____

This journal contains notarial acts from _____ to _____
performed by this notary public.

ABOUT THE JOURNAL

Like other notaries public, I attempt to follow a standard of care for journaling, but I was unable to find a journal that would accommodate the process I wanted to follow. At times, I felt penalized as I tried to fit the required information into the small or limited boxes provided to me in most journals, as my writing is a bit large and a little sloppy. It was customary for me to use multiple entry lines for a single signing as I documented pertinent circumstances. Furthermore, I would fill a couple of pages of my journal for common signings such as estate planning, adoptions, real estate transactions/loan closings, etc. due to the number of documents and individuals signing.

This was my starting point. I set out to design a journal that would mirror my work flow and aid me as I followed a standard of care. From different design layouts, reviews with notary public experts and loan signing trainers, and a beta trial with notaries public, the Integrity Notary Journal™ emerged.

The Integrity Notary Journal™ is designed to be efficient and complement the standard of care a notary public provides. The comprehensive list of common documents and notarial acts makes it easy to quickly identify and note each. The visual layout provides prompts to a standard of care to which we all aspire. These prompts include cues for willingness and competence of signer and initialing when an oath is administered. There are also areas designated to capture signing location, others in attendance, client/lender information, and notarization format (paper, electronic, remote online notarization, a.k.a. RON). Most importantly, the single-signing-view™ ensures information remains private. A large notes section is provided, which allows the notary public to capture unique situations, further document information collected in other parts of the journal, or any other information relevant to the signing.

Feedback is the life blood to any instrument attempting to support a process. This is undoubtably true for a notary public journal. Standard of care practices evolve, and statutes change. I welcome your constructive feedback as you include the Integrity Notary Journal™ in your signings.

I am honored you chose to purchase the Integrity Notary Journal™. I am confident you will find it a good investment for your practice.

Best,

Clyde Heppner
Mobile Notary KC LLC

INSTRUCTIONS

It is extremely important to know your state's requirements for journaling notarial acts. Always follow your state's requirements, and guidance from your secretary of state or state office for notary commissions.

Signings are recorded on two pages—an upper and lower page—constituting the single-signing-view™. Signer information is captured on each page and linked by the Signer Number on the left side of the page. Hence, it is important to match each signer by their Signer Number across the two pages.

Upper Page Information

#	DATE / TIME	NAME	IDENTITY VERIFIED	WILLINGNESS & COMPETENCE	FORMAT
1	DATE **A** 8/15/2020 — TIME **B** 2:00 pm	NAME ☑ Signer ☐ Witness **C** — John A. Signer	☑ D.L. ☐ Passport ☐ Credible Witness **D** — #D1234567 exp 7/10/2023 MO — ☐ Other	☑ Expressed willingness **E** — ☑ Mentally alert — ☑ Indicated understanding	☑ Paper **F** — ☐ Electronic — ☐ RON
2	DATE 8/15/2020 — TIME 2:00 pm	NAME ☑ Signer ☐ Witness — Teddy B. Signer	☐ D.L. ☐ Passport ☑ Credible Witness — Mary T. Witness — ☐ Other	☑ Expressed willingness — ☑ Mentally alert — ☑ Indicated understanding	☑ Paper — ☐ Electronic — ☐ RON
3	DATE 8/15/2020 — TIME 2:00 pm	NAME ☐ Signer ☑ Witness - credible — Mary T. Witness	☑ D.L. ☐ Passport ☐ Credible Witness — #D891011 exp 6/15/2021 MO — ☐ Other	☑ Expressed willingness — ☑ Mentally alert — ☑ Indicated understanding	☐ Paper — ☐ Electronic — ☐ RON
4	DATE — TIME	NAME ☐ Signer ☐ Witness	☐ D.L. ☐ Passport ☐ Credible Witness — ☐ Other	☐ Expressed willingness — ☐ Mentally alert — ☐ Indicated understanding	☐ Paper — ☐ Electronic — ☐ RON

DOCUMENT(S) SIGNED   **G**   SIGNER / SIGNER / **H**

Document	Type	Signer	Document	Type	Signer	H
☐ Borrower's Aff	Acknowledgment Jurat ____	1 2 3 4	☐ Minor Medical Consent	Acknowledgment Jurat ____	1 2 3 4	☐ _____
☑ Compliance Agrmt	(Acknowledgment) Jurat ____	(1)(2) 3 4	☐ Minor Passport Consent	Acknowledgment Jurat ____	1 2 3 4	Acknowledgment Jurat Copy Oath SW 1 2 3 4
☐ Correction Agrmt	Acknowledgment Jurat ____	1 2 3 4	☐ Minor Travel Consent	Acknowledgment Jurat ____	1 2 3 4	
☐ Debts/Leins Aff	Acknowledgment Jurat ____	1 2 3 4				☐ _____
☐ Deed of Trust	Acknowledgment Jurat ____	1 2 3 4	☐ Vehicle Duplicate Title	Acknowledgment Jurat ____	1 2 3 4	Acknowledgment Jurat Copy Oath SW 1 2 3 4
☐ Distrib of Proceeds	Acknowledgment Jurat ____	1 2 3 4	☐ Vehicle Lein Release	Acknowledgment Jurat ____	1 2 3 4	
☐ E&O Agrmt	Acknowledgment Jurat ____	1 2 3 4	☐ Vehicle Odom/Vin Ver	Acknowledgment Jurat ____	1 2 3 4	☐ _____
☐ Grant Deed	Acknowledgment Jurat ____	1 2 3 4	☐ Vehicle Title Transfer	Acknowledgment Jurat ____	1 2 3 4	Acknowledgment Jurat Copy Oath SW 1 2 3 4
☑ Marital Stat Aff	Acknowledgment (Jurat) ____	(1)(2) 3 4				
☐ Mortgage	Acknowledgment Jurat ____	1 2 3 4	☐ Adv Health Care Dir	Acknowledgment Jurat ____	1 2 3 4	☐ _____
☐ Occupancy/Fin Aff	Acknowledgment Jurat ____	1 2 3 4	☐ Assign of Digital Assets	Acknowledgment Jurat ____	1 2 3 4	Acknowledgment Jurat Copy Oath SW 1 2 3 4
☑ Owner's Aff	Acknowledgment (Jurat) ____	(1) 2 3 4	☐ Assign of Personal Prop	Acknowledgment Jurat ____	1 2 3 4	
☑ Payoff Aff	Acknowledgment (Jurat) ____	(1) 2 3 4	☐ HIPAA Release	Acknowledgment Jurat ____	1 2 3 4	☐ _____
☐ Quit-Claim Deed	Acknowledgment Jurat ____	1 2 3 4	☐ Living Trust ____	Acknowledgment Jurat ____	1 2 3 4	Acknowledgment Jurat Copy Oath SW 1 2 3 4
☐ Sig/Name Aff	Acknowledgment Jurat ____	1 2 3 4	☐ Last Will & Testament	Acknowledgment Jurat ____	1 2 3 4	
☐ Survey Aff	Acknowledgment Jurat ____	1 2 3 4	☐ POA ____	Acknowledgment Jurat ____	1 2 3 4	☐ _____
☐ Warranty Deed	Acknowledgment Jurat ____	1 2 3 4	☑ Trust Certification	(Acknowledgment) Jurat ____	(1)(2) 3 4	Acknowledgment Jurat Copy Oath SW 1 2 3 4

A   Date the notarial act took place.

B   Time the notarial act took place.

C   Name of signer or witness. Check appropriate box and enter the name.

D   How was identify verified? Check appropriate box(es) and enter required information for your state. Typically, information includes the ID document expiration date, state/country where issued, and the ID number.

E   Assess the willingness and competence of the signer/witness. Check boxes as to what you assessed.

F   What is the format of how the notarial act is recorded? Check the appropriate box.
- Paper. The signer and notary public are physically together and sign paper document(s). The notary public applies an ink or embossed seal to the paper document(s).
- Electronic. The signer and notary public are physically together and sign electronic document(s) with an electronic signature. The notary public applies an electronic seal to the electronic document(s).
- RON (Remote Online Notarization). The signer and notary public meet virtually (online) using an approved

platform authorized by your state. Signer and notary public are physically located in different places and sign electronic with an electronic signature. The notary public applies an electronic seal to the electronic documents.

G Check the box next to the document(s) notarized.
- If the notarial act is an Acknowledgment or Jurat, circle the appropriate act.
- If the notarial act is a Certified Copy, Signature Witness or something else, note the act in the blank and circle it.
- Circle the Signer Number(s) of the individual(s) who signed the document.

H Documents not listed in Section G can be entered in this area.
- Write the name of the document above the line.
- Circle the notarial act performed.
- Circle the Signer Number(s) of the individual(s) who signed the document.

Lower Page Information

SIGNING ADDRESS I	OTHERS IN ATTENDANCE J	CLIENT / SIGNING SERVICE K	FEE L
123 Main street City, State 12345	None	Best Signing Service LENDER / LOAN NUMBER Best Lender #123456789	$125

NOTES **M**

Additional details about the signing can be entered here.

_____

Q

	ADDRESS N	PHONE O	SIGNATURE P	INITIAL IF OATH/AFF TAKEN	RIGHT THUMB PRINT R
1	123 Main street City, State Zip	123-456-7890 EMAIL NA	*John A. Signer*	J.A.S	
2	123 Main street City, State Zip	123-456-7890 EMAIL NA	*Teddy B. Signer*	T.B.S	
3	222 Oak Avenue City, State Zip	123-456-0001 EMAIL myemail@service.com	*Mary T. Witness*	M.T.W	
4	ADDRESS	PHONE EMAIL	SIGNATURE	INITIAL IF OATH/AFF TAKEN	

I Address where the signing took place.
J List others who were in attendance but did not sign.
K Enter the client or signing service name. If appropriate, enter the lender name and loan number.
L Enter the fee paid by the signing service or the fee charged for notarial acts completed.
M Provide additional information about a situation, clarify details, or enter any other relevant information about the signing such as the name of RON platform used.
N Address of signer or witness.
O Phone number and/or email address of signer or witness.
P Signature of signer or witness.
Q Initials are entered by the signer or witness, if s/he took an oath/affirmation.
R Right thumb print of signer or witness.

SAMPLE OATHS AND AFFIRMATIONS

The following oaths/affirmations are provided only as samples, which I encourage you to modify to meet the requirements of your state. It is always important to contact your secretary of state or state office for notary commissions when you are unsure of the expected notary practice requirements.

Jurat

Do you solemnly swear/affirm, under the penalties of perjury that:
- *You are [name]?*
- *You are completing this document of your own free will?*
- *The information in the document is accurate to the best of your knowledge?*

Loan Document Package

Some notaries public begin their loan closings by having the signers take an oath. Signers are informed that they will be under oath during the entire session. In this situation, the notary public may remind the signers they are under oath before they sign documents with a jurat notarial certificate.

Do you solemnly swear/affirm, under the penalties of perjury, that:
- *You are executing these documents of your own free will;*
- *The information in these documents is accurate to the best of your knowledge;*
- *You agree to and will abide by to the terms in the documents?*

Other notaries public administer an oath for each document with a jurat notarial certificate.

Testimony

Please state your name.
Please raise your right hand.
Do you solemnly swear/affirm that the testimony you shall give in this matter will be the truth, the whole truth, and nothing but the truth, so help you God?

Credible Witness

Do you solemnly swear/affirm under penalties of perjury that you personally know this person as [name of person whose signature is to be notarized], that he/she is the person named in the document, and that you have no financial interest in and are not a party to this transaction so help you God?

Entry Log

#	DATE / TIME	NAME	IDENTITY VERIFIED	WILLINGNESS & COMPETENCE	FORMAT
1	DATE ___ / TIME ___	☐ Signer ☐ Witness	☐ D.L. ☐ Passport ☐ Credible Witness ☐ Other	☐ Expressed willingness ☐ Mentally alert ☐ Indicated understanding	☐ Paper ☐ Electronic ☐ RON
2	DATE ___ / TIME ___	☐ Signer ☐ Witness	☐ D.L. ☐ Passport ☐ Credible Witness ☐ Other	☐ Expressed willingness ☐ Mentally alert ☐ Indicated understanding	☐ Paper ☐ Electronic ☐ RON
3	DATE ___ / TIME ___	☐ Signer ☐ Witness	☐ D.L. ☐ Passport ☐ Credible Witness ☐ Other	☐ Expressed willingness ☐ Mentally alert ☐ Indicated understanding	☐ Paper ☐ Electronic ☐ RON
4	DATE ___ / TIME ___	☐ Signer ☐ Witness	☐ D.L. ☐ Passport ☐ Credible Witness ☐ Other	☐ Expressed willingness ☐ Mentally alert ☐ Indicated understanding	☐ Paper ☐ Electronic ☐ RON

DOCUMENT(S) SIGNED

Document	Act			SIGNER 1	2	3	4
☐ Borrower's Aff	Acknowledgment	Jurat		1	2	3	4
☐ Compliance Agrmt	Acknowledgment	Jurat		1	2	3	4
☐ Correction Agrmt	Acknowledgment	Jurat		1	2	3	4
☐ Debts/Leins Aff	Acknowledgment	Jurat		1	2	3	4
☐ Deed of Trust	Acknowledgment	Jurat		1	2	3	4
☐ Distrib of Proceeds	Acknowledgment	Jurat		1	2	3	4
☐ E&O Agrmt	Acknowledgment	Jurat		1	2	3	4
☐ Grant Deed	Acknowledgment	Jurat		1	2	3	4
☐ Marital Stat Aff	Acknowledgment	Jurat		1	2	3	4
☐ Mortgage	Acknowledgment	Jurat		1	2	3	4
☐ Occupancy/Fin Aff	Acknowledgment	Jurat		1	2	3	4
☐ Owner's Aff	Acknowledgment	Jurat		1	2	3	4
☐ Payoff Aff	Acknowledgment	Jurat		1	2	3	4
☐ Quit-Claim Deed	Acknowledgment	Jurat		1	2	3	4
☐ Sig/Name Aff	Acknowledgment	Jurat		1	2	3	4
☐ Survey Aff	Acknowledgment	Jurat		1	2	3	4
☐ Warranty Deed	Acknowledgment	Jurat		1	2	3	4

Document	Act					SIGNER 1	2	3	4
☐ Minor Medical Consent	Acknowledgment	Jurat				1	2	3	4
☐ Minor Passport Consent	Acknowledgment	Jurat	Copy	Oath	SW	1	2	3	4
☐ Minor Travel Consent	Acknowledgment	Jurat				1	2	3	4
☐ Vehicle Duplicate Title	Acknowledgment	Jurat	Copy	Oath	SW	1	2	3	4
☐ Vehicle Lein Release	Acknowledgment	Jurat				1	2	3	4
☐ Vehicle Odom/Vin Ver	Acknowledgment	Jurat				1	2	3	4
☐ Vehicle Title Transfer	Acknowledgment	Jurat	Copy	Oath	SW	1	2	3	4
☐ Adv Health Care Dir	Acknowledgment	Jurat				1	2	3	4
☐ Assign of Digital Assets	Acknowledgment	Jurat	Copy	Oath	SW	1	2	3	4
☐ Assign of Personal Prop	Acknowledgment	Jurat				1	2	3	4
☐ HIPAA Release	Acknowledgment	Jurat				1	2	3	4
☐ Living Trust	Acknowledgment	Jurat				1	2	3	4
☐ Last Will & Testament	Acknowledgment	Jurat	Copy	Oath	SW	1	2	3	4
☐ POA	Acknowledgment	Jurat				1	2	3	4
☐ Trust Certification	Acknowledgment	Jurat	Copy	Oath	SW	1	2	3	4

SIGNING ADDRESS	OTHERS IN ATTENDANCE	CLIENT / SIGNING SERVICE	FEE
		LENDER / LOAN NUMBER	

NOTES

	ADDRESS	PHONE / EMAIL	SIGNATURE	INITIAL IF OATH/AFF TAKEN	RIGHT THUMB PRINT
1		PHONE / EMAIL			
2		PHONE / EMAIL			
3		PHONE / EMAIL			
4		PHONE / EMAIL			

1	DATE TIME	NAME ❑ Signer ❑ Witness	IDENTITY VERIFIED ❑ D.L. ❑ Passport ❑ Credible Witness ❑ Other	WILLINGNESS & COMPETENCE ❑ Expressed willingness ❑ Mentally alert ❑ Indicated understanding	FORMAT ❑ Paper ❑ Electronic ❑ RON
2	DATE TIME	NAME ❑ Signer ❑ Witness	IDENTITY VERIFIED ❑ D.L. ❑ Passport ❑ Credible Witness ❑ Other	WILLINGNESS & COMPETENCE ❑ Expressed willingness ❑ Mentally alert ❑ Indicated understanding	FORMAT ❑ Paper ❑ Electronic ❑ RON
3	DATE TIME	NAME ❑ Signer ❑ Witness	IDENTITY VERIFIED ❑ D.L. ❑ Passport ❑ Credible Witness ❑ Other	WILLINGNESS & COMPETENCE ❑ Expressed willingness ❑ Mentally alert ❑ Indicated understanding	FORMAT ❑ Paper ❑ Electronic ❑ RON
4	DATE TIME	NAME ❑ Signer ❑ Witness	IDENTITY VERIFIED ❑ D.L. ❑ Passport ❑ Credible Witness ❑ Other	WILLINGNESS & COMPETENCE ❑ Expressed willingness ❑ Mentally alert ❑ Indicated understanding	FORMAT ❑ Paper ❑ Electronic ❑ RON

DOCUMENT(S) SIGNED		SIGNER			SIGNER	
❑ Borrower's Aff	Acknowledgment Jurat _____	1 2 3 4	❑ Minor Medical Consent	Acknowledgment Jurat _____	1 2 3 4	❑ _______________
❑ Compliance Agrmt	Acknowledgment Jurat _____	1 2 3 4	❑ Minor Passport Consent	Acknowledgment Jurat _____	1 2 3 4	Acknowledgment Jurat Copy Oath SW 1 2 3 4
❑ Correction Agrmt	Acknowledgment Jurat _____	1 2 3 4	❑ Minor Travel Consent	Acknowledgment Jurat _____	1 2 3 4	
❑ Debts/Leins Aff	Acknowledgment Jurat _____	1 2 3 4				❑ _______________
❑ Deed of Trust	Acknowledgment Jurat _____	1 2 3 4	❑ Vehicle Duplicate Title	Acknowledgment Jurat _____	1 2 3 4	Acknowledgment Jurat Copy Oath SW 1 2 3 4
❑ Distrib of Proceeds	Acknowledgment Jurat _____	1 2 3 4	❑ Vehicle Lein Release	Acknowledgment Jurat _____	1 2 3 4	
❑ E&O Agrmt	Acknowledgment Jurat _____	1 2 3 4	❑ Vehicle Odom/Vin Ver	Acknowledgment Jurat _____	1 2 3 4	❑ _______________
❑ Grant Deed	Acknowledgment Jurat _____	1 2 3 4	❑ Vehicle Title Transfer	Acknowledgment Jurat _____	1 2 3 4	Acknowledgment Jurat Copy Oath SW 1 2 3 4
❑ Marital Stat Aff	Acknowledgment Jurat _____	1 2 3 4				
❑ Mortgage	Acknowledgment Jurat _____	1 2 3 4	❑ Adv Health Care Dir	Acknowledgment Jurat _____	1 2 3 4	❑ _______________
❑ Occupancy/Fin Aff	Acknowledgment Jurat _____	1 2 3 4	❑ Assign of Digital Assets	Acknowledgment Jurat _____	1 2 3 4	Acknowledgment Jurat Copy Oath SW 1 2 3 4
❑ Owner's Aff	Acknowledgment Jurat _____	1 2 3 4	❑ Assign of Personal Prop	Acknowledgment Jurat _____	1 2 3 4	
❑ Payoff Aff	Acknowledgment Jurat _____	1 2 3 4	❑ HIPAA Release	Acknowledgment Jurat _____	1 2 3 4	❑ _______________
❑ Quit-Claim Deed	Acknowledgment Jurat _____	1 2 3 4	❑ Living Trust _________	Acknowledgment Jurat _____	1 2 3 4	Acknowledgment Jurat Copy Oath SW 1 2 3 4
❑ Sig/Name Aff	Acknowledgment Jurat _____	1 2 3 4	❑ Last Will & Testament	Acknowledgment Jurat _____	1 2 3 4	
❑ Survey Aff	Acknowledgment Jurat _____	1 2 3 4	❑ POA _______________	Acknowledgment Jurat _____	1 2 3 4	❑ _______________
❑ Warranty Deed	Acknowledgment Jurat _____	1 2 3 4	❑ Trust Certification	Acknowledgment Jurat _____	1 2 3 4	Acknowledgment Jurat Copy Oath SW 1 2 3 4

SIGNING ADDRESS	OTHERS IN ATTENDANCE	CLIENT / SIGNING SERVICE	FEE
		LENDER / LOAN NUMBER	

NOTES

	ADDRESS	PHONE	EMAIL	SIGNATURE	INITIAL IF OATH/AFF TAKEN	RIGHT THUMB PRINT
1						
2						
3						
4						

Notary Journal Entries

#	DATE / TIME	NAME	IDENTITY VERIFIED	WILLINGNESS & COMPETENCE	FORMAT
1	DATE _____ / TIME _____	□ Signer □ Witness	□ D.L. □ Passport □ Credible Witness □ Other	□ Expressed willingness □ Mentally alert □ Indicated understanding	□ Paper □ Electronic □ RON
2	DATE _____ / TIME _____	□ Signer □ Witness	□ D.L. □ Passport □ Credible Witness □ Other	□ Expressed willingness □ Mentally alert □ Indicated understanding	□ Paper □ Electronic □ RON
3	DATE _____ / TIME _____	□ Signer □ Witness	□ D.L. □ Passport □ Credible Witness □ Other	□ Expressed willingness □ Mentally alert □ Indicated understanding	□ Paper □ Electronic □ RON
4	DATE _____ / TIME _____	□ Signer □ Witness	□ D.L. □ Passport □ Credible Witness □ Other	□ Expressed willingness □ Mentally alert □ Indicated understanding	□ Paper □ Electronic □ RON

DOCUMENT(S) SIGNED

Document	Type	SIGNER
□ Borrower's Aff	Acknowledgment Jurat	1 2 3 4
□ Compliance Agrmt	Acknowledgment Jurat	1 2 3 4
□ Correction Agrmt	Acknowledgment Jurat	1 2 3 4
□ Debts/Leins Aff	Acknowledgment Jurat	1 2 3 4
□ Deed of Trust	Acknowledgment Jurat	1 2 3 4
□ Distrib of Proceeds	Acknowledgment Jurat	1 2 3 4
□ E&O Agrmt	Acknowledgment Jurat	1 2 3 4
□ Grant Deed	Acknowledgment Jurat	1 2 3 4
□ Marital Stat Aff	Acknowledgment Jurat	1 2 3 4
□ Mortgage	Acknowledgment Jurat	1 2 3 4
□ Occupancy/Fin Aff	Acknowledgment Jurat	1 2 3 4
□ Owner's Aff	Acknowledgment Jurat	1 2 3 4
□ Payoff Aff	Acknowledgment Jurat	1 2 3 4
□ Quit-Claim Deed	Acknowledgment Jurat	1 2 3 4
□ Sig/Name Aff	Acknowledgment Jurat	1 2 3 4
□ Survey Aff	Acknowledgment Jurat	1 2 3 4
□ Warranty Deed	Acknowledgment Jurat	1 2 3 4
□ Minor Medical Consent	Acknowledgment Jurat Copy Oath SW	1 2 3 4
□ Minor Passport Consent	Acknowledgment Jurat Copy Oath SW	1 2 3 4
□ Minor Travel Consent	Acknowledgment Jurat Copy Oath SW	1 2 3 4
□ Vehicle Duplicate Title	Acknowledgment Jurat Copy Oath SW	1 2 3 4
□ Vehicle Lein Release	Acknowledgment Jurat Copy Oath SW	1 2 3 4
□ Vehicle Odom/Vin Ver	Acknowledgment Jurat Copy Oath SW	1 2 3 4
□ Vehicle Title Transfer	Acknowledgment Jurat Copy Oath SW	1 2 3 4
□ Adv Health Care Dir	Acknowledgment Jurat Copy Oath SW	1 2 3 4
□ Assign of Digital Assets	Acknowledgment Jurat Copy Oath SW	1 2 3 4
□ Assign of Personal Prop	Acknowledgment Jurat Copy Oath SW	1 2 3 4
□ HIPAA Release	Acknowledgment Jurat Copy Oath SW	1 2 3 4
□ Living Trust	Acknowledgment Jurat Copy Oath SW	1 2 3 4
□ Last Will & Testament	Acknowledgment Jurat Copy Oath SW	1 2 3 4
□ POA	Acknowledgment Jurat Copy Oath SW	1 2 3 4
□ Trust Certification	Acknowledgment Jurat Copy Oath SW	1 2 3 4

SIGNING ADDRESS	OTHERS IN ATTENDANCE	CLIENT / SIGNING SERVICE	FEE
		LENDER / LOAN NUMBER	

NOTES

	ADDRESS	SIGNATURE	PHONE	INITIAL IF OATH/AFF TAKEN	RIGHT THUMB PRINT
1			EMAIL		
2	ADDRESS	SIGNATURE	PHONE	INITIAL IF OATH/AFF TAKEN	RIGHT THUMB PRINT
			EMAIL		
3	ADDRESS	SIGNATURE	PHONE	INITIAL IF OATH/AFF TAKEN	RIGHT THUMB PRINT
			EMAIL		
4	ADDRESS	SIGNATURE	PHONE	INITIAL IF OATH/AFF TAKEN	RIGHT THUMB PRINT
			EMAIL		

Entry 1

DATE	
TIME	

NAME: ☐ Signer ☐ Witness

IDENTITY VERIFIED: ☐ D.L. ☐ Passport ☐ Credible Witness ☐ Other

WILLINGNESS & COMPETENCE: ☐ Expressed willingness ☐ Mentally alert ☐ Indicated understanding

FORMAT: ☐ Paper ☐ Electronic ☐ RON

Entry 2

DATE	
TIME	

NAME: ☐ Signer ☐ Witness

IDENTITY VERIFIED: ☐ D.L. ☐ Passport ☐ Credible Witness ☐ Other

WILLINGNESS & COMPETENCE: ☐ Expressed willingness ☐ Mentally alert ☐ Indicated understanding

FORMAT: ☐ Paper ☐ Electronic ☐ RON

Entry 3

DATE	
TIME	

NAME: ☐ Signer ☐ Witness

IDENTITY VERIFIED: ☐ D.L. ☐ Passport ☐ Credible Witness ☐ Other

WILLINGNESS & COMPETENCE: ☐ Expressed willingness ☐ Mentally alert ☐ Indicated understanding

FORMAT: ☐ Paper ☐ Electronic ☐ RON

Entry 4

DATE	
TIME	

NAME: ☐ Signer ☐ Witness

IDENTITY VERIFIED: ☐ D.L. ☐ Passport ☐ Credible Witness ☐ Other

WILLINGNESS & COMPETENCE: ☐ Expressed willingness ☐ Mentally alert ☐ Indicated understanding

FORMAT: ☐ Paper ☐ Electronic ☐ RON

DOCUMENT(S) SIGNED

Document	Acknowledgment	Jurat	Signer 1 2 3 4
☐ Borrower's Aff	Acknowledgment	Jurat	1 2 3 4
☐ Compliance Agrmt	Acknowledgment	Jurat	1 2 3 4
☐ Correction Agrmt	Acknowledgment	Jurat	1 2 3 4
☐ Debts/Leins Aff	Acknowledgment	Jurat	1 2 3 4
☐ Deed of Trust	Acknowledgment	Jurat	1 2 3 4
☐ Distrib of Proceeds	Acknowledgment	Jurat	1 2 3 4
☐ E&O Agrmt	Acknowledgment	Jurat	1 2 3 4
☐ Grant Deed	Acknowledgment	Jurat	1 2 3 4
☐ Marital Stat Aff	Acknowledgment	Jurat	1 2 3 4
☐ Mortgage	Acknowledgment	Jurat	1 2 3 4
☐ Occupancy/Fin Aff	Acknowledgment	Jurat	1 2 3 4
☐ Owner's Aff	Acknowledgment	Jurat	1 2 3 4
☐ Payoff Aff	Acknowledgment	Jurat	1 2 3 4
☐ Quit-Claim Deed	Acknowledgment	Jurat	1 2 3 4
☐ Sig/Name Aff	Acknowledgment	Jurat	1 2 3 4
☐ Survey Aff	Acknowledgment	Jurat	1 2 3 4
☐ Warranty Deed	Acknowledgment	Jurat	1 2 3 4

Document	Acknowledgment	Jurat	Copy	Oath	SW	Signer 1 2 3 4
☐ Minor Medical Consent	Acknowledgment	Jurat	Copy	Oath	SW	1 2 3 4
☐ Minor Passport Consent	Acknowledgment	Jurat	Copy	Oath	SW	1 2 3 4
☐ Minor Travel Consent	Acknowledgment	Jurat	Copy	Oath	SW	1 2 3 4
☐ Vehicle Duplicate Title	Acknowledgment	Jurat	Copy	Oath	SW	1 2 3 4
☐ Vehicle Lein Release	Acknowledgment	Jurat	Copy	Oath	SW	1 2 3 4
☐ Vehicle Odom/Vin Ver	Acknowledgment	Jurat	Copy	Oath	SW	1 2 3 4
☐ Vehicle Title Transfer	Acknowledgment	Jurat	Copy	Oath	SW	1 2 3 4
☐ Adv Health Care Dir	Acknowledgment	Jurat	Copy	Oath	SW	1 2 3 4
☐ Assign of Digital Assets	Acknowledgment	Jurat	Copy	Oath	SW	1 2 3 4
☐ Assign of Personal Prop	Acknowledgment	Jurat	Copy	Oath	SW	1 2 3 4
☐ HIPAA Release	Acknowledgment	Jurat	Copy	Oath	SW	1 2 3 4
☐ Living Trust	Acknowledgment	Jurat	Copy	Oath	SW	1 2 3 4
☐ Last Will & Testament	Acknowledgment	Jurat	Copy	Oath	SW	1 2 3 4
☐ POA	Acknowledgment	Jurat	Copy	Oath	SW	1 2 3 4
☐ Trust Certification	Acknowledgment	Jurat	Copy	Oath	SW	1 2 3 4

SIGNING ADDRESS	OTHERS IN ATTENDANCE	CLIENT / SIGNING SERVICE	FEE
		LENDER / LOAN NUMBER	

NOTES

#	ADDRESS	PHONE / EMAIL	SIGNATURE	INITIAL IF OATH/AFF TAKEN	RIGHT THUMB PRINT
1		PHONE / EMAIL	SIGNATURE		RIGHT THUMB PRINT
2		PHONE / EMAIL	SIGNATURE		RIGHT THUMB PRINT
3		PHONE / EMAIL	SIGNATURE		RIGHT THUMB PRINT
4		PHONE / EMAIL	SIGNATURE		RIGHT THUMB PRINT

Notary Entries (1–4)

#		NAME	IDENTITY VERIFIED	WILLINGNESS & COMPETENCE	FORMAT
1	DATE _____ / TIME _____	☐ Signer ☐ Witness	☐ D.L. ☐ Passport ☐ Credible Witness ☐ Other	☐ Expressed willingness ☐ Mentally alert ☐ Indicated understanding	☐ Paper ☐ Electronic ☐ RON
2	DATE _____ / TIME _____	☐ Signer ☐ Witness	☐ D.L. ☐ Passport ☐ Credible Witness ☐ Other	☐ Expressed willingness ☐ Mentally alert ☐ Indicated understanding	☐ Paper ☐ Electronic ☐ RON
3	DATE _____ / TIME _____	☐ Signer ☐ Witness	☐ D.L. ☐ Passport ☐ Credible Witness ☐ Other	☐ Expressed willingness ☐ Mentally alert ☐ Indicated understanding	☐ Paper ☐ Electronic ☐ RON
4	DATE _____ / TIME _____	☐ Signer ☐ Witness	☐ D.L. ☐ Passport ☐ Credible Witness ☐ Other	☐ Expressed willingness ☐ Mentally alert ☐ Indicated understanding	☐ Paper ☐ Electronic ☐ RON

DOCUMENT(S) SIGNED

Document	Type	SIGNER
☐ Borrower's Aff	Acknowledgment Jurat	1 2 3 4
☐ Compliance Agrmt	Acknowledgment Jurat	1 2 3 4
☐ Correction Agrmt	Acknowledgment Jurat	1 2 3 4
☐ Debts/Leins Aff	Acknowledgment Jurat	1 2 3 4
☐ Deed of Trust	Acknowledgment Jurat	1 2 3 4
☐ Distrib of Proceeds	Acknowledgment Jurat	1 2 3 4
☐ E&O Agrmt	Acknowledgment Jurat	1 2 3 4
☐ Grant Deed	Acknowledgment Jurat	1 2 3 4
☐ Marital Stat Aff	Acknowledgment Jurat	1 2 3 4
☐ Mortgage	Acknowledgment Jurat	1 2 3 4
☐ Occupancy/Fin Aff	Acknowledgment Jurat	1 2 3 4
☐ Owner's Aff	Acknowledgment Jurat	1 2 3 4
☐ Payoff Aff	Acknowledgment Jurat	1 2 3 4
☐ Quit-Claim Deed	Acknowledgment Jurat	1 2 3 4
☐ Sig/Name Aff	Acknowledgment Jurat	1 2 3 4
☐ Survey Aff	Acknowledgment Jurat	1 2 3 4
☐ Warranty Deed	Acknowledgment Jurat	1 2 3 4

Document	Type	SIGNER
☐ Minor Medical Consent	Acknowledgment Jurat	1 2 3 4
☐ Minor Passport Consent	Acknowledgment Jurat	1 2 3 4
☐ Minor Travel Consent	Acknowledgment Jurat	1 2 3 4
☐ Vehicle Duplicate Title	Acknowledgment Jurat	1 2 3 4
☐ Vehicle Lein Release	Acknowledgment Jurat	1 2 3 4
☐ Vehicle Odom/Vin Ver	Acknowledgment Jurat	1 2 3 4
☐ Vehicle Title Transfer	Acknowledgment Jurat	1 2 3 4
☐ Adv Health Care Dir	Acknowledgment Jurat	1 2 3 4
☐ Assign of Digital Assets	Acknowledgment Jurat	1 2 3 4
☐ Assign of Personal Prop	Acknowledgment Jurat	1 2 3 4
☐ HIPAA Release	Acknowledgment Jurat	1 2 3 4
☐ Living Trust	Acknowledgment Jurat Copy Oath SW	1 2 3 4
☐ Last Will & Testament	Acknowledgment Jurat	1 2 3 4
☐ POA	Acknowledgment Jurat	1 2 3 4
☐ Trust Certification	Acknowledgment Jurat Copy Oath SW	1 2 3 4

SIGNING ADDRESS	OTHERS IN ATTENDANCE	CLIENT / SIGNING SERVICE	FEE
		LENDER / LOAN NUMBER	

NOTES

#	ADDRESS / PHONE / EMAIL	SIGNATURE	INITIAL IF OATH/AFF TAKEN	RIGHT THUMB PRINT
1	ADDRESS / PHONE / EMAIL	SIGNATURE	INITIAL IF OATH/AFF TAKEN	RIGHT THUMB PRINT
2	ADDRESS / PHONE / EMAIL	SIGNATURE	INITIAL IF OATH/AFF TAKEN	RIGHT THUMB PRINT
3	ADDRESS / PHONE / EMAIL	SIGNATURE	INITIAL IF OATH/AFF TAKEN	RIGHT THUMB PRINT
4	ADDRESS / PHONE / EMAIL	SIGNATURE	INITIAL IF OATH/AFF TAKEN	RIGHT THUMB PRINT

Signer / Witness Records

Entry 1
- **DATE:** _____
- **TIME:** _____
- **NAME:** ☐ Signer ☐ Witness
- **IDENTITY VERIFIED:** ☐ D.L. ☐ Passport ☐ Credible Witness ☐ Other
- **WILLINGNESS & COMPETENCE:** ☐ Expressed willingness ☐ Mentally alert ☐ Indicated understanding
- **FORMAT:** ☐ Paper ☐ Electronic ☐ RON

Entry 2
- **DATE:** _____
- **TIME:** _____
- **NAME:** ☐ Signer ☐ Witness
- **IDENTITY VERIFIED:** ☐ D.L. ☐ Passport ☐ Credible Witness ☐ Other
- **WILLINGNESS & COMPETENCE:** ☐ Expressed willingness ☐ Mentally alert ☐ Indicated understanding
- **FORMAT:** ☐ Paper ☐ Electronic ☐ RON

Entry 3
- **DATE:** _____
- **TIME:** _____
- **NAME:** ☐ Signer ☐ Witness
- **IDENTITY VERIFIED:** ☐ D.L. ☐ Passport ☐ Credible Witness ☐ Other
- **WILLINGNESS & COMPETENCE:** ☐ Expressed willingness ☐ Mentally alert ☐ Indicated understanding
- **FORMAT:** ☐ Paper ☐ Electronic ☐ RON

Entry 4
- **DATE:** _____
- **TIME:** _____
- **NAME:** ☐ Signer ☐ Witness
- **IDENTITY VERIFIED:** ☐ D.L. ☐ Passport ☐ Credible Witness ☐ Other
- **WILLINGNESS & COMPETENCE:** ☐ Expressed willingness ☐ Mentally alert ☐ Indicated understanding
- **FORMAT:** ☐ Paper ☐ Electronic ☐ RON

DOCUMENT(S) SIGNED

Document	Type	SIGNER
☐ Borrower's Aff	Acknowledgment / Jurat	1 2 3 4
☐ Compliance Agrmt	Acknowledgment / Jurat	1 2 3 4
☐ Correction Agrmt	Acknowledgment / Jurat	1 2 3 4
☐ Debs/Leins Aff	Acknowledgment / Jurat	1 2 3 4
☐ Deed of Trust	Acknowledgment / Jurat	1 2 3 4
☐ Distrib of Proceeds	Acknowledgment / Jurat	1 2 3 4
☐ E&O Agrmt	Acknowledgment / Jurat	1 2 3 4
☐ Grant Deed	Acknowledgment / Jurat	1 2 3 4
☐ Marital Stat Aff	Acknowledgment / Jurat	1 2 3 4
☐ Mortgage	Acknowledgment / Jurat	1 2 3 4
☐ Occupancy/Fin Aff	Acknowledgment / Jurat	1 2 3 4
☐ Owner's Aff	Acknowledgment / Jurat	1 2 3 4
☐ Payoff Aff	Acknowledgment / Jurat	1 2 3 4
☐ Quit-Claim Deed	Acknowledgment / Jurat	1 2 3 4
☐ Sig/Name Aff	Acknowledgment / Jurat	1 2 3 4
☐ Survey Aff	Acknowledgment / Jurat	1 2 3 4
☐ Warranty Deed	Acknowledgment / Jurat	1 2 3 4

Document	Type	SIGNER
☐ Minor Medical Consent	Acknowledgment / Jurat	1 2 3 4
☐ Minor Passport Consent	Acknowledgment / Jurat	1 2 3 4
☐ Minor Travel Consent	Acknowledgment / Jurat	1 2 3 4
☐ Vehicle Duplicate Title	Acknowledgment / Jurat	1 2 3 4
☐ Vehicle Lein Release	Acknowledgment / Jurat	1 2 3 4
☐ Vehicle Odom/Vin Ver	Acknowledgment / Jurat	1 2 3 4
☐ Vehicle Title Transfer	Acknowledgment / Jurat	1 2 3 4
☐ Adv Health Care Dir	Acknowledgment / Jurat	1 2 3 4
☐ Assign of Digital Assets	Acknowledgment / Jurat	1 2 3 4
☐ Assign of Personal Prop	Acknowledgment / Jurat	1 2 3 4
☐ HIPAA Release	Acknowledgment / Jurat	1 2 3 4
☐ Living Trust	Acknowledgment / Jurat	1 2 3 4
☐ Last Will & Testament	Acknowledgment / Jurat	1 2 3 4
☐ POA	Acknowledgment / Jurat	1 2 3 4
☐ Trust Certification	Acknowledgment / Jurat / Copy / Oath / SW	1 2 3 4

(Right-column documents also include: Acknowledgment, Jurat, Copy, Oath, SW)

SIGNING ADDRESS	OTHERS IN ATTENDANCE	CLIENT / SIGNING SERVICE	FEE
		LENDER / LOAN NUMBER	

NOTES

	ADDRESS	PHONE	EMAIL	SIGNATURE	INITIAL IF OATH/AFF TAKEN	RIGHT THUMB PRINT
1						
2						
3						
4						

Notary Journal Entries

#	DATE / TIME	NAME	IDENTITY VERIFIED	WILLINGNESS & COMPETENCE	FORMAT
1	DATE ____ / TIME ____	☐ Signer ☐ Witness	☐ D.L. ☐ Passport ☐ Credible Witness ☐ Other	☐ Expressed willingness ☐ Mentally alert ☐ Indicated understanding	☐ Paper ☐ Electronic ☐ RON
2	DATE ____ / TIME ____	☐ Signer ☐ Witness	☐ D.L. ☐ Passport ☐ Credible Witness ☐ Other	☐ Expressed willingness ☐ Mentally alert ☐ Indicated understanding	☐ Paper ☐ Electronic ☐ RON
3	DATE ____ / TIME ____	☐ Signer ☐ Witness	☐ D.L. ☐ Passport ☐ Credible Witness ☐ Other	☐ Expressed willingness ☐ Mentally alert ☐ Indicated understanding	☐ Paper ☐ Electronic ☐ RON
4	DATE ____ / TIME ____	☐ Signer ☐ Witness	☐ D.L. ☐ Passport ☐ Credible Witness ☐ Other	☐ Expressed willingness ☐ Mentally alert ☐ Indicated understanding	☐ Paper ☐ Electronic ☐ RON

DOCUMENT(S) SIGNED

Document	Type	SIGNER
☐ Borrower's Aff	Acknowledgment Jurat	1 2 3 4
☐ Compliance Agrmt	Acknowledgment Jurat	1 2 3 4
☐ Correction Agrmt	Acknowledgment Jurat	1 2 3 4
☐ Debts/Leins Aff	Acknowledgment Jurat	1 2 3 4
☐ Deed of Trust	Acknowledgment Jurat	1 2 3 4
☐ Distrib of Proceeds	Acknowledgment Jurat	1 2 3 4
☐ E&O Agrmt	Acknowledgment Jurat	1 2 3 4
☐ Grant Deed	Acknowledgment Jurat	1 2 3 4
☐ Marital Stat Aff	Acknowledgment Jurat	1 2 3 4
☐ Mortgage	Acknowledgment Jurat	1 2 3 4
☐ Occupancy/Fin Aff	Acknowledgment Jurat	1 2 3 4
☐ Owner's Aff	Acknowledgment Jurat	1 2 3 4
☐ Payoff Aff	Acknowledgment Jurat	1 2 3 4
☐ Quit-Claim Deed	Acknowledgment Jurat	1 2 3 4
☐ Sig/Name Aff	Acknowledgment Jurat	1 2 3 4
☐ Survey Aff	Acknowledgment Jurat	1 2 3 4
☐ Warranty Deed	Acknowledgment Jurat	1 2 3 4
☐ Minor Medical Consent	Acknowledgment Jurat Copy Oath SW	1 2 3 4
☐ Minor Passport Consent	Acknowledgment Jurat	1 2 3 4
☐ Minor Travel Consent	Acknowledgment Jurat	1 2 3 4
☐ Vehicle Duplicate Title	Acknowledgment Jurat Copy Oath SW	1 2 3 4
☐ Vehicle Lein Release	Acknowledgment Jurat	1 2 3 4
☐ Vehicle Odom/Vin Ver	Acknowledgment Jurat	1 2 3 4
☐ Vehicle Title Transfer	Acknowledgment Jurat Copy Oath SW	1 2 3 4
☐ Adv Health Care Dir	Acknowledgment Jurat	1 2 3 4
☐ Assign of Digital Assets	Acknowledgment Jurat	1 2 3 4
☐ Assign of Personal Prop	Acknowledgment Jurat	1 2 3 4
☐ HIPAA Release	Acknowledgment Jurat	1 2 3 4
☐ Living Trust	Acknowledgment Jurat Copy Oath SW	1 2 3 4
☐ Last Will & Testament	Acknowledgment Jurat	1 2 3 4
☐ POA	Acknowledgment Jurat	1 2 3 4
☐ Trust Certification	Acknowledgment Jurat Copy Oath SW	1 2 3 4

SIGNING ADDRESS	OTHERS IN ATTENDANCE	CLIENT / SIGNING SERVICE
		LENDER / LOAN NUMBER
		FEE

NOTES

	ADDRESS	PHONE	EMAIL	SIGNATURE	INITIAL IF OATH/AFF TAKEN	RIGHT THUMB PRINT
1						
2						
3						
4						

Notary Journal Entries (1–4)

#	DATE / TIME	NAME	IDENTITY VERIFIED	WILLINGNESS & COMPETENCE	FORMAT
1	DATE ___ TIME ___	☐ Signer ☐ Witness	☐ D.L. ☐ Passport ☐ Credible Witness ☐ Other	☐ Expressed willingness ☐ Mentally alert ☐ Indicated understanding	☐ Paper ☐ Electronic ☐ RON
2	DATE ___ TIME ___	☐ Signer ☐ Witness	☐ D.L. ☐ Passport ☐ Credible Witness ☐ Other	☐ Expressed willingness ☐ Mentally alert ☐ Indicated understanding	☐ Paper ☐ Electronic ☐ RON
3	DATE ___ TIME ___	☐ Signer ☐ Witness	☐ D.L. ☐ Passport ☐ Credible Witness ☐ Other	☐ Expressed willingness ☐ Mentally alert ☐ Indicated understanding	☐ Paper ☐ Electronic ☐ RON
4	DATE ___ TIME ___	☐ Signer ☐ Witness	☐ D.L. ☐ Passport ☐ Credible Witness ☐ Other	☐ Expressed willingness ☐ Mentally alert ☐ Indicated understanding	☐ Paper ☐ Electronic ☐ RON

DOCUMENT(S) SIGNED

Document	Type	SIGNER 1 2 3 4
☐ Borrower's Aff	Acknowledgment Jurat	1 2 3 4
☐ Compliance Agrmt	Acknowledgment Jurat	1 2 3 4
☐ Correction Agrmt	Acknowledgment Jurat	1 2 3 4
☐ Debts/Leins Aff	Acknowledgment Jurat	1 2 3 4
☐ Deed of Trust	Acknowledgment Jurat	1 2 3 4
☐ Distrib of Proceeds	Acknowledgment Jurat	1 2 3 4
☐ E&O Agrmt	Acknowledgment Jurat	1 2 3 4
☐ Grant Deed	Acknowledgment Jurat	1 2 3 4
☐ Marital Stat Aff	Acknowledgment Jurat	1 2 3 4
☐ Mortgage	Acknowledgment Jurat	1 2 3 4
☐ Occupancy/Fin Aff	Acknowledgment Jurat	1 2 3 4
☐ Owner's Aff	Acknowledgment Jurat	1 2 3 4
☐ Payoff Aff	Acknowledgment Jurat	1 2 3 4
☐ Quit-Claim Deed	Acknowledgment Jurat	1 2 3 4
☐ Sig/Name Aff	Acknowledgment Jurat	1 2 3 4
☐ Survey Aff	Acknowledgment Jurat	1 2 3 4
☐ Warranty Deed	Acknowledgment Jurat	1 2 3 4

Document	Type	SIGNER 1 2 3 4	Extra
☐ Minor Medical Consent	Acknowledgment Jurat	1 2 3 4	☐
☐ Minor Passport Consent	Acknowledgment Jurat	1 2 3 4	Acknowledgment Jurat Copy Oath SW 1 2 3 4
☐ Minor Travel Consent	Acknowledgment Jurat	1 2 3 4	
☐ Vehicle Duplicate Title	Acknowledgment Jurat	1 2 3 4	☐ Acknowledgment Jurat Copy Oath SW 1 2 3 4
☐ Vehicle Lein Release	Acknowledgment Jurat	1 2 3 4	
☐ Vehicle Odom/Vin Ver	Acknowledgment Jurat	1 2 3 4	☐
☐ Vehicle Title Transfer	Acknowledgment Jurat	1 2 3 4	Acknowledgment Jurat Copy Oath SW 1 2 3 4
☐ Adv Health Care Dir	Acknowledgment Jurat	1 2 3 4	☐
☐ Assign of Digital Assets	Acknowledgment Jurat	1 2 3 4	Acknowledgment Jurat Copy Oath SW 1 2 3 4
☐ Assign of Personal Prop	Acknowledgment Jurat	1 2 3 4	
☐ HIPAA Release	Acknowledgment Jurat	1 2 3 4	☐
☐ Living Trust ___	Acknowledgment Jurat	1 2 3 4	Acknowledgment Jurat Copy Oath SW 1 2 3 4
☐ Last Will & Testament	Acknowledgment Jurat	1 2 3 4	
☐ POA ___	Acknowledgment Jurat	1 2 3 4	☐
☐ Trust Certification	Acknowledgment Jurat	1 2 3 4	Acknowledgment Jurat Copy Oath SW 1 2 3 4

SIGNING ADDRESS	OTHERS IN ATTENDANCE	CLIENT / SIGNING SERVICE	FEE
		LENDER / LOAN NUMBER	

NOTES

#	ADDRESS	PHONE / EMAIL	SIGNATURE	INITIAL IF OATH/AFF TAKEN	RIGHT THUMB PRINT
1		PHONE / EMAIL			
2		PHONE / EMAIL			
3		PHONE / EMAIL			
4		PHONE / EMAIL			

Entries 1–4

#	DATE / TIME	NAME	IDENTITY VERIFIED	WILLINGNESS & COMPETENCE	FORMAT
1	DATE ___ / TIME ___	☐ Signer ☐ Witness	☐ D.L. ☐ Passport ☐ Credible Witness ☐ Other	☐ Expressed willingness ☐ Mentally alert ☐ Indicated understanding	☐ Paper ☐ Electronic ☐ RON
2	DATE ___ / TIME ___	☐ Signer ☐ Witness	☐ D.L. ☐ Passport ☐ Credible Witness ☐ Other	☐ Expressed willingness ☐ Mentally alert ☐ Indicated understanding	☐ Paper ☐ Electronic ☐ RON
3	DATE ___ / TIME ___	☐ Signer ☐ Witness	☐ D.L. ☐ Passport ☐ Credible Witness ☐ Other	☐ Expressed willingness ☐ Mentally alert ☐ Indicated understanding	☐ Paper ☐ Electronic ☐ RON
4	DATE ___ / TIME ___	☐ Signer ☐ Witness	☐ D.L. ☐ Passport ☐ Credible Witness ☐ Other	☐ Expressed willingness ☐ Mentally alert ☐ Indicated understanding	☐ Paper ☐ Electronic ☐ RON

DOCUMENT(S) SIGNED

Document	Type	SIGNER
☐ Borrower's Aff	Acknowledgment Jurat	1 2 3 4
☐ Compliance Agrmt	Acknowledgment Jurat	1 2 3 4
☐ Correction Agrmt	Acknowledgment Jurat	1 2 3 4
☐ Debts/Leins Aff	Acknowledgment Jurat	1 2 3 4
☐ Deed of Trust	Acknowledgment Jurat	1 2 3 4
☐ Distrib of Proceeds	Acknowledgment Jurat	1 2 3 4
☐ E&O Agrmt	Acknowledgment Jurat	1 2 3 4
☐ Grant Deed	Acknowledgment Jurat	1 2 3 4
☐ Marital Stat Aff	Acknowledgment Jurat	1 2 3 4
☐ Mortgage	Acknowledgment Jurat	1 2 3 4
☐ Occupancy/Fin Aff	Acknowledgment Jurat	1 2 3 4
☐ Owner's Aff	Acknowledgment Jurat	1 2 3 4
☐ Payoff Aff	Acknowledgment Jurat	1 2 3 4
☐ Quit-Claim Deed	Acknowledgment Jurat	1 2 3 4
☐ Sig/Name Aff	Acknowledgment Jurat	1 2 3 4
☐ Survey Aff	Acknowledgment Jurat	1 2 3 4
☐ Warranty Deed	Acknowledgment Jurat	1 2 3 4
☐ Minor Medical Consent	Acknowledgment Jurat	1 2 3 4
☐ Minor Passport Consent	Acknowledgment Jurat	1 2 3 4
☐ Minor Travel Consent	Acknowledgment Jurat	1 2 3 4
☐ Vehicle Duplicate Title	Acknowledgment Jurat	1 2 3 4
☐ Vehicle Lein Release	Acknowledgment Jurat	1 2 3 4
☐ Vehicle Odom/Vin Ver	Acknowledgment Jurat	1 2 3 4
☐ Vehicle Title Transfer	Acknowledgment Jurat	1 2 3 4
☐ Adv Health Care Dir	Acknowledgment Jurat	1 2 3 4
☐ Assign of Digital Assets	Acknowledgment Jurat	1 2 3 4
☐ Assign of Personal Prop	Acknowledgment Jurat	1 2 3 4
☐ HIPAA Release	Acknowledgment Jurat	1 2 3 4
☐ Living Trust _____	Acknowledgment Jurat Copy Oath SW	1 2 3 4
☐ Last Will & Testament	Acknowledgment Jurat Copy Oath SW	1 2 3 4
☐ POA	Acknowledgment Jurat Copy Oath SW	1 2 3 4
☐ Trust Certification	Acknowledgment Jurat Copy Oath SW	1 2 3 4

SIGNING ADDRESS	OTHERS IN ATTENDANCE	CLIENT / SIGNING SERVICE	FEE
		LENDER / LOAN NUMBER	

NOTES

_____
_____
_____
_____
_____
_____
_____
_____
_____
_____
_____
_____

	ADDRESS	PHONE	SIGNATURE	INITIAL IF OATH/AFF TAKEN	RIGHT THUMB PRINT
1		EMAIL			
2	ADDRESS	PHONE	SIGNATURE	INITIAL IF OATH/AFF TAKEN	RIGHT THUMB PRINT
		EMAIL			
3	ADDRESS	PHONE	SIGNATURE	INITIAL IF OATH/AFF TAKEN	RIGHT THUMB PRINT
		EMAIL			
4	ADDRESS	PHONE	SIGNATURE	INITIAL IF OATH/AFF TAKEN	RIGHT THUMB PRINT
		EMAIL			

Notary Entries 1–4

#	DATE / TIME	NAME	IDENTITY VERIFIED	WILLINGNESS & COMPETENCE	FORMAT
1	DATE: ___ TIME: ___	☐ Signer ☐ Witness	☐ D.L. ☐ Passport ☐ Credible Witness ☐ Other	☐ Expressed willingness ☐ Mentally alert ☐ Indicated understanding	☐ Paper ☐ Electronic ☐ RON
2	DATE: ___ TIME: ___	☐ Signer ☐ Witness	☐ D.L. ☐ Passport ☐ Credible Witness ☐ Other	☐ Expressed willingness ☐ Mentally alert ☐ Indicated understanding	☐ Paper ☐ Electronic ☐ RON
3	DATE: ___ TIME: ___	☐ Signer ☐ Witness	☐ D.L. ☐ Passport ☐ Credible Witness ☐ Other	☐ Expressed willingness ☐ Mentally alert ☐ Indicated understanding	☐ Paper ☐ Electronic ☐ RON
4	DATE: ___ TIME: ___	☐ Signer ☐ Witness	☐ D.L. ☐ Passport ☐ Credible Witness ☐ Other	☐ Expressed willingness ☐ Mentally alert ☐ Indicated understanding	☐ Paper ☐ Electronic ☐ RON

DOCUMENT(S) SIGNED

Document	Type	Signer
☐ Borrower's Aff	Acknowledgment Jurat	1 2 3 4
☐ Compliance Agrmt	Acknowledgment Jurat	1 2 3 4
☐ Correction Agrmt	Acknowledgment Jurat	1 2 3 4
☐ Debs/Leins Aff	Acknowledgment Jurat	1 2 3 4
☐ Deed of Trust	Acknowledgment Jurat	1 2 3 4
☐ Distrib of Proceeds	Acknowledgment Jurat	1 2 3 4
☐ E&O Agrmt	Acknowledgment Jurat	1 2 3 4
☐ Grant Deed	Acknowledgment Jurat	1 2 3 4
☐ Marital Stat Aff	Acknowledgment Jurat	1 2 3 4
☐ Mortgage	Acknowledgment Jurat	1 2 3 4
☐ Occupancy/Fin Aff	Acknowledgment Jurat	1 2 3 4
☐ Owner's Aff	Acknowledgment Jurat	1 2 3 4
☐ Payoff Aff	Acknowledgment Jurat	1 2 3 4
☐ Quit-Claim Deed	Acknowledgment Jurat	1 2 3 4
☐ Sig/Name Aff	Acknowledgment Jurat	1 2 3 4
☐ Survey Aff	Acknowledgment Jurat	1 2 3 4
☐ Warranty Deed	Acknowledgment Jurat	1 2 3 4

Document	Type	Signer
☐ Minor Medical Consent	Acknowledgment Jurat	1 2 3 4
☐ Minor Passport Consent	Acknowledgment Jurat Copy Oath SW	1 2 3 4
☐ Minor Travel Consent	Acknowledgment Jurat	1 2 3 4
☐ Vehicle Duplicate Title	Acknowledgment Jurat Copy Oath SW	1 2 3 4
☐ Vehicle Lein Release	Acknowledgment Jurat	1 2 3 4
☐ Vehicle Odom/Vin Ver	Acknowledgment Jurat	1 2 3 4
☐ Vehicle Title Transfer	Acknowledgment Jurat Copy Oath SW	1 2 3 4
☐ Adv Health Care Dir	Acknowledgment Jurat	1 2 3 4
☐ Assign of Digital Assets	Acknowledgment Jurat Copy Oath SW	1 2 3 4
☐ Assign of Personal Prop	Acknowledgment Jurat	1 2 3 4
☐ HIPAA Release	Acknowledgment Jurat	1 2 3 4
☐ Living Trust	Acknowledgment Jurat Copy Oath SW	1 2 3 4
☐ Last Will & Testament	Acknowledgment Jurat	1 2 3 4
☐ POA	Acknowledgment Jurat	1 2 3 4
☐ Trust Certification	Acknowledgment Jurat Copy Oath SW	1 2 3 4

SIGNING ADDRESS	OTHERS IN ATTENDANCE	CLIENT / SIGNING SERVICE	FEE
		LENDER / LOAN NUMBER	

NOTES

	ADDRESS	PHONE	SIGNATURE	INITIAL IF OATH/AFF TAKEN	RIGHT THUMB PRINT
1		EMAIL			
2	ADDRESS	PHONE	SIGNATURE	INITIAL IF OATH/AFF TAKEN	RIGHT THUMB PRINT
		EMAIL			
3	ADDRESS	PHONE	SIGNATURE	INITIAL IF OATH/AFF TAKEN	RIGHT THUMB PRINT
		EMAIL			
4	ADDRESS	PHONE	SIGNATURE	INITIAL IF OATH/AFF TAKEN	RIGHT THUMB PRINT
		EMAIL			

1	DATE TIME	NAME ☐ Signer ☐ Witness	IDENTITY VERIFIED ☐ D.L. ☐ Passport ☐ Credible Witness ☐ Other	WILLINGNESS & COMPETENCE ☐ Expressed willingness ☐ Mentally alert ☐ Indicated understanding	FORMAT ☐ Paper ☐ Electronic ☐ RON
2	DATE TIME	NAME ☐ Signer ☐ Witness	IDENTITY VERIFIED ☐ D.L. ☐ Passport ☐ Credible Witness ☐ Other	WILLINGNESS & COMPETENCE ☐ Expressed willingness ☐ Mentally alert ☐ Indicated understanding	FORMAT ☐ Paper ☐ Electronic ☐ RON
3	DATE TIME	NAME ☐ Signer ☐ Witness	IDENTITY VERIFIED ☐ D.L. ☐ Passport ☐ Credible Witness ☐ Other	WILLINGNESS & COMPETENCE ☐ Expressed willingness ☐ Mentally alert ☐ Indicated understanding	FORMAT ☐ Paper ☐ Electronic ☐ RON
4	DATE TIME	NAME ☐ Signer ☐ Witness	IDENTITY VERIFIED ☐ D.L. ☐ Passport ☐ Credible Witness ☐ Other	WILLINGNESS & COMPETENCE ☐ Expressed willingness ☐ Mentally alert ☐ Indicated understanding	FORMAT ☐ Paper ☐ Electronic ☐ RON

DOCUMENT(S) SIGNED

Document				Signer
☐ Borrower's Aff	Acknowledgment	Jurat	______	1 2 3 4
☐ Compliance Agrmt	Acknowledgment	Jurat	______	1 2 3 4
☐ Correction Agrmt	Acknowledgment	Jurat	______	1 2 3 4
☐ Debts/Leins Aff	Acknowledgment	Jurat	______	1 2 3 4
☐ Deed of Trust	Acknowledgment	Jurat	______	1 2 3 4
☐ Distrib of Proceeds	Acknowledgment	Jurat	______	1 2 3 4
☐ E&O Agrmt	Acknowledgment	Jurat	______	1 2 3 4
☐ Grant Deed	Acknowledgment	Jurat	______	1 2 3 4
☐ Marital Stat Aff	Acknowledgment	Jurat	______	1 2 3 4
☐ Mortgage	Acknowledgment	Jurat	______	1 2 3 4
☐ Occupancy/Fin Aff	Acknowledgment	Jurat	______	1 2 3 4
☐ Owner's Aff	Acknowledgment	Jurat	______	1 2 3 4
☐ Payoff Aff	Acknowledgment	Jurat	______	1 2 3 4
☐ Quit-Claim Deed	Acknowledgment	Jurat	______	1 2 3 4
☐ Sig/Name Aff	Acknowledgment	Jurat	______	1 2 3 4
☐ Survey Aff	Acknowledgment	Jurat	______	1 2 3 4
☐ Warranty Deed	Acknowledgment	Jurat	______	1 2 3 4

Document				Signer
☐ Minor Medical Consent	Acknowledgment	Jurat	______	1 2 3 4
☐ Minor Passport Consent	Acknowledgment	Jurat	______	1 2 3 4
☐ Minor Travel Consent	Acknowledgment	Jurat	______	1 2 3 4
☐ Vehicle Duplicate Title	Acknowledgment	Jurat	______	1 2 3 4
☐ Vehicle Lein Release	Acknowledgment	Jurat	______	1 2 3 4
☐ Vehicle Odom/Vin Ver	Acknowledgment	Jurat	______	1 2 3 4
☐ Vehicle Title Transfer	Acknowledgment	Jurat	______	1 2 3 4
☐ Adv Health Care Dir	Acknowledgment	Jurat	______	1 2 3 4
☐ Assign of Digital Assets	Acknowledgment	Jurat	______	1 2 3 4
☐ Assign of Personal Prop	Acknowledgment	Jurat	______	1 2 3 4
☐ HIPAA Release	Acknowledgment	Jurat	______	1 2 3 4
☐ Living Trust ______	Acknowledgment	Jurat	______	1 2 3 4
☐ Last Will & Testament	Acknowledgment	Jurat	______	1 2 3 4
☐ POA ______	Acknowledgment	Jurat	______	1 2 3 4
☐ Trust Certification	Acknowledgment	Jurat	______	1 2 3 4

☐ ______					
Acknowledgment	Jurat	Copy	Oath	SW	1 2 3 4
☐ ______					
Acknowledgment	Jurat	Copy	Oath	SW	1 2 3 4
☐ ______					
Acknowledgment	Jurat	Copy	Oath	SW	1 2 3 4
☐ ______					
Acknowledgment	Jurat	Copy	Oath	SW	1 2 3 4
☐ ______					
Acknowledgment	Jurat	Copy	Oath	SW	1 2 3 4
☐ ______					
Acknowledgment	Jurat	Copy	Oath	SW	1 2 3 4

SIGNING ADDRESS	OTHERS IN ATTENDANCE	CLIENT / SIGNING SERVICE	FEE
		LENDER / LOAN NUMBER	

NOTES

_____
_____
_____
_____
_____
_____
_____
_____
_____
_____
_____
_____
_____

	ADDRESS	PHONE / EMAIL	SIGNATURE	INITIAL IF OATH/AFF TAKEN	RIGHT THUMB PRINT
1		PHONE / EMAIL	SIGNATURE		RIGHT THUMB PRINT
2		PHONE / EMAIL	SIGNATURE		RIGHT THUMB PRINT
3		PHONE / EMAIL	SIGNATURE		RIGHT THUMB PRINT
4		PHONE / EMAIL	SIGNATURE		RIGHT THUMB PRINT

Notary Journal Entries

Entry 1
DATE		**FORMAT**
TIME		☐ Paper ☐ Electronic ☐ RON

NAME: ☐ Signer ☐ Witness

IDENTITY VERIFIED: ☐ D.L. ☐ Passport ☐ Credible Witness ☐ Other

WILLINGNESS & COMPETENCE: ☐ Expressed willingness ☐ Mentally alert ☐ Indicated understanding

Entry 2
DATE		**FORMAT**
TIME		☐ Paper ☐ Electronic ☐ RON

NAME: ☐ Signer ☐ Witness

IDENTITY VERIFIED: ☐ D.L. ☐ Passport ☐ Credible Witness ☐ Other

WILLINGNESS & COMPETENCE: ☐ Expressed willingness ☐ Mentally alert ☐ Indicated understanding

Entry 3
DATE		**FORMAT**
TIME		☐ Paper ☐ Electronic ☐ RON

NAME: ☐ Signer ☐ Witness

IDENTITY VERIFIED: ☐ D.L. ☐ Passport ☐ Credible Witness ☐ Other

WILLINGNESS & COMPETENCE: ☐ Expressed willingness ☐ Mentally alert ☐ Indicated understanding

Entry 4
DATE		**FORMAT**
TIME		☐ Paper ☐ Electronic ☐ RON

NAME: ☐ Signer ☐ Witness

IDENTITY VERIFIED: ☐ D.L. ☐ Passport ☐ Credible Witness ☐ Other

WILLINGNESS & COMPETENCE: ☐ Expressed willingness ☐ Mentally alert ☐ Indicated understanding

DOCUMENT(S) SIGNED

Document	Type	Type	SIGNER
☐ Borrower's Aff	Acknowledgment	Jurat	1 2 3 4
☐ Compliance Agrmt	Acknowledgment	Jurat	1 2 3 4
☐ Correction Agrmt	Acknowledgment	Jurat	1 2 3 4
☐ Debts/Leins Aff	Acknowledgment	Jurat	1 2 3 4
☐ Deed of Trust	Acknowledgment	Jurat	1 2 3 4
☐ Distrib of Proceeds	Acknowledgment	Jurat	1 2 3 4
☐ E&O Agrmt	Acknowledgment	Jurat	1 2 3 4
☐ Grant Deed	Acknowledgment	Jurat	1 2 3 4
☐ Marital Stat Aff	Acknowledgment	Jurat	1 2 3 4
☐ Mortgage	Acknowledgment	Jurat	1 2 3 4
☐ Occupancy/Fin Aff	Acknowledgment	Jurat	1 2 3 4
☐ Owner's Aff	Acknowledgment	Jurat	1 2 3 4
☐ Payoff Aff	Acknowledgment	Jurat	1 2 3 4
☐ Quit-Claim Deed	Acknowledgment	Jurat	1 2 3 4
☐ Sig/Name Aff	Acknowledgment	Jurat	1 2 3 4
☐ Survey Aff	Acknowledgment	Jurat	1 2 3 4
☐ Warranty Deed	Acknowledgment	Jurat	1 2 3 4

Document	Type	Type	SIGNER
☐ Minor Medical Consent	Acknowledgment	Jurat	1 2 3 4
☐ Minor Passport Consent	Acknowledgment	Jurat	1 2 3 4
☐ Minor Travel Consent	Acknowledgment	Jurat	1 2 3 4
☐ Vehicle Duplicate Title	Acknowledgment	Jurat	1 2 3 4
☐ Vehicle Lein Release	Acknowledgment	Jurat	1 2 3 4
☐ Vehicle Odom/Vin Ver	Acknowledgment	Jurat	1 2 3 4
☐ Vehicle Title Transfer	Acknowledgment	Jurat	1 2 3 4
☐ Adv Health Care Dir	Acknowledgment	Jurat	1 2 3 4
☐ Assign of Digital Assets	Acknowledgment	Jurat	1 2 3 4
☐ Assign of Personal Prop	Acknowledgment	Jurat	1 2 3 4
☐ HIPAA Release	Acknowledgment	Jurat	1 2 3 4
☐ Living Trust	Acknowledgment	Jurat	1 2 3 4
☐ Last Will & Testament	Acknowledgment	Jurat	1 2 3 4
☐ POA	Acknowledgment	Jurat	1 2 3 4
☐ Trust Certification	Acknowledgment	Jurat	1 2 3 4

For the second document column, each row additionally provides: Acknowledgment Jurat Copy Oath SW 1 2 3 4 with checkbox.

SIGNING ADDRESS	OTHERS IN ATTENDANCE	CLIENT / SIGNING SERVICE	FEE
		LENDER / LOAN NUMBER	

NOTES

	ADDRESS	PHONE	SIGNATURE	INITIAL IF OATH/AFF TAKEN	RIGHT THUMB PRINT
1		EMAIL			
2	ADDRESS	PHONE	SIGNATURE	INITIAL IF OATH/AFF TAKEN	RIGHT THUMB PRINT
		EMAIL			
3	ADDRESS	PHONE	SIGNATURE	INITIAL IF OATH/AFF TAKEN	RIGHT THUMB PRINT
		EMAIL			
4	ADDRESS	PHONE	SIGNATURE	INITIAL IF OATH/AFF TAKEN	RIGHT THUMB PRINT
		EMAIL			

Notary Journal Entries

#		IDENTITY VERIFIED	WILLINGNESS & COMPETENCE	FORMAT
1	DATE / TIME — NAME: ☐ Signer ☐ Witness	☐ D.L. ☐ Passport ☐ Credible Witness ☐ Other	☐ Expressed willingness ☐ Mentally alert ☐ Indicated understanding	☐ Paper ☐ Electronic ☐ RON
2	DATE / TIME — NAME: ☐ Signer ☐ Witness	☐ D.L. ☐ Passport ☐ Credible Witness ☐ Other	☐ Expressed willingness ☐ Mentally alert ☐ Indicated understanding	☐ Paper ☐ Electronic ☐ RON
3	DATE / TIME — NAME: ☐ Signer ☐ Witness	☐ D.L. ☐ Passport ☐ Credible Witness ☐ Other	☐ Expressed willingness ☐ Mentally alert ☐ Indicated understanding	☐ Paper ☐ Electronic ☐ RON
4	DATE / TIME — NAME: ☐ Signer ☐ Witness	☐ D.L. ☐ Passport ☐ Credible Witness ☐ Other	☐ Expressed willingness ☐ Mentally alert ☐ Indicated understanding	☐ Paper ☐ Electronic ☐ RON

DOCUMENT(S) SIGNED

Document	Type	SIGNER
☐ Borrower's Aff	Acknowledgment Jurat	1 2 3 4
☐ Compliance Agrmt	Acknowledgment Jurat	1 2 3 4
☐ Correction Agrmt	Acknowledgment Jurat	1 2 3 4
☐ Debts/Leins Aff	Acknowledgment Jurat	1 2 3 4
☐ Deed of Trust	Acknowledgment Jurat	1 2 3 4
☐ Distrib of Proceeds	Acknowledgment Jurat	1 2 3 4
☐ E&O Agrmt	Acknowledgment Jurat	1 2 3 4
☐ Grant Deed	Acknowledgment Jurat	1 2 3 4
☐ Marital Stat Aff	Acknowledgment Jurat	1 2 3 4
☐ Mortgage	Acknowledgment Jurat	1 2 3 4
☐ Occupancy/Fin Aff	Acknowledgment Jurat	1 2 3 4
☐ Owner's Aff	Acknowledgment Jurat	1 2 3 4
☐ Payoff Aff	Acknowledgment Jurat	1 2 3 4
☐ Quit-Claim Deed	Acknowledgment Jurat	1 2 3 4
☐ Sig/Name Aff	Acknowledgment Jurat	1 2 3 4
☐ Survey Aff	Acknowledgment Jurat	1 2 3 4
☐ Warranty Deed	Acknowledgment Jurat	1 2 3 4
☐ Minor Medical Consent	Acknowledgment Jurat	1 2 3 4
☐ Minor Passport Consent	Acknowledgment Jurat	1 2 3 4
☐ Minor Travel Consent	Acknowledgment Jurat	1 2 3 4
☐ Vehicle Duplicate Title	Acknowledgment Jurat	1 2 3 4
☐ Vehicle Lein Release	Acknowledgment Jurat	1 2 3 4
☐ Vehicle Odom/Vin Ver	Acknowledgment Jurat	1 2 3 4
☐ Vehicle Title Transfer	Acknowledgment Jurat	1 2 3 4
☐ Adv Health Care Dir	Acknowledgment Jurat	1 2 3 4
☐ Assign of Digital Assets	Acknowledgment Jurat	1 2 3 4
☐ Assign of Personal Prop	Acknowledgment Jurat	1 2 3 4
☐ HIPAA Release	Acknowledgment Jurat	1 2 3 4
☐ Living Trust	Acknowledgment Jurat	1 2 3 4
☐ Last Will & Testament	Acknowledgment Jurat	1 2 3 4
☐ POA	Acknowledgment Jurat	1 2 3 4
☐ Trust Certification	Acknowledgment Jurat	1 2 3 4

Additional options (right column): ☐ Acknowledgment Jurat Copy Oath SW — 1 2 3 4

SIGNING ADDRESS	OTHERS IN ATTENDANCE	CLIENT / SIGNING SERVICE	FEE
		LENDER / LOAN NUMBER	

NOTES

_____
_____
_____
_____
_____
_____
_____
_____
_____
_____
_____
_____

	ADDRESS	PHONE	SIGNATURE	INITIAL IF OATH/AFF TAKEN	RIGHT THUMB PRINT
1		PHONE / EMAIL	SIGNATURE	INITIAL IF OATH/AFF TAKEN	RIGHT THUMB PRINT
2	ADDRESS	PHONE / EMAIL	SIGNATURE	INITIAL IF OATH/AFF TAKEN	RIGHT THUMB PRINT
3	ADDRESS	PHONE / EMAIL	SIGNATURE	INITIAL IF OATH/AFF TAKEN	RIGHT THUMB PRINT
4	ADDRESS	PHONE / EMAIL	SIGNATURE	INITIAL IF OATH/AFF TAKEN	RIGHT THUMB PRINT

1	DATE TIME	NAME ❑ Signer ❑ Witness	IDENTITY VERIFIED ❑ D.L. ❑ Passport ❑ Credible Witness ❑ Other	WILLINGNESS & COMPETENCE ❑ Expressed willingness ❑ Mentally alert ❑ Indicated understanding	FORMAT ❑ Paper ❑ Electronic ❑ RON
2	DATE TIME	NAME ❑ Signer ❑ Witness	IDENTITY VERIFIED ❑ D.L. ❑ Passport ❑ Credible Witness ❑ Other	WILLINGNESS & COMPETENCE ❑ Expressed willingness ❑ Mentally alert ❑ Indicated understanding	FORMAT ❑ Paper ❑ Electronic ❑ RON
3	DATE TIME	NAME ❑ Signer ❑ Witness	IDENTITY VERIFIED ❑ D.L. ❑ Passport ❑ Credible Witness ❑ Other	WILLINGNESS & COMPETENCE ❑ Expressed willingness ❑ Mentally alert ❑ Indicated understanding	FORMAT ❑ Paper ❑ Electronic ❑ RON
4	DATE TIME	NAME ❑ Signer ❑ Witness	IDENTITY VERIFIED ❑ D.L. ❑ Passport ❑ Credible Witness ❑ Other	WILLINGNESS & COMPETENCE ❑ Expressed willingness ❑ Mentally alert ❑ Indicated understanding	FORMAT ❑ Paper ❑ Electronic ❑ RON

DOCUMENT(S) SIGNED		SIGNER			SIGNER	
❑ Borrower's Aff	Acknowledgment Jurat ______	1 2 3 4	❑ Minor Medical Consent	Acknowledgment Jurat ______	1 2 3 4	❑ ______
❑ Compliance Agrmt	Acknowledgment Jurat ______	1 2 3 4	❑ Minor Passport Consent	Acknowledgment Jurat ______	1 2 3 4	Acknowledgment Jurat Copy Oath SW 1 2 3 4
❑ Correction Agrmt	Acknowledgment Jurat ______	1 2 3 4	❑ Minor Travel Consent	Acknowledgment Jurat ______	1 2 3 4	
❑ Debts/Leins Aff	Acknowledgment Jurat ______	1 2 3 4				❑ ______
❑ Deed of Trust	Acknowledgment Jurat ______	1 2 3 4	❑ Vehicle Duplicate Title	Acknowledgment Jurat ______	1 2 3 4	Acknowledgment Jurat Copy Oath SW 1 2 3 4
❑ Distrib of Proceeds	Acknowledgment Jurat ______	1 2 3 4	❑ Vehicle Lein Release	Acknowledgment Jurat ______	1 2 3 4	
❑ E&O Agrmt	Acknowledgment Jurat ______	1 2 3 4	❑ Vehicle Odom/Vin Ver	Acknowledgment Jurat ______	1 2 3 4	❑ ______
❑ Grant Deed	Acknowledgment Jurat ______	1 2 3 4	❑ Vehicle Title Transfer	Acknowledgment Jurat ______	1 2 3 4	Acknowledgment Jurat Copy Oath SW 1 2 3 4
❑ Marital Stat Aff	Acknowledgment Jurat ______	1 2 3 4				
❑ Mortgage	Acknowledgment Jurat ______	1 2 3 4	❑ Adv Health Care Dir	Acknowledgment Jurat ______	1 2 3 4	❑ ______
❑ Occupancy/Fin Aff	Acknowledgment Jurat ______	1 2 3 4	❑ Assign of Digital Assets	Acknowledgment Jurat ______	1 2 3 4	Acknowledgment Jurat Copy Oath SW 1 2 3 4
❑ Owner's Aff	Acknowledgment Jurat ______	1 2 3 4	❑ Assign of Personal Prop	Acknowledgment Jurat ______	1 2 3 4	
❑ Payoff Aff	Acknowledgment Jurat ______	1 2 3 4	❑ HIPAA Release	Acknowledgment Jurat ______	1 2 3 4	❑ ______
❑ Quit-Claim Deed	Acknowledgment Jurat ______	1 2 3 4	❑ Living Trust ______	Acknowledgment Jurat ______	1 2 3 4	Acknowledgment Jurat Copy Oath SW 1 2 3 4
❑ Sig/Name Aff	Acknowledgment Jurat ______	1 2 3 4	❑ Last Will & Testament	Acknowledgment Jurat ______	1 2 3 4	
❑ Survey Aff	Acknowledgment Jurat ______	1 2 3 4	❑ POA ______	Acknowledgment Jurat ______	1 2 3 4	❑ ______
❑ Warranty Deed	Acknowledgment Jurat ______	1 2 3 4	❑ Trust Certification	Acknowledgment Jurat ______	1 2 3 4	Acknowledgment Jurat Copy Oath SW 1 2 3 4

SIGNING ADDRESS	OTHERS IN ATTENDANCE	CLIENT / SIGNING SERVICE	FEE
		LENDER / LOAN NUMBER	

NOTES

_____
_____
_____
_____
_____
_____
_____
_____
_____
_____
_____
_____

	ADDRESS	SIGNATURE	PHONE	EMAIL	INITIAL IF OATH/AFF TAKEN	RIGHT THUMB PRINT
1						
2						
3						
4						

Notary Entries

Entry 1
Field	Details
DATE	
TIME	
NAME	☐ Signer ☐ Witness
IDENTITY VERIFIED	☐ D.L. ☐ Passport ☐ Credible Witness ☐ Other
WILLINGNESS & COMPETENCE	☐ Expressed willingness ☐ Mentally alert ☐ Indicated understanding
FORMAT	☐ Paper ☐ Electronic ☐ RON

Entry 2
Field	Details
DATE	
TIME	
NAME	☐ Signer ☐ Witness
IDENTITY VERIFIED	☐ D.L. ☐ Passport ☐ Credible Witness ☐ Other
WILLINGNESS & COMPETENCE	☐ Expressed willingness ☐ Mentally alert ☐ Indicated understanding
FORMAT	☐ Paper ☐ Electronic ☐ RON

Entry 3
Field	Details
DATE	
TIME	
NAME	☐ Signer ☐ Witness
IDENTITY VERIFIED	☐ D.L. ☐ Passport ☐ Credible Witness ☐ Other
WILLINGNESS & COMPETENCE	☐ Expressed willingness ☐ Mentally alert ☐ Indicated understanding
FORMAT	☐ Paper ☐ Electronic ☐ RON

Entry 4
Field	Details
DATE	
TIME	
NAME	☐ Signer ☐ Witness
IDENTITY VERIFIED	☐ D.L. ☐ Passport ☐ Credible Witness ☐ Other
WILLINGNESS & COMPETENCE	☐ Expressed willingness ☐ Mentally alert ☐ Indicated understanding
FORMAT	☐ Paper ☐ Electronic ☐ RON

DOCUMENT(S) SIGNED

Document	Type				SIGNER			
					1	2	3	4
☐ Borrower's Aff	Acknowledgment	Jurat			1	2	3	4
☐ Compliance Agrmt	Acknowledgment	Jurat			1	2	3	4
☐ Correction Agrmt	Acknowledgment	Jurat			1	2	3	4
☐ Debts/Leins Aff	Acknowledgment	Jurat			1	2	3	4
☐ Deed of Trust	Acknowledgment	Jurat			1	2	3	4
☐ Distrib of Proceeds	Acknowledgment	Jurat			1	2	3	4
☐ E&O Agrmt	Acknowledgment	Jurat			1	2	3	4
☐ Grant Deed	Acknowledgment	Jurat			1	2	3	4
☐ Marital Stat Aff	Acknowledgment	Jurat			1	2	3	4
☐ Mortgage	Acknowledgment	Jurat			1	2	3	4
☐ Occupancy/Fin Aff	Acknowledgment	Jurat			1	2	3	4
☐ Owner's Aff	Acknowledgment	Jurat			1	2	3	4
☐ Payoff Aff	Acknowledgment	Jurat			1	2	3	4
☐ Quit-Claim Deed	Acknowledgment	Jurat			1	2	3	4
☐ Sig/Name Aff	Acknowledgment	Jurat			1	2	3	4
☐ Survey Aff	Acknowledgment	Jurat			1	2	3	4
☐ Warranty Deed	Acknowledgment	Jurat			1	2	3	4

Document	Acknowledgment	Jurat	Copy	Oath	SW	SIGNER			
						1	2	3	4
☐ Minor Medical Consent	Acknowledgment	Jurat				1	2	3	4
☐ Minor Passport Consent	Acknowledgment	Jurat				1	2	3	4
☐ Minor Travel Consent	Acknowledgment	Jurat				1	2	3	4
☐ Vehicle Duplicate Title	Acknowledgment	Jurat				1	2	3	4
☐ Vehicle Lein Release	Acknowledgment	Jurat				1	2	3	4
☐ Vehicle Odom/Vin Ver	Acknowledgment	Jurat				1	2	3	4
☐ Vehicle Title Transfer	Acknowledgment	Jurat				1	2	3	4
☐ Adv Health Care Dir	Acknowledgment	Jurat	Copy	Oath	SW	1	2	3	4
☐ Assign of Digital Assets	Acknowledgment	Jurat				1	2	3	4
☐ Assign of Personal Prop	Acknowledgment	Jurat				1	2	3	4
☐ HIPAA Release	Acknowledgment	Jurat				1	2	3	4
☐ Living Trust	Acknowledgment	Jurat	Copy	Oath	SW	1	2	3	4
☐ Last Will & Testament	Acknowledgment	Jurat				1	2	3	4
☐ POA	Acknowledgment	Jurat	Copy	Oath	SW	1	2	3	4
☐ Trust Certification	Acknowledgment	Jurat				1	2	3	4

SIGNING ADDRESS	OTHERS IN ATTENDANCE	CLIENT / SIGNING SERVICE	FEE
		LENDER / LOAN NUMBER	

NOTES

_____

	ADDRESS	PHONE	SIGNATURE	INITIAL IF OATH/AFF TAKEN	RIGHT THUMB PRINT
1		PHONE / EMAIL	SIGNATURE	INITIAL IF OATH/AFF TAKEN	RIGHT THUMB PRINT
2	ADDRESS	PHONE / EMAIL	SIGNATURE	INITIAL IF OATH/AFF TAKEN	RIGHT THUMB PRINT
3	ADDRESS	PHONE / EMAIL	SIGNATURE	INITIAL IF OATH/AFF TAKEN	RIGHT THUMB PRINT
4	ADDRESS	PHONE / EMAIL	SIGNATURE	INITIAL IF OATH/AFF TAKEN	RIGHT THUMB PRINT

Notary Journal Entry

#	DATE / TIME	NAME	IDENTITY VERIFIED	WILLINGNESS & COMPETENCE	FORMAT
1	DATE _____ TIME _____	□ Signer □ Witness	□ D.L. □ Passport □ Credible Witness / □ Other	□ Expressed willingness □ Mentally alert □ Indicated understanding	□ Paper □ Electronic □ RON
2	DATE _____ TIME _____	□ Signer □ Witness	□ D.L. □ Passport □ Credible Witness / □ Other	□ Expressed willingness □ Mentally alert □ Indicated understanding	□ Paper □ Electronic □ RON
3	DATE _____ TIME _____	□ Signer □ Witness	□ D.L. □ Passport □ Credible Witness / □ Other	□ Expressed willingness □ Mentally alert □ Indicated understanding	□ Paper □ Electronic □ RON
4	DATE _____ TIME _____	□ Signer □ Witness	□ D.L. □ Passport □ Credible Witness / □ Other	□ Expressed willingness □ Mentally alert □ Indicated understanding	□ Paper □ Electronic □ RON

DOCUMENT(S) SIGNED

Document	Type	SIGNER 1 2 3 4
□ Borrower's Aff	Acknowledgment Jurat	1 2 3 4
□ Compliance Agrmt	Acknowledgment Jurat	1 2 3 4
□ Correction Agrmt	Acknowledgment Jurat	1 2 3 4
□ Debts/Leins Aff	Acknowledgment Jurat	1 2 3 4
□ Deed of Trust	Acknowledgment Jurat	1 2 3 4
□ Distrib of Proceeds	Acknowledgment Jurat	1 2 3 4
□ E&O Agrmt	Acknowledgment Jurat	1 2 3 4
□ Grant Deed	Acknowledgment Jurat	1 2 3 4
□ Marital Stat Aff	Acknowledgment Jurat	1 2 3 4
□ Mortgage	Acknowledgment Jurat	1 2 3 4
□ Occupancy/Fin Aff	Acknowledgment Jurat	1 2 3 4
□ Owner's Aff	Acknowledgment Jurat	1 2 3 4
□ Payoff Aff	Acknowledgment Jurat	1 2 3 4
□ Quit-Claim Deed	Acknowledgment Jurat	1 2 3 4
□ Sig/Name Aff	Acknowledgment Jurat	1 2 3 4
□ Survey Aff	Acknowledgment Jurat	1 2 3 4
□ Warranty Deed	Acknowledgment Jurat	1 2 3 4

Document	Type	SIGNER 1 2 3 4
□ Minor Medical Consent	Acknowledgment Jurat	1 2 3 4
□ Minor Passport Consent	Acknowledgment Jurat / Acknowledgment Jurat Copy Oath SW	1 2 3 4
□ Minor Travel Consent	Acknowledgment Jurat	1 2 3 4
□ Vehicle Duplicate Title	Acknowledgment Jurat Copy Oath SW	1 2 3 4
□ Vehicle Lein Release	Acknowledgment Jurat	1 2 3 4
□ Vehicle Odom/Vin Ver	Acknowledgment Jurat	1 2 3 4
□ Vehicle Title Transfer	Acknowledgment Jurat Copy Oath SW	1 2 3 4
□ Adv Health Care Dir	Acknowledgment Jurat	1 2 3 4
□ Assign of Digital Assets	Acknowledgment Jurat Copy Oath SW	1 2 3 4
□ Assign of Personal Prop	Acknowledgment Jurat	1 2 3 4
□ HIPAA Release	Acknowledgment Jurat	1 2 3 4
□ Living Trust	Acknowledgment Jurat Copy Oath SW	1 2 3 4
□ Last Will & Testament	Acknowledgment Jurat	1 2 3 4
□ POA	Acknowledgment Jurat	1 2 3 4
□ Trust Certification	Acknowledgment Jurat Copy Oath SW	1 2 3 4

SIGNING ADDRESS	OTHERS IN ATTENDANCE	CLIENT / SIGNING SERVICE	FEE
		LENDER / LOAN NUMBER	

NOTES

_____
_____
_____
_____
_____
_____
_____
_____
_____
_____
_____
_____
_____

	ADDRESS	PHONE	SIGNATURE	INITIAL IF OATH/AFF TAKEN	RIGHT THUMB PRINT
1		EMAIL			
2	ADDRESS	PHONE / EMAIL	SIGNATURE	INITIAL IF OATH/AFF TAKEN	RIGHT THUMB PRINT
3	ADDRESS	PHONE / EMAIL	SIGNATURE	INITIAL IF OATH/AFF TAKEN	RIGHT THUMB PRINT
4	ADDRESS	PHONE / EMAIL	SIGNATURE	INITIAL IF OATH/AFF TAKEN	RIGHT THUMB PRINT

Notary Journal Entries

Entry 1
DATE		
TIME		

NAME: ☐ Signer ☐ Witness

IDENTITY VERIFIED: ☐ D.L. ☐ Passport ☐ Credible Witness ☐ Other

WILLINGNESS & COMPETENCE: ☐ Expressed willingness ☐ Mentally alert ☐ Indicated understanding

FORMAT: ☐ Paper ☐ Electronic ☐ RON

Entry 2
DATE		
TIME		

NAME: ☐ Signer ☐ Witness

IDENTITY VERIFIED: ☐ D.L. ☐ Passport ☐ Credible Witness ☐ Other

WILLINGNESS & COMPETENCE: ☐ Expressed willingness ☐ Mentally alert ☐ Indicated understanding

FORMAT: ☐ Paper ☐ Electronic ☐ RON

Entry 3
DATE		
TIME		

NAME: ☐ Signer ☐ Witness

IDENTITY VERIFIED: ☐ D.L. ☐ Passport ☐ Credible Witness ☐ Other

WILLINGNESS & COMPETENCE: ☐ Expressed willingness ☐ Mentally alert ☐ Indicated understanding

FORMAT: ☐ Paper ☐ Electronic ☐ RON

Entry 4
DATE		
TIME		

NAME: ☐ Signer ☐ Witness

IDENTITY VERIFIED: ☐ D.L. ☐ Passport ☐ Credible Witness ☐ Other

WILLINGNESS & COMPETENCE: ☐ Expressed willingness ☐ Mentally alert ☐ Indicated understanding

FORMAT: ☐ Paper ☐ Electronic ☐ RON

DOCUMENT(S) SIGNED

Document	Type	Type		SIGNER			
☐ Minor Medical Consent	Acknowledgment	Jurat	Copy Oath SW	1	2	3	4
☐ Minor Passport Consent	Acknowledgment	Jurat	Copy Oath SW	1	2	3	4
☐ Minor Travel Consent	Acknowledgment	Jurat	Copy Oath SW	1	2	3	4
☐ Vehicle Duplicate Title	Acknowledgment	Jurat	Copy Oath SW	1	2	3	4
☐ Vehicle Lein Release	Acknowledgment	Jurat	Copy Oath SW	1	2	3	4
☐ Vehicle Odom/Vin Ver	Acknowledgment	Jurat	Copy Oath SW	1	2	3	4
☐ Vehicle Title Transfer	Acknowledgment	Jurat	Copy Oath SW	1	2	3	4
☐ Adv Health Care Dir	Acknowledgment	Jurat	Copy Oath SW	1	2	3	4
☐ Assign of Digital Assets	Acknowledgment	Jurat	Copy Oath SW	1	2	3	4
☐ Assign of Personal Prop	Acknowledgment	Jurat	Copy Oath SW	1	2	3	4
☐ HIPAA Release	Acknowledgment	Jurat	Copy Oath SW	1	2	3	4
☐ Living Trust	Acknowledgment	Jurat	Copy Oath SW	1	2	3	4
☐ Last Will & Testament	Acknowledgment	Jurat	Copy Oath SW	1	2	3	4
☐ POA	Acknowledgment	Jurat	Copy Oath SW	1	2	3	4
☐ Trust Certification	Acknowledgment	Jurat	Copy Oath SW	1	2	3	4

Document	Type	Type	SIGNER			
☐ Borrower's Aff	Acknowledgment	Jurat	1	2	3	4
☐ Compliance Agrmt	Acknowledgment	Jurat	1	2	3	4
☐ Correction Agrmt	Acknowledgment	Jurat	1	2	3	4
☐ Debts/Leins Aff	Acknowledgment	Jurat	1	2	3	4
☐ Deed of Trust	Acknowledgment	Jurat	1	2	3	4
☐ Distrib of Proceeds	Acknowledgment	Jurat	1	2	3	4
☐ E&O Agrmt	Acknowledgment	Jurat	1	2	3	4
☐ Grant Deed	Acknowledgment	Jurat	1	2	3	4
☐ Marital Stat Aff	Acknowledgment	Jurat	1	2	3	4
☐ Mortgage	Acknowledgment	Jurat	1	2	3	4
☐ Occupancy/Fin Aff	Acknowledgment	Jurat	1	2	3	4
☐ Owner's Aff	Acknowledgment	Jurat	1	2	3	4
☐ Payoff Aff	Acknowledgment	Jurat	1	2	3	4
☐ Quit-Claim Deed	Acknowledgment	Jurat	1	2	3	4
☐ Sig/Name Aff	Acknowledgment	Jurat	1	2	3	4
☐ Survey Aff	Acknowledgment	Jurat	1	2	3	4
☐ Warranty Deed	Acknowledgment	Jurat	1	2	3	4

SIGNING ADDRESS	OTHERS IN ATTENDANCE	CLIENT / SIGNING SERVICE	FEE
		LENDER / LOAN NUMBER	

NOTES

	ADDRESS	PHONE	EMAIL	SIGNATURE	INITIAL IF OATH/AFF TAKEN	RIGHT THUMB PRINT
1						
2						
3						
4						

Signer/Witness Record

#	DATE / TIME	NAME	IDENTITY VERIFIED	WILLINGNESS & COMPETENCE	FORMAT
1	DATE ___ / TIME ___	☐ Signer ☐ Witness	☐ D.L. ☐ Passport ☐ Credible Witness ☐ Other	☐ Expressed willingness ☐ Mentally alert ☐ Indicated understanding	☐ Paper ☐ Electronic ☐ RON
2	DATE ___ / TIME ___	☐ Signer ☐ Witness	☐ D.L. ☐ Passport ☐ Credible Witness ☐ Other	☐ Expressed willingness ☐ Mentally alert ☐ Indicated understanding	☐ Paper ☐ Electronic ☐ RON
3	DATE ___ / TIME ___	☐ Signer ☐ Witness	☐ D.L. ☐ Passport ☐ Credible Witness ☐ Other	☐ Expressed willingness ☐ Mentally alert ☐ Indicated understanding	☐ Paper ☐ Electronic ☐ RON
4	DATE ___ / TIME ___	☐ Signer ☐ Witness	☐ D.L. ☐ Passport ☐ Credible Witness ☐ Other	☐ Expressed willingness ☐ Mentally alert ☐ Indicated understanding	☐ Paper ☐ Electronic ☐ RON

DOCUMENT(S) SIGNED

Document	Type		SIGNER			
			1	2	3	4
☐ Borrower's Aff	Acknowledgment	Jurat	1	2	3	4
☐ Compliance Agrmt	Acknowledgment	Jurat	1	2	3	4
☐ Correction Agrmt	Acknowledgment	Jurat	1	2	3	4
☐ Debts/Leins Aff	Acknowledgment	Jurat	1	2	3	4
☐ Deed of Trust	Acknowledgment	Jurat	1	2	3	4
☐ Distrib of Proceeds	Acknowledgment	Jurat	1	2	3	4
☐ E&O Agrmt	Acknowledgment	Jurat	1	2	3	4
☐ Grant Deed	Acknowledgment	Jurat	1	2	3	4
☐ Marital Stat Aff	Acknowledgment	Jurat	1	2	3	4
☐ Mortgage	Acknowledgment	Jurat	1	2	3	4
☐ Occupancy/Fin Aff	Acknowledgment	Jurat	1	2	3	4
☐ Owner's Aff	Acknowledgment	Jurat	1	2	3	4
☐ Payoff Aff	Acknowledgment	Jurat	1	2	3	4
☐ Quit-Claim Deed	Acknowledgment	Jurat	1	2	3	4
☐ Sig/Name Aff	Acknowledgment	Jurat	1	2	3	4
☐ Survey Aff	Acknowledgment	Jurat	1	2	3	4
☐ Warranty Deed	Acknowledgment	Jurat	1	2	3	4

Document	Type				SIGNER			
					1	2	3	4
☐ Minor Medical Consent	Acknowledgment	Jurat			1	2	3	4
☐ Minor Passport Consent	Acknowledgment	Jurat			1	2	3	4
☐ Minor Travel Consent	Acknowledgment	Jurat			1	2	3	4
☐ Vehicle Duplicate Title	Acknowledgment	Jurat			1	2	3	4
☐ Vehicle Lein Release	Acknowledgment	Jurat			1	2	3	4
☐ Vehicle Odom/Vin Ver	Acknowledgment	Jurat			1	2	3	4
☐ Vehicle Title Transfer	Acknowledgment	Jurat			1	2	3	4
☐ Adv Health Care Dir	Acknowledgment	Jurat			1	2	3	4
☐ Assign of Digital Assets	Acknowledgment	Jurat			1	2	3	4
☐ Assign of Personal Prop	Acknowledgment	Jurat			1	2	3	4
☐ HIPAA Release	Acknowledgment	Jurat			1	2	3	4
☐ Living Trust	Acknowledgment	Jurat			1	2	3	4
☐ Last Will & Testament	Acknowledgment	Jurat			1	2	3	4
☐ POA	Acknowledgment	Jurat	Copy	Oath	SW	1	2	3	4
☐ Trust Certification	Acknowledgment	Jurat	Copy	Oath	SW	1	2	3	4

(Right-hand documents also include: ☐ Acknowledgment Jurat Copy Oath SW 1 2 3 4 grouped columns)

SIGNING ADDRESS	OTHERS IN ATTENDANCE	CLIENT / SIGNING SERVICE	FEE
		LENDER / LOAN NUMBER	

NOTES

_____
_____
_____
_____
_____
_____
_____
_____
_____
_____
_____
_____
_____

	ADDRESS	PHONE / EMAIL	SIGNATURE	INITIAL IF OATH/AFF TAKEN	RIGHT THUMB PRINT
1		PHONE / EMAIL	SIGNATURE		RIGHT THUMB PRINT
2		PHONE / EMAIL	SIGNATURE		RIGHT THUMB PRINT
3		PHONE / EMAIL	SIGNATURE		RIGHT THUMB PRINT
4		PHONE / EMAIL	SIGNATURE		RIGHT THUMB PRINT

Notary Journal Entries

Entry 1
DATE	
TIME	

NAME: ☐ Signer ☐ Witness

IDENTITY VERIFIED: ☐ D.L. ☐ Passport ☐ Credible Witness ☐ Other

WILLINGNESS & COMPETENCE: ☐ Expressed willingness ☐ Mentally alert ☐ Indicated understanding

FORMAT: ☐ Paper ☐ Electronic ☐ RON

Entry 2
DATE	
TIME	

NAME: ☐ Signer ☐ Witness

IDENTITY VERIFIED: ☐ D.L. ☐ Passport ☐ Credible Witness ☐ Other

WILLINGNESS & COMPETENCE: ☐ Expressed willingness ☐ Mentally alert ☐ Indicated understanding

FORMAT: ☐ Paper ☐ Electronic ☐ RON

Entry 3
DATE	
TIME	

NAME: ☐ Signer ☐ Witness

IDENTITY VERIFIED: ☐ D.L. ☐ Passport ☐ Credible Witness ☐ Other

WILLINGNESS & COMPETENCE: ☐ Expressed willingness ☐ Mentally alert ☐ Indicated understanding

FORMAT: ☐ Paper ☐ Electronic ☐ RON

Entry 4
DATE	
TIME	

NAME: ☐ Signer ☐ Witness

IDENTITY VERIFIED: ☐ D.L. ☐ Passport ☐ Credible Witness ☐ Other

WILLINGNESS & COMPETENCE: ☐ Expressed willingness ☐ Mentally alert ☐ Indicated understanding

FORMAT: ☐ Paper ☐ Electronic ☐ RON

DOCUMENT(S) SIGNED

Document	SIGNER 1 2 3 4	Act Type
☐ Borrower's Aff	1 2 3 4	Acknowledgment Jurat
☐ Compliance Agrmt	1 2 3 4	Acknowledgment Jurat
☐ Correction Agrmt	1 2 3 4	Acknowledgment Jurat
☐ Debts/Leins Aff	1 2 3 4	Acknowledgment Jurat
☐ Deed of Trust	1 2 3 4	Acknowledgment Jurat
☐ Distrib of Proceeds	1 2 3 4	Acknowledgment Jurat
☐ E&O Agrmt	1 2 3 4	Acknowledgment Jurat
☐ Grant Deed	1 2 3 4	Acknowledgment Jurat
☐ Marital Stat Aff	1 2 3 4	Acknowledgment Jurat
☐ Mortgage	1 2 3 4	Acknowledgment Jurat
☐ Occupancy/Fin Aff	1 2 3 4	Acknowledgment Jurat
☐ Owner's Aff	1 2 3 4	Acknowledgment Jurat
☐ Payoff Aff	1 2 3 4	Acknowledgment Jurat
☐ Quit-Claim Deed	1 2 3 4	Acknowledgment Jurat
☐ Sig/Name Aff	1 2 3 4	Acknowledgment Jurat
☐ Survey Aff	1 2 3 4	Acknowledgment Jurat
☐ Warranty Deed	1 2 3 4	Acknowledgment Jurat

Document	SIGNER 1 2 3 4	Act Type
☐ Minor Medical Consent	1 2 3 4	Acknowledgment Jurat
☐ Minor Passport Consent	1 2 3 4	Acknowledgment Jurat
☐ Minor Travel Consent	1 2 3 4	Acknowledgment Jurat
☐ Vehicle Duplicate Title	1 2 3 4	Acknowledgment Jurat
☐ Vehicle Lein Release	1 2 3 4	Acknowledgment Jurat
☐ Vehicle Odom/Vin Ver	1 2 3 4	Acknowledgment Jurat
☐ Vehicle Title Transfer	1 2 3 4	Acknowledgment Jurat
☐ Adv Health Care Dir	1 2 3 4	Acknowledgment Jurat
☐ Assign of Digital Assets	1 2 3 4	Acknowledgment Jurat
☐ Assign of Personal Prop	1 2 3 4	Acknowledgment Jurat
☐ HIPAA Release	1 2 3 4	Acknowledgment Jurat
☐ Living Trust	1 2 3 4	Acknowledgment Jurat
☐ Last Will & Testament	1 2 3 4	Acknowledgment Jurat
☐ POA	1 2 3 4	Acknowledgment Jurat
☐ Trust Certification	1 2 3 4	Acknowledgment Jurat

Additional act columns (right portion): ☐ Acknowledgment Jurat Copy Oath SW — 1 2 3 4 (grouped in sets)

SIGNING ADDRESS	OTHERS IN ATTENDANCE	CLIENT / SIGNING SERVICE	FEE
		LENDER / LOAN NUMBER	

NOTES

#	ADDRESS	SIGNATURE	PHONE	EMAIL	INITIAL IF OATH/AFF TAKEN	RIGHT THUMB PRINT
1						
2						
3						
4						

Notary Journal Entries

Entry 1

Field	Details
DATE	
TIME	
NAME	□ Signer □ Witness
IDENTITY VERIFIED	□ D.L. □ Passport □ Credible Witness □ Other
WILLINGNESS & COMPETENCE	□ Expressed willingness □ Mentally alert □ Indicated understanding
FORMAT	□ Paper □ Electronic □ RON

Entry 2

Field	Details
DATE	
TIME	
NAME	□ Signer □ Witness
IDENTITY VERIFIED	□ D.L. □ Passport □ Credible Witness □ Other
WILLINGNESS & COMPETENCE	□ Expressed willingness □ Mentally alert □ Indicated understanding
FORMAT	□ Paper □ Electronic □ RON

Entry 3

Field	Details
DATE	
TIME	
NAME	□ Signer □ Witness
IDENTITY VERIFIED	□ D.L. □ Passport □ Credible Witness □ Other
WILLINGNESS & COMPETENCE	□ Expressed willingness □ Mentally alert □ Indicated understanding
FORMAT	□ Paper □ Electronic □ RON

Entry 4

Field	Details
DATE	
TIME	
NAME	□ Signer □ Witness
IDENTITY VERIFIED	□ D.L. □ Passport □ Credible Witness □ Other
WILLINGNESS & COMPETENCE	□ Expressed willingness □ Mentally alert □ Indicated understanding
FORMAT	□ Paper □ Electronic □ RON

DOCUMENT(S) SIGNED

Document	Type					SIGNER			
						1	2	3	4
□ Borrower's Aff	Acknowledgment	Jurat				1	2	3	4
□ Compliance Agrmt	Acknowledgment	Jurat				1	2	3	4
□ Correction Agrmt	Acknowledgment	Jurat				1	2	3	4
□ Debts/Leins Aff	Acknowledgment	Jurat				1	2	3	4
□ Deed of Trust	Acknowledgment	Jurat				1	2	3	4
□ Distrib of Proceeds	Acknowledgment	Jurat				1	2	3	4
□ E&O Agrmt	Acknowledgment	Jurat				1	2	3	4
□ Grant Deed	Acknowledgment	Jurat				1	2	3	4
□ Marital Stat Aff	Acknowledgment	Jurat				1	2	3	4
□ Mortgage	Acknowledgment	Jurat				1	2	3	4
□ Occupancy/Fin Aff	Acknowledgment	Jurat				1	2	3	4
□ Owner's Aff	Acknowledgment	Jurat				1	2	3	4
□ Payoff Aff	Acknowledgment	Jurat				1	2	3	4
□ Quit-Claim Deed	Acknowledgment	Jurat				1	2	3	4
□ Sig/Name Aff	Acknowledgment	Jurat				1	2	3	4
□ Survey Aff	Acknowledgment	Jurat				1	2	3	4
□ Warranty Deed	Acknowledgment	Jurat				1	2	3	4

Document	Type					SIGNER			
						1	2	3	4
□ Minor Medical Consent	Acknowledgment	Jurat							
□ Minor Passport Consent	Acknowledgment	Jurat	Copy	Oath	SW	1	2	3	4
□ Minor Travel Consent	Acknowledgment	Jurat	Copy	Oath	SW	1	2	3	4
□ Vehicle Duplicate Title	Acknowledgment	Jurat							
□ Vehicle Lein Release	Acknowledgment	Jurat	Copy	Oath	SW	1	2	3	4
□ Vehicle Odom/Vin Ver	Acknowledgment	Jurat							
□ Vehicle Title Transfer	Acknowledgment	Jurat	Copy	Oath	SW	1	2	3	4
□ Adv Health Care Dir	Acknowledgment	Jurat							
□ Assign of Digital Assets	Acknowledgment	Jurat	Copy	Oath	SW	1	2	3	4
□ Assign of Personal Prop	Acknowledgment	Jurat							
□ HIPAA Release	Acknowledgment	Jurat							
□ Living Trust	Acknowledgment	Jurat	Copy	Oath	SW	1	2	3	4
□ Last Will & Testament	Acknowledgment	Jurat							
□ POA	Acknowledgment	Jurat							
□ Trust Certification	Acknowledgment	Jurat	Copy	Oath	SW	1	2	3	4

SIGNING ADDRESS	OTHERS IN ATTENDANCE	CLIENT / SIGNING SERVICE	FEE
		LENDER / LOAN NUMBER	

NOTES

	ADDRESS	PHONE	SIGNATURE	INITIAL IF OATH/AFF TAKEN	RIGHT THUMB PRINT
1		EMAIL			
2	ADDRESS	PHONE	SIGNATURE	INITIAL IF OATH/AFF TAKEN	RIGHT THUMB PRINT
		EMAIL			
3	ADDRESS	PHONE	SIGNATURE	INITIAL IF OATH/AFF TAKEN	RIGHT THUMB PRINT
		EMAIL			
4	ADDRESS	PHONE	SIGNATURE	INITIAL IF OATH/AFF TAKEN	RIGHT THUMB PRINT
		EMAIL			

Notary Journal Entry (Entries 1–4)

Entry 1
- DATE: _____ TIME: _____
- NAME: ☐ Signer ☐ Witness
- IDENTITY VERIFIED: ☐ D.L. ☐ Passport ☐ Credible Witness ☐ Other
- WILLINGNESS & COMPETENCE: ☐ Expressed willingness ☐ Mentally alert ☐ Indicated understanding
- FORMAT: ☐ Paper ☐ Electronic ☐ RON

Entry 2
- DATE: _____ TIME: _____
- NAME: ☐ Signer ☐ Witness
- IDENTITY VERIFIED: ☐ D.L. ☐ Passport ☐ Credible Witness ☐ Other
- WILLINGNESS & COMPETENCE: ☐ Expressed willingness ☐ Mentally alert ☐ Indicated understanding
- FORMAT: ☐ Paper ☐ Electronic ☐ RON

Entry 3
- DATE: _____ TIME: _____
- NAME: ☐ Signer ☐ Witness
- IDENTITY VERIFIED: ☐ D.L. ☐ Passport ☐ Credible Witness ☐ Other
- WILLINGNESS & COMPETENCE: ☐ Expressed willingness ☐ Mentally alert ☐ Indicated understanding
- FORMAT: ☐ Paper ☐ Electronic ☐ RON

Entry 4
- DATE: _____ TIME: _____
- NAME: ☐ Signer ☐ Witness
- IDENTITY VERIFIED: ☐ D.L. ☐ Passport ☐ Credible Witness ☐ Other
- WILLINGNESS & COMPETENCE: ☐ Expressed willingness ☐ Mentally alert ☐ Indicated understanding
- FORMAT: ☐ Paper ☐ Electronic ☐ RON

DOCUMENT(S) SIGNED

Document	Notarial Act	SIGNER 1	2	3	4
☐ Borrower's Aff	Acknowledgment Jurat	1	2	3	4
☐ Compliance Agrmt	Acknowledgment Jurat	1	2	3	4
☐ Correction Agrmt	Acknowledgment Jurat	1	2	3	4
☐ Debs/Leins Aff	Acknowledgment Jurat	1	2	3	4
☐ Deed of Trust	Acknowledgment Jurat	1	2	3	4
☐ Distrib of Proceeds	Acknowledgment Jurat	1	2	3	4
☐ E&O Agrmt	Acknowledgment Jurat	1	2	3	4
☐ Grant Deed	Acknowledgment Jurat	1	2	3	4
☐ Marital Stat Aff	Acknowledgment Jurat	1	2	3	4
☐ Mortgage	Acknowledgment Jurat	1	2	3	4
☐ Occupancy/Fin Aff	Acknowledgment Jurat	1	2	3	4
☐ Owner's Aff	Acknowledgment Jurat	1	2	3	4
☐ Payoff Aff	Acknowledgment Jurat	1	2	3	4
☐ Quit-Claim Deed	Acknowledgment Jurat	1	2	3	4
☐ Sig/Name Aff	Acknowledgment Jurat	1	2	3	4
☐ Survey Aff	Acknowledgment Jurat	1	2	3	4
☐ Warranty Deed	Acknowledgment Jurat	1	2	3	4

Document	Notarial Act	SIGNER 1	2	3	4
☐ Minor Medical Consent	Acknowledgment Jurat	1	2	3	4
☐ Minor Passport Consent	Acknowledgment Jurat	1	2	3	4
☐ Minor Travel Consent	Acknowledgment Jurat	1	2	3	4
☐ Vehicle Duplicate Title	Acknowledgment Jurat	1	2	3	4
☐ Vehicle Lein Release	Acknowledgment Jurat	1	2	3	4
☐ Vehicle Odom/Vin Ver	Acknowledgment Jurat	1	2	3	4
☐ Vehicle Title Transfer	Acknowledgment Jurat	1	2	3	4
☐ Adv Health Care Dir	Acknowledgment Jurat	1	2	3	4
☐ Assign of Digital Assets	Acknowledgment Jurat	1	2	3	4
☐ Assign of Personal Prop	Acknowledgment Jurat	1	2	3	4
☐ HIPAA Release	Acknowledgment Jurat	1	2	3	4
☐ Living Trust	Acknowledgment Jurat	1	2	3	4
☐ Last Will & Testament	Acknowledgment Jurat	1	2	3	4
☐ POA	Acknowledgment Jurat	1	2	3	4
☐ Trust Certification	Acknowledgment Jurat	1	2	3	4

Additional acts (right column): Acknowledgment Jurat Copy Oath SW — 1 2 3 4

SIGNING ADDRESS	OTHERS IN ATTENDANCE	CLIENT / SIGNING SERVICE	FEE
		LENDER / LOAN NUMBER	

NOTES

_____
_____
_____
_____
_____
_____
_____
_____
_____
_____
_____
_____
_____

#	ADDRESS	PHONE / EMAIL	SIGNATURE	INITIAL IF OATH/AFF TAKEN	RIGHT THUMB PRINT
1		PHONE / EMAIL	SIGNATURE		RIGHT THUMB PRINT
2		PHONE / EMAIL	SIGNATURE		RIGHT THUMB PRINT
3		PHONE / EMAIL	SIGNATURE		RIGHT THUMB PRINT
4		PHONE / EMAIL	SIGNATURE		RIGHT THUMB PRINT

Signer Entries 1–4

#	DATE / TIME	NAME	WILLINGNESS & COMPETENCE	IDENTITY VERIFIED	FORMAT
1	DATE ___ TIME ___	☐ Signer ☐ Witness	☐ Expressed willingness ☐ Mentally alert ☐ Indicated understanding	☐ D.L. ☐ Passport ☐ Credible Witness ☐ Other	☐ Paper ☐ Electronic ☐ RON
2	DATE ___ TIME ___	☐ Signer ☐ Witness	☐ Expressed willingness ☐ Mentally alert ☐ Indicated understanding	☐ D.L. ☐ Passport ☐ Credible Witness ☐ Other	☐ Paper ☐ Electronic ☐ RON
3	DATE ___ TIME ___	☐ Signer ☐ Witness	☐ Expressed willingness ☐ Mentally alert ☐ Indicated understanding	☐ D.L. ☐ Passport ☐ Credible Witness ☐ Other	☐ Paper ☐ Electronic ☐ RON
4	DATE ___ TIME ___	☐ Signer ☐ Witness	☐ Expressed willingness ☐ Mentally alert ☐ Indicated understanding	☐ D.L. ☐ Passport ☐ Credible Witness ☐ Other	☐ Paper ☐ Electronic ☐ RON

DOCUMENT(S) SIGNED

Document	Type	SIGNER 1 2 3 4
☐ Borrower's Aff	Acknowledgment Jurat ___	1 2 3 4
☐ Compliance Agrmt	Acknowledgment Jurat ___	1 2 3 4
☐ Correction Agrmt	Acknowledgment Jurat ___	1 2 3 4
☐ Debts/Leins Aff	Acknowledgment Jurat ___	1 2 3 4
☐ Deed of Trust	Acknowledgment Jurat ___	1 2 3 4
☐ Distrib of Proceeds	Acknowledgment Jurat ___	1 2 3 4
☐ E&O Agrmt	Acknowledgment Jurat ___	1 2 3 4
☐ Grant Deed	Acknowledgment Jurat ___	1 2 3 4
☐ Marital Stat Aff	Acknowledgment Jurat ___	1 2 3 4
☐ Mortgage	Acknowledgment Jurat ___	1 2 3 4
☐ Occupancy/Fin Aff	Acknowledgment Jurat ___	1 2 3 4
☐ Owner's Aff	Acknowledgment Jurat ___	1 2 3 4
☐ Payoff Aff	Acknowledgment Jurat ___	1 2 3 4
☐ Quit-Claim Deed	Acknowledgment Jurat ___	1 2 3 4
☐ Sig/Name Aff	Acknowledgment Jurat ___	1 2 3 4
☐ Survey Aff	Acknowledgment Jurat ___	1 2 3 4
☐ Warranty Deed	Acknowledgment Jurat ___	1 2 3 4

Document	Type	SIGNER 1 2 3 4
☐ Minor Medical Consent	Acknowledgment Jurat	1 2 3 4
☐ Minor Passport Consent	Acknowledgment Jurat	1 2 3 4
☐ Minor Travel Consent	Acknowledgment Jurat	1 2 3 4
☐ Vehicle Duplicate Title	Acknowledgment Jurat	1 2 3 4
☐ Vehicle Lein Release	Acknowledgment Jurat	1 2 3 4
☐ Vehicle Odom/Vin Ver	Acknowledgment Jurat	1 2 3 4
☐ Vehicle Title Transfer	Acknowledgment Jurat	1 2 3 4
☐ Adv Health Care Dir	Acknowledgment Jurat	1 2 3 4
☐ Assign of Digital Assets	Acknowledgment Jurat	1 2 3 4
☐ Assign of Personal Prop	Acknowledgment Jurat	1 2 3 4
☐ HIPAA Release	Acknowledgment Jurat	1 2 3 4
☐ Living Trust	Acknowledgment Jurat ___	1 2 3 4
☐ Last Will & Testament	Acknowledgment Jurat	1 2 3 4
☐ POA	Acknowledgment Jurat ___	1 2 3 4
☐ Trust Certification	Acknowledgment Jurat ___	1 2 3 4

For the right-hand documents, additional options apply: ☐ Acknowledgment Jurat Copy Oath SW — 1 2 3 4

			FEE
SIGNING ADDRESS	OTHERS IN ATTENDANCE	CLIENT / SIGNING SERVICE	
		LENDER / LOAN NUMBER	

NOTES

#	SIGNATURE	PHONE	EMAIL	ADDRESS	INITIAL IF OATH/AFF TAKEN	RIGHT THUMB PRINT
1						
2						
3						
4						

1	DATE TIME	NAME ❑ Signer ❑ Witness	IDENTITY VERIFIED ❑ D.L. ❑ Passport ❑ Credible Witness ❑ Other	WILLINGNESS & COMPETENCE ❑ Expressed willingness ❑ Mentally alert ❑ Indicated understanding	FORMAT ❑ Paper ❑ Electronic ❑ RON
2	DATE TIME	NAME ❑ Signer ❑ Witness	IDENTITY VERIFIED ❑ D.L. ❑ Passport ❑ Credible Witness ❑ Other	WILLINGNESS & COMPETENCE ❑ Expressed willingness ❑ Mentally alert ❑ Indicated understanding	FORMAT ❑ Paper ❑ Electronic ❑ RON
3	DATE TIME	NAME ❑ Signer ❑ Witness	IDENTITY VERIFIED ❑ D.L. ❑ Passport ❑ Credible Witness ❑ Other	WILLINGNESS & COMPETENCE ❑ Expressed willingness ❑ Mentally alert ❑ Indicated understanding	FORMAT ❑ Paper ❑ Electronic ❑ RON
4	DATE TIME	NAME ❑ Signer ❑ Witness	IDENTITY VERIFIED ❑ D.L. ❑ Passport ❑ Credible Witness ❑ Other	WILLINGNESS & COMPETENCE ❑ Expressed willingness ❑ Mentally alert ❑ Indicated understanding	FORMAT ❑ Paper ❑ Electronic ❑ RON

DOCUMENT(S) SIGNED			SIGNER				SIGNER	
❑ Borrower's Aff	Acknowledgment	Jurat ______	1 2 3 4	❑ Minor Medical Consent	Acknowledgment	Jurat ______	1 2 3 4	❑ ______
❑ Compliance Agrmt	Acknowledgment	Jurat ______	1 2 3 4	❑ Minor Passport Consent	Acknowledgment	Jurat ______	1 2 3 4	Acknowledgment Jurat Copy Oath SW 1 2 3 4
❑ Correction Agrmt	Acknowledgment	Jurat ______	1 2 3 4	❑ Minor Travel Consent	Acknowledgment	Jurat ______	1 2 3 4	
❑ Debts/Leins Aff	Acknowledgment	Jurat ______	1 2 3 4					❑ ______
❑ Deed of Trust	Acknowledgment	Jurat ______	1 2 3 4	❑ Vehicle Duplicate Title	Acknowledgment	Jurat ______	1 2 3 4	Acknowledgment Jurat Copy Oath SW 1 2 3 4
❑ Distrib of Proceeds	Acknowledgment	Jurat ______	1 2 3 4	❑ Vehicle Lein Release	Acknowledgment	Jurat ______	1 2 3 4	
❑ E&O Agrmt	Acknowledgment	Jurat ______	1 2 3 4	❑ Vehicle Odom/Vin Ver	Acknowledgment	Jurat ______	1 2 3 4	❑ ______
❑ Grant Deed	Acknowledgment	Jurat ______	1 2 3 4	❑ Vehicle Title Transfer	Acknowledgment	Jurat ______	1 2 3 4	Acknowledgment Jurat Copy Oath SW 1 2 3 4
❑ Marital Stat Aff	Acknowledgment	Jurat ______	1 2 3 4					
❑ Mortgage	Acknowledgment	Jurat ______	1 2 3 4	❑ Adv Health Care Dir	Acknowledgment	Jurat ______	1 2 3 4	❑ ______
❑ Occupancy/Fin Aff	Acknowledgment	Jurat ______	1 2 3 4	❑ Assign of Digital Assets	Acknowledgment	Jurat ______	1 2 3 4	Acknowledgment Jurat Copy Oath SW 1 2 3 4
❑ Owner's Aff	Acknowledgment	Jurat ______	1 2 3 4	❑ Assign of Personal Prop	Acknowledgment	Jurat ______	1 2 3 4	
❑ Payoff Aff	Acknowledgment	Jurat ______	1 2 3 4	❑ HIPAA Release	Acknowledgment	Jurat ______	1 2 3 4	❑ ______
❑ Quit-Claim Deed	Acknowledgment	Jurat ______	1 2 3 4	❑ Living Trust ______	Acknowledgment	Jurat ______	1 2 3 4	Acknowledgment Jurat Copy Oath SW 1 2 3 4
❑ Sig/Name Aff	Acknowledgment	Jurat ______	1 2 3 4	❑ Last Will & Testament	Acknowledgment	Jurat ______	1 2 3 4	
❑ Survey Aff	Acknowledgment	Jurat ______	1 2 3 4	❑ POA ______	Acknowledgment	Jurat ______	1 2 3 4	❑ ______
❑ Warranty Deed	Acknowledgment	Jurat ______	1 2 3 4	❑ Trust Certification	Acknowledgment	Jurat ______	1 2 3 4	Acknowledgment Jurat Copy Oath SW 1 2 3 4

Signing Address	Others in Attendance	Client / Signing Service Lender / Loan Number	Fee

Notes

1	Address	Phone Email	Signature	Initial if oath/aff taken	Right Thumb Print
2	Address	Phone Email	Signature	Initial if oath/aff taken	Right Thumb Print
3	Address	Phone Email	Signature	Initial if oath/aff taken	Right Thumb Print
4	Address	Phone Email	Signature	Initial if oath/aff taken	Right Thumb Print

Notary Journal Entries

Entry 1
DATE		
TIME		

NAME: ☐ Signer ☐ Witness

IDENTITY VERIFIED: ☐ D.L. ☐ Passport ☐ Credible Witness ☐ Other

WILLINGNESS & COMPETENCE: ☐ Expressed willingness ☐ Mentally alert ☐ Indicated understanding

FORMAT: ☐ Paper ☐ Electronic ☐ RON

Entry 2
DATE		
TIME		

NAME: ☐ Signer ☐ Witness

IDENTITY VERIFIED: ☐ D.L. ☐ Passport ☐ Credible Witness ☐ Other

WILLINGNESS & COMPETENCE: ☐ Expressed willingness ☐ Mentally alert ☐ Indicated understanding

FORMAT: ☐ Paper ☐ Electronic ☐ RON

Entry 3
DATE		
TIME		

NAME: ☐ Signer ☐ Witness

IDENTITY VERIFIED: ☐ D.L. ☐ Passport ☐ Credible Witness ☐ Other

WILLINGNESS & COMPETENCE: ☐ Expressed willingness ☐ Mentally alert ☐ Indicated understanding

FORMAT: ☐ Paper ☐ Electronic ☐ RON

Entry 4
DATE		
TIME		

NAME: ☐ Signer ☐ Witness

IDENTITY VERIFIED: ☐ D.L. ☐ Passport ☐ Credible Witness ☐ Other

WILLINGNESS & COMPETENCE: ☐ Expressed willingness ☐ Mentally alert ☐ Indicated understanding

FORMAT: ☐ Paper ☐ Electronic ☐ RON

DOCUMENT(S) SIGNED

Document	Notarial Act		SIGNER 1 2 3 4
☐ Borrower's Aff	Acknowledgment	Jurat	1 2 3 4
☐ Compliance Agrmt	Acknowledgment	Jurat	1 2 3 4
☐ Correction Agrmt	Acknowledgment	Jurat	1 2 3 4
☐ Debts/Leins Aff	Acknowledgment	Jurat	1 2 3 4
☐ Deed of Trust	Acknowledgment	Jurat	1 2 3 4
☐ Distrib of Proceeds	Acknowledgment	Jurat	1 2 3 4
☐ E&O Agrmt	Acknowledgment	Jurat	1 2 3 4
☐ Grant Deed	Acknowledgment	Jurat	1 2 3 4
☐ Marital Stat Aff	Acknowledgment	Jurat	1 2 3 4
☐ Mortgage	Acknowledgment	Jurat	1 2 3 4
☐ Occupancy/Fin Aff	Acknowledgment	Jurat	1 2 3 4
☐ Owner's Aff	Acknowledgment	Jurat	1 2 3 4
☐ Payoff Aff	Acknowledgment	Jurat	1 2 3 4
☐ Quit-Claim Deed	Acknowledgment	Jurat	1 2 3 4
☐ Sig/Name Aff	Acknowledgment	Jurat	1 2 3 4
☐ Survey Aff	Acknowledgment	Jurat	1 2 3 4
☐ Warranty Deed	Acknowledgment	Jurat	1 2 3 4

Document	Notarial Act		SIGNER 1 2 3 4
☐ Minor Medical Consent	Acknowledgment	Jurat	1 2 3 4
☐ Minor Passport Consent	Acknowledgment	Jurat	1 2 3 4
☐ Minor Travel Consent	Acknowledgment	Jurat	1 2 3 4
☐ Vehicle Duplicate Title	Acknowledgment	Jurat	1 2 3 4
☐ Vehicle Lein Release	Acknowledgment	Jurat	1 2 3 4
☐ Vehicle Odom/Vin Ver	Acknowledgment	Jurat	1 2 3 4
☐ Vehicle Title Transfer	Acknowledgment	Jurat	1 2 3 4
☐ Adv Health Care Dir	Acknowledgment	Jurat	1 2 3 4
☐ Assign of Digital Assets	Acknowledgment	Jurat	1 2 3 4
☐ Assign of Personal Prop	Acknowledgment	Jurat	1 2 3 4
☐ HIPAA Release	Acknowledgment	Jurat	1 2 3 4
☐ Living Trust ____	Acknowledgment	Jurat	1 2 3 4
☐ Last Will & Testament	Acknowledgment	Jurat	1 2 3 4
☐ POA ____	Acknowledgment	Jurat	1 2 3 4
☐ Trust Certification	Acknowledgment	Jurat	1 2 3 4

The following rows include additional columns — **Copy**, **Oath**, **SW** — with SIGNER 1 2 3 4:

Document	Acknowledgment	Jurat	Copy	Oath	SW	SIGNER 1 2 3 4	☐
	Acknowledgment	Jurat	Copy	Oath	SW	1 2 3 4	☐
	Acknowledgment	Jurat	Copy	Oath	SW	1 2 3 4	☐
	Acknowledgment	Jurat	Copy	Oath	SW	1 2 3 4	☐
	Acknowledgment	Jurat	Copy	Oath	SW	1 2 3 4	☐
	Acknowledgment	Jurat	Copy	Oath	SW	1 2 3 4	☐

SIGNING ADDRESS	OTHERS IN ATTENDANCE	CLIENT / SIGNING SERVICE	FEE
		LENDER / LOAN NUMBER	

NOTES

	ADDRESS	PHONE	EMAIL	SIGNATURE	INITIAL IF OATH/AFF TAKEN	RIGHT THUMB PRINT
1						
2						
3						
4						

Notary Journal Entry (Entries 1–4)

#	DATE / TIME	NAME	IDENTITY VERIFIED	WILLINGNESS & COMPETENCE	FORMAT
1	DATE __ / TIME __	☐ Signer ☐ Witness	☐ D.L. ☐ Passport ☐ Credible Witness ☐ Other	☐ Expressed willingness ☐ Mentally alert ☐ Indicated understanding	☐ Paper ☐ Electronic ☐ RON
2	DATE __ / TIME __	☐ Signer ☐ Witness	☐ D.L. ☐ Passport ☐ Credible Witness ☐ Other	☐ Expressed willingness ☐ Mentally alert ☐ Indicated understanding	☐ Paper ☐ Electronic ☐ RON
3	DATE __ / TIME __	☐ Signer ☐ Witness	☐ D.L. ☐ Passport ☐ Credible Witness ☐ Other	☐ Expressed willingness ☐ Mentally alert ☐ Indicated understanding	☐ Paper ☐ Electronic ☐ RON
4	DATE __ / TIME __	☐ Signer ☐ Witness	☐ D.L. ☐ Passport ☐ Credible Witness ☐ Other	☐ Expressed willingness ☐ Mentally alert ☐ Indicated understanding	☐ Paper ☐ Electronic ☐ RON

DOCUMENT(S) SIGNED

Column 1 (SIGNER 1 2 3 4)

Document	Notarial Act	Signer
☐ Borrower's Aff	Acknowledgment Jurat	1 2 3 4
☐ Compliance Agrmt	Acknowledgment Jurat	1 2 3 4
☐ Correction Agrmt	Acknowledgment Jurat	1 2 3 4
☐ Debts/Leins Aff	Acknowledgment Jurat	1 2 3 4
☐ Deed of Trust	Acknowledgment Jurat	1 2 3 4
☐ Distrib of Proceeds	Acknowledgment Jurat	1 2 3 4
☐ E&O Agrmt	Acknowledgment Jurat	1 2 3 4
☐ Grant Deed	Acknowledgment Jurat	1 2 3 4
☐ Marital Stat Aff	Acknowledgment Jurat	1 2 3 4
☐ Mortgage	Acknowledgment Jurat	1 2 3 4
☐ Occupancy/Fin Aff	Acknowledgment Jurat	1 2 3 4
☐ Owner's Aff	Acknowledgment Jurat	1 2 3 4
☐ Payoff Aff	Acknowledgment Jurat	1 2 3 4
☐ Quit-Claim Deed	Acknowledgment Jurat	1 2 3 4
☐ Sig/Name Aff	Acknowledgment Jurat	1 2 3 4
☐ Survey Aff	Acknowledgment Jurat	1 2 3 4
☐ Warranty Deed	Acknowledgment Jurat	1 2 3 4

Column 2 (SIGNER 1 2 3 4)

Document	Notarial Act	Signer	Additional Act	Signer
☐ Minor Medical Consent	Acknowledgment Jurat	1 2 3 4		
☐ Minor Passport Consent	Acknowledgment Jurat	1 2 3 4	Copy Oath SW	1 2 3 4
☐ Minor Travel Consent	Acknowledgment Jurat	1 2 3 4		
☐ Vehicle Duplicate Title	Acknowledgment Jurat	1 2 3 4	Copy Oath SW	1 2 3 4
☐ Vehicle Lein Release	Acknowledgment Jurat	1 2 3 4		
☐ Vehicle Odom/Vin Ver	Acknowledgment Jurat	1 2 3 4		
☐ Vehicle Title Transfer	Acknowledgment Jurat	1 2 3 4	Copy Oath SW	1 2 3 4
☐ Adv Health Care Dir	Acknowledgment Jurat	1 2 3 4		
☐ Assign of Digital Assets	Acknowledgment Jurat	1 2 3 4	Copy Oath SW	1 2 3 4
☐ Assign of Personal Prop	Acknowledgment Jurat	1 2 3 4		
☐ HIPAA Release	Acknowledgment Jurat	1 2 3 4		
☐ Living Trust	Acknowledgment Jurat	1 2 3 4	Copy Oath SW	1 2 3 4
☐ Last Will & Testament	Acknowledgment Jurat	1 2 3 4		
☐ POA	Acknowledgment Jurat	1 2 3 4		
☐ Trust Certification	Acknowledgment Jurat	1 2 3 4	Copy Oath SW	1 2 3 4

SIGNING ADDRESS	OTHERS IN ATTENDANCE	CLIENT / SIGNING SERVICE	FEE
		LENDER / LOAN NUMBER	

NOTES

	ADDRESS	PHONE	EMAIL	SIGNATURE	INITIAL IF OATH/AFF TAKEN	RIGHT THUMB PRINT
1						
2						
3						
4						

Left Section — Notarial Acts

#	DATE / TIME	NAME	IDENTITY VERIFIED	WILLINGNESS & COMPETENCE	FORMAT
1	DATE ___ TIME ___	☐ Signer ☐ Witness	☐ D.L. ☐ Passport ☐ Credible Witness ☐ Other	☐ Expressed willingness ☐ Mentally alert ☐ Indicated understanding	☐ Paper ☐ Electronic ☐ RON
2	DATE ___ TIME ___	☐ Signer ☐ Witness	☐ D.L. ☐ Passport ☐ Credible Witness ☐ Other	☐ Expressed willingness ☐ Mentally alert ☐ Indicated understanding	☐ Paper ☐ Electronic ☐ RON
3	DATE ___ TIME ___	☐ Signer ☐ Witness	☐ D.L. ☐ Passport ☐ Credible Witness ☐ Other	☐ Expressed willingness ☐ Mentally alert ☐ Indicated understanding	☐ Paper ☐ Electronic ☐ RON
4	DATE ___ TIME ___	☐ Signer ☐ Witness	☐ D.L. ☐ Passport ☐ Credible Witness ☐ Other	☐ Expressed willingness ☐ Mentally alert ☐ Indicated understanding	☐ Paper ☐ Electronic ☐ RON

DOCUMENT(S) SIGNED

Document	Act			SIGNER
☐ Borrower's Aff	Acknowledgment	Jurat	_____	1 2 3 4
☐ Compliance Agrmt	Acknowledgment	Jurat	_____	1 2 3 4
☐ Correction Agrmt	Acknowledgment	Jurat	_____	1 2 3 4
☐ Debts/Leins Aff	Acknowledgment	Jurat	_____	1 2 3 4
☐ Deed of Trust	Acknowledgment	Jurat	_____	1 2 3 4
☐ Distrib of Proceeds	Acknowledgment	Jurat	_____	1 2 3 4
☐ E&O Agrmt	Acknowledgment	Jurat	_____	1 2 3 4
☐ Grant Deed	Acknowledgment	Jurat	_____	1 2 3 4
☐ Marital Stat Aff	Acknowledgment	Jurat	_____	1 2 3 4
☐ Mortgage	Acknowledgment	Jurat	_____	1 2 3 4
☐ Occupancy/Fin Aff	Acknowledgment	Jurat	_____	1 2 3 4
☐ Owner's Aff	Acknowledgment	Jurat	_____	1 2 3 4
☐ Payoff Aff	Acknowledgment	Jurat	_____	1 2 3 4
☐ Quit-Claim Deed	Acknowledgment	Jurat	_____	1 2 3 4
☐ Sig/Name Aff	Acknowledgment	Jurat	_____	1 2 3 4
☐ Survey Aff	Acknowledgment	Jurat	_____	1 2 3 4
☐ Warranty Deed	Acknowledgment	Jurat	_____	1 2 3 4

Document	Act			SIGNER
☐ Minor Medical Consent	Acknowledgment	Jurat	_____	1 2 3 4
☐ Minor Passport Consent	Acknowledgment	Jurat	_____	1 2 3 4
☐ Minor Travel Consent	Acknowledgment	Jurat	_____	1 2 3 4
☐ Vehicle Duplicate Title	Acknowledgment	Jurat	_____	1 2 3 4
☐ Vehicle Lein Release	Acknowledgment	Jurat	_____	1 2 3 4
☐ Vehicle Odom/Vin Ver	Acknowledgment	Jurat	_____	1 2 3 4
☐ Vehicle Title Transfer	Acknowledgment	Jurat	_____	1 2 3 4
☐ Adv Health Care Dir	Acknowledgment	Jurat	_____	1 2 3 4
☐ Assign of Digital Assets	Acknowledgment	Jurat	_____	1 2 3 4
☐ Assign of Personal Prop	Acknowledgment	Jurat	_____	1 2 3 4
☐ HIPAA Release	Acknowledgment	Jurat	_____	1 2 3 4
☐ Living Trust	Acknowledgment	Jurat	_____	1 2 3 4
☐ Last Will & Testament	Acknowledgment	Jurat	_____	1 2 3 4
☐ POA	Acknowledgment	Jurat	_____	1 2 3 4
☐ Trust Certification	Acknowledgment	Jurat	_____	1 2 3 4

Additional act columns (Acknowledgment / Jurat / Copy / Oath / SW) with SIGNER 1 2 3 4 are provided alongside the right-hand document list (☐).

SIGNING ADDRESS	OTHERS IN ATTENDANCE	CLIENT / SIGNING SERVICE	FEE
		LENDER / LOAN NUMBER	

NOTES

_____

	ADDRESS	PHONE	SIGNATURE	INITIAL IF OATH/AFF TAKEN	RIGHT THUMB PRINT
1		PHONE / EMAIL	SIGNATURE	INITIAL IF OATH/AFF TAKEN	RIGHT THUMB PRINT
2	ADDRESS	PHONE / EMAIL	SIGNATURE	INITIAL IF OATH/AFF TAKEN	RIGHT THUMB PRINT
3	ADDRESS	PHONE / EMAIL	SIGNATURE	INITIAL IF OATH/AFF TAKEN	RIGHT THUMB PRINT
4	ADDRESS	PHONE / EMAIL	SIGNATURE	INITIAL IF OATH/AFF TAKEN	RIGHT THUMB PRINT

Notary Journal Entries (1–4)

Each numbered entry (1, 2, 3, 4) contains the following fields:

DATE	
TIME	
NAME	☐ Signer ☐ Witness
IDENTITY VERIFIED	☐ D.L. ☐ Passport ☐ Credible Witness ☐ Other
WILLINGNESS & COMPETENCE	☐ Expressed willingness ☐ Mentally alert ☐ Indicated understanding
FORMAT	☐ Paper ☐ Electronic ☐ RON

DOCUMENT(S) SIGNED

DOCUMENT(S) SIGNED	Act Type		SIGNER 1	2	3	4
☐ Borrower's Aff	Acknowledgment	Jurat	1	2	3	4
☐ Compliance Agrmt	Acknowledgment	Jurat	1	2	3	4
☐ Correction Agrmt	Acknowledgment	Jurat	1	2	3	4
☐ Debts/Leins Aff	Acknowledgment	Jurat	1	2	3	4
☐ Deed of Trust	Acknowledgment	Jurat	1	2	3	4
☐ Distrib of Proceeds	Acknowledgment	Jurat	1	2	3	4
☐ E&O Agrmt	Acknowledgment	Jurat	1	2	3	4
☐ Grant Deed	Acknowledgment	Jurat	1	2	3	4
☐ Marital Stat Aff	Acknowledgment	Jurat	1	2	3	4
☐ Mortgage	Acknowledgment	Jurat	1	2	3	4
☐ Occupancy/Fin Aff	Acknowledgment	Jurat	1	2	3	4
☐ Owner's Aff	Acknowledgment	Jurat	1	2	3	4
☐ Payoff Aff	Acknowledgment	Jurat	1	2	3	4
☐ Quit-Claim Deed	Acknowledgment	Jurat	1	2	3	4
☐ Sig/Name Aff	Acknowledgment	Jurat	1	2	3	4
☐ Survey Aff	Acknowledgment	Jurat	1	2	3	4
☐ Warranty Deed	Acknowledgment	Jurat	1	2	3	4

DOCUMENT(S) SIGNED	Act Type		SIGNER 1	2	3	4
☐ Minor Medical Consent	Acknowledgment	Jurat	1	2	3	4
☐ Minor Passport Consent	Acknowledgment	Jurat	1	2	3	4
☐ Minor Travel Consent	Acknowledgment	Jurat	1	2	3	4
☐ Vehicle Duplicate Title	Acknowledgment	Jurat	1	2	3	4
☐ Vehicle Lein Release	Acknowledgment	Jurat	1	2	3	4
☐ Vehicle Odom/Vin Ver	Acknowledgment	Jurat	1	2	3	4
☐ Vehicle Title Transfer	Acknowledgment	Jurat	1	2	3	4
☐ Adv Health Care Dir	Acknowledgment	Jurat	1	2	3	4
☐ Assign of Digital Assets	Acknowledgment	Jurat	1	2	3	4
☐ Assign of Personal Prop	Acknowledgment	Jurat	1	2	3	4
☐ HIPAA Release	Acknowledgment	Jurat	1	2	3	4
☐ Living Trust	Acknowledgment	Jurat	1	2	3	4
☐ Last Will & Testament	Acknowledgment	Jurat	1	2	3	4
☐ POA	Acknowledgment	Jurat	1	2	3	4
☐ Trust Certification	Acknowledgment	Jurat	1	2	3	4

Certificate types (right column header area): Acknowledgment, Jurat, Copy, Oath, SW — 1 2 3 4

SIGNING ADDRESS	OTHERS IN ATTENDANCE	CLIENT / SIGNING SERVICE	FEE
		LENDER / LOAN NUMBER	

NOTES

	ADDRESS	PHONE	EMAIL	SIGNATURE	INITIAL IF OATH/AFF TAKEN	RIGHT THUMB PRINT
1						
2						
3						
4						

Notary Journal Entries

Entry 1
- **DATE:**
- **TIME:**
- **NAME:** □ Signer □ Witness
- **IDENTITY VERIFIED:** □ D.L. □ Passport □ Credible Witness / □ Other
- **WILLINGNESS & COMPETENCE:** □ Expressed willingness □ Mentally alert □ Indicated understanding
- **FORMAT:** □ Paper □ Electronic □ RON

Entry 2
- **DATE:**
- **TIME:**
- **NAME:** □ Signer □ Witness
- **IDENTITY VERIFIED:** □ D.L. □ Passport □ Credible Witness / □ Other
- **WILLINGNESS & COMPETENCE:** □ Expressed willingness □ Mentally alert □ Indicated understanding
- **FORMAT:** □ Paper □ Electronic □ RON

Entry 3
- **DATE:**
- **TIME:**
- **NAME:** □ Signer □ Witness
- **IDENTITY VERIFIED:** □ D.L. □ Passport □ Credible Witness / □ Other
- **WILLINGNESS & COMPETENCE:** □ Expressed willingness □ Mentally alert □ Indicated understanding
- **FORMAT:** □ Paper □ Electronic □ RON

Entry 4
- **DATE:**
- **TIME:**
- **NAME:** □ Signer □ Witness
- **IDENTITY VERIFIED:** □ D.L. □ Passport □ Credible Witness / □ Other
- **WILLINGNESS & COMPETENCE:** □ Expressed willingness □ Mentally alert □ Indicated understanding
- **FORMAT:** □ Paper □ Electronic □ RON

DOCUMENT(S) SIGNED

Document	Type		SIGNER 1	2	3	4
□ Borrower's Aff	Acknowledgment	Jurat	1	2	3	4
□ Compliance Agrmt	Acknowledgment	Jurat	1	2	3	4
□ Correction Agrmt	Acknowledgment	Jurat	1	2	3	4
□ Debts/Leins Aff	Acknowledgment	Jurat	1	2	3	4
□ Deed of Trust	Acknowledgment	Jurat	1	2	3	4
□ Distrib of Proceeds	Acknowledgment	Jurat	1	2	3	4
□ E&O Agrmt	Acknowledgment	Jurat	1	2	3	4
□ Grant Deed	Acknowledgment	Jurat	1	2	3	4
□ Marital Stat Aff	Acknowledgment	Jurat	1	2	3	4
□ Mortgage	Acknowledgment	Jurat	1	2	3	4
□ Occupancy/Fin Aff	Acknowledgment	Jurat	1	2	3	4
□ Owner's Aff	Acknowledgment	Jurat	1	2	3	4
□ Payoff Aff	Acknowledgment	Jurat	1	2	3	4
□ Quit-Claim Deed	Acknowledgment	Jurat	1	2	3	4
□ Sig/Name Aff	Acknowledgment	Jurat	1	2	3	4
□ Survey Aff	Acknowledgment	Jurat	1	2	3	4
□ Warranty Deed	Acknowledgment	Jurat	1	2	3	4

Document	Type		SIGNER 1	2	3	4	Extra
□ Minor Medical Consent	Acknowledgment	Jurat	1	2	3	4	
□ Minor Passport Consent	Acknowledgment	Jurat	1	2	3	4	Copy Oath SW 1 2 3 4
□ Minor Travel Consent	Acknowledgment	Jurat	1	2	3	4	
□ Vehicle Duplicate Title	Acknowledgment	Jurat	1	2	3	4	
□ Vehicle Lein Release	Acknowledgment	Jurat	1	2	3	4	Copy Oath SW 1 2 3 4
□ Vehicle Odom/Vin Ver	Acknowledgment	Jurat	1	2	3	4	
□ Vehicle Title Transfer	Acknowledgment	Jurat	1	2	3	4	Copy Oath SW 1 2 3 4
□ Adv Health Care Dir	Acknowledgment	Jurat	1	2	3	4	Copy Oath SW 1 2 3 4
□ Assign of Digital Assets	Acknowledgment	Jurat	1	2	3	4	Copy Oath SW 1 2 3 4
□ Assign of Personal Prop	Acknowledgment	Jurat	1	2	3	4	
□ HIPAA Release	Acknowledgment	Jurat	1	2	3	4	Copy Oath SW 1 2 3 4
□ Living Trust _____	Acknowledgment	Jurat	1	2	3	4	Copy Oath SW 1 2 3 4
□ Last Will & Testament	Acknowledgment	Jurat	1	2	3	4	
□ POA _____	Acknowledgment	Jurat	1	2	3	4	
□ Trust Certification	Acknowledgment	Jurat	1	2	3	4	Copy Oath SW 1 2 3 4

SIGNING ADDRESS	OTHERS IN ATTENDANCE	CLIENT / SIGNING SERVICE	FEE
		LENDER / LOAN NUMBER	

NOTES

_____
_____
_____
_____
_____
_____
_____
_____
_____
_____
_____
_____

	ADDRESS	SIGNATURE	PHONE	EMAIL	INITIAL IF OATH/AFF TAKEN	RIGHT THUMB PRINT
1						
2						
3						
4						

Notary Journal Entry

Records

1

DATE	TIME

- **NAME:** ☐ Signer ☐ Witness
- **IDENTITY VERIFIED:** ☐ D.L. ☐ Passport ☐ Credible Witness ☐ Other
- **WILLINGNESS & COMPETENCE:** ☐ Expressed willingness ☐ Mentally alert ☐ Indicated understanding
- **FORMAT:** ☐ Paper ☐ Electronic ☐ RON

2

DATE	TIME

- **NAME:** ☐ Signer ☐ Witness
- **IDENTITY VERIFIED:** ☐ D.L. ☐ Passport ☐ Credible Witness ☐ Other
- **WILLINGNESS & COMPETENCE:** ☐ Expressed willingness ☐ Mentally alert ☐ Indicated understanding
- **FORMAT:** ☐ Paper ☐ Electronic ☐ RON

3

DATE	TIME

- **NAME:** ☐ Signer ☐ Witness
- **IDENTITY VERIFIED:** ☐ D.L. ☐ Passport ☐ Credible Witness ☐ Other
- **WILLINGNESS & COMPETENCE:** ☐ Expressed willingness ☐ Mentally alert ☐ Indicated understanding
- **FORMAT:** ☐ Paper ☐ Electronic ☐ RON

4

DATE	TIME

- **NAME:** ☐ Signer ☐ Witness
- **IDENTITY VERIFIED:** ☐ D.L. ☐ Passport ☐ Credible Witness ☐ Other
- **WILLINGNESS & COMPETENCE:** ☐ Expressed willingness ☐ Mentally alert ☐ Indicated understanding
- **FORMAT:** ☐ Paper ☐ Electronic ☐ RON

DOCUMENT(S) SIGNED

☐ Document	Type	SIGNER
☐ Borrower's Aff	Acknowledgment Jurat	1 2 3 4
☐ Compliance Agrmt	Acknowledgment Jurat	1 2 3 4
☐ Correction Agrmt	Acknowledgment Jurat	1 2 3 4
☐ Debts/Leins Aff	Acknowledgment Jurat	1 2 3 4
☐ Deed of Trust	Acknowledgment Jurat	1 2 3 4
☐ Distrib of Proceeds	Acknowledgment Jurat	1 2 3 4
☐ E&O Agrmt	Acknowledgment Jurat	1 2 3 4
☐ Grant Deed	Acknowledgment Jurat	1 2 3 4
☐ Marital Stat Aff	Acknowledgment Jurat	1 2 3 4
☐ Mortgage	Acknowledgment Jurat	1 2 3 4
☐ Occupancy/Fin Aff	Acknowledgment Jurat	1 2 3 4
☐ Owner's Aff	Acknowledgment Jurat	1 2 3 4
☐ Payoff Aff	Acknowledgment Jurat	1 2 3 4
☐ Quit-Claim Deed	Acknowledgment Jurat	1 2 3 4
☐ Sig/Name Aff	Acknowledgment Jurat	1 2 3 4
☐ Survey Aff	Acknowledgment Jurat	1 2 3 4
☐ Warranty Deed	Acknowledgment Jurat	1 2 3 4

☐ Document	Type	SIGNER
☐ Minor Medical Consent	Acknowledgment Jurat	1 2 3 4
☐ Minor Passport Consent	Acknowledgment Jurat Copy Oath SW	1 2 3 4
☐ Minor Travel Consent	Acknowledgment Jurat	1 2 3 4
☐ Vehicle Duplicate Title	Acknowledgment Jurat Copy Oath SW	1 2 3 4
☐ Vehicle Lein Release	Acknowledgment Jurat	1 2 3 4
☐ Vehicle Odom/Vin Ver	Acknowledgment Jurat Copy	1 2 3 4
☐ Vehicle Title Transfer	Acknowledgment Jurat	1 2 3 4
☐ Adv Health Care Dir	Acknowledgment Jurat Copy Oath SW	1 2 3 4
☐ Assign of Digital Assets	Acknowledgment Jurat	1 2 3 4
☐ Assign of Personal Prop	Acknowledgment Jurat	1 2 3 4
☐ HIPAA Release	Acknowledgment Jurat	1 2 3 4
☐ Living Trust	Acknowledgment Jurat Copy Oath SW	1 2 3 4
☐ Last Will & Testament	Acknowledgment Jurat	1 2 3 4
☐ POA	Acknowledgment Jurat	1 2 3 4
☐ Trust Certification	Acknowledgment Jurat Copy Oath SW	1 2 3 4

SIGNING ADDRESS	OTHERS IN ATTENDANCE	CLIENT / SIGNING SERVICE	FEE
		LENDER / LOAN NUMBER	

NOTES

_____
_____
_____
_____
_____
_____
_____
_____
_____
_____
_____

#	ADDRESS	SIGNATURE	PHONE	EMAIL	INITIAL IF OATH/AFF TAKEN	RIGHT THUMB PRINT
1						
2						
3						
4						

Notary Journal Entries

For each entry (1, 2, 3, 4):

DATE / TIME	
NAME	☐ Signer ☐ Witness
IDENTITY VERIFIED	☐ D.L. ☐ Passport ☐ Credible Witness ☐ Other
WILLINGNESS & COMPETENCE	☐ Expressed willingness ☐ Mentally alert ☐ Indicated understanding
FORMAT	☐ Paper ☐ Electronic ☐ RON

DOCUMENT(S) SIGNED

Document	Type		SIGNER			
			1	2	3	4
☐ Borrower's Aff	Acknowledgment	Jurat	1	2	3	4
☐ Compliance Agrmt	Acknowledgment	Jurat	1	2	3	4
☐ Correction Agrmt	Acknowledgment	Jurat	1	2	3	4
☐ Debts/Leins Aff	Acknowledgment	Jurat	1	2	3	4
☐ Deed of Trust	Acknowledgment	Jurat	1	2	3	4
☐ Distrib of Proceeds	Acknowledgment	Jurat	1	2	3	4
☐ E&O Agrmt	Acknowledgment	Jurat	1	2	3	4
☐ Grant Deed	Acknowledgment	Jurat	1	2	3	4
☐ Marital Stat Aff	Acknowledgment	Jurat	1	2	3	4
☐ Mortgage	Acknowledgment	Jurat	1	2	3	4
☐ Occupancy/Fin Aff	Acknowledgment	Jurat	1	2	3	4
☐ Owner's Aff	Acknowledgment	Jurat	1	2	3	4
☐ Payoff Aff	Acknowledgment	Jurat	1	2	3	4
☐ Quit-Claim Deed	Acknowledgment	Jurat	1	2	3	4
☐ Sig/Name Aff	Acknowledgment	Jurat	1	2	3	4
☐ Survey Aff	Acknowledgment	Jurat	1	2	3	4
☐ Warranty Deed	Acknowledgment	Jurat	1	2	3	4

Document	Type				SIGNER			
					1	2	3	4
☐ Minor Medical Consent	Acknowledgment	Jurat			1	2	3	4
☐ Minor Passport Consent	Acknowledgment	Jurat			1	2	3	4
☐ Minor Travel Consent	Acknowledgment	Jurat			1	2	3	4
☐ Vehicle Duplicate Title	Acknowledgment	Jurat			1	2	3	4
☐ Vehicle Lein Release	Acknowledgment	Jurat			1	2	3	4
☐ Vehicle Odom/Vin Ver	Acknowledgment	Jurat			1	2	3	4
☐ Vehicle Title Transfer	Acknowledgment	Jurat			1	2	3	4
☐ Adv Health Care Dir	Acknowledgment	Jurat			1	2	3	4
☐ Assign of Digital Assets	Acknowledgment	Jurat			1	2	3	4
☐ Assign of Personal Prop	Acknowledgment	Jurat			1	2	3	4
☐ HIPAA Release	Acknowledgment	Jurat			1	2	3	4
☐ Living Trust	Acknowledgment	Jurat			1	2	3	4
☐ Last Will & Testament	Acknowledgment	Jurat			1	2	3	4
☐ POA	Acknowledgment	Jurat	Copy	Oath	1	2	3	4
☐ Trust Certification	Acknowledgment	Jurat	Copy	Oath SW	1	2	3	4

(Notarial act columns for the right-hand list: Acknowledgment, Jurat, Copy, Oath, SW — with additional ☐ per document)

SIGNING ADDRESS	OTHERS IN ATTENDANCE	CLIENT / SIGNING SERVICE	FEE
		LENDER / LOAN NUMBER	

NOTES

	ADDRESS	PHONE	EMAIL	SIGNATURE	INITIAL IF OATH/AFF TAKEN	RIGHT THUMB PRINT
1						
2						
3						
4						

Entries 1–4

Entry 1
- **DATE:**
- **TIME:**
- **NAME:** ☐ Signer ☐ Witness
- **IDENTITY VERIFIED:** ☐ D.L. ☐ Passport ☐ Credible Witness ☐ Other
- **WILLINGNESS & COMPETENCE:** ☐ Expressed willingness ☐ Mentally alert ☐ Indicated understanding
- **FORMAT:** ☐ Paper ☐ Electronic ☐ RON

Entry 2
- **DATE:**
- **TIME:**
- **NAME:** ☐ Signer ☐ Witness
- **IDENTITY VERIFIED:** ☐ D.L. ☐ Passport ☐ Credible Witness ☐ Other
- **WILLINGNESS & COMPETENCE:** ☐ Expressed willingness ☐ Mentally alert ☐ Indicated understanding
- **FORMAT:** ☐ Paper ☐ Electronic ☐ RON

Entry 3
- **DATE:**
- **TIME:**
- **NAME:** ☐ Signer ☐ Witness
- **IDENTITY VERIFIED:** ☐ D.L. ☐ Passport ☐ Credible Witness ☐ Other
- **WILLINGNESS & COMPETENCE:** ☐ Expressed willingness ☐ Mentally alert ☐ Indicated understanding
- **FORMAT:** ☐ Paper ☐ Electronic ☐ RON

Entry 4
- **DATE:**
- **TIME:**
- **NAME:** ☐ Signer ☐ Witness
- **IDENTITY VERIFIED:** ☐ D.L. ☐ Passport ☐ Credible Witness ☐ Other
- **WILLINGNESS & COMPETENCE:** ☐ Expressed willingness ☐ Mentally alert ☐ Indicated understanding
- **FORMAT:** ☐ Paper ☐ Electronic ☐ RON

DOCUMENT(S) SIGNED

Document	Type		SIGNER			
			1	2	3	4
☐ Borrower's Aff	Acknowledgment	Jurat	1	2	3	4
☐ Compliance Agrmt	Acknowledgment	Jurat	1	2	3	4
☐ Correction Agrmt	Acknowledgment	Jurat	1	2	3	4
☐ Debts/Leins Aff	Acknowledgment	Jurat	1	2	3	4
☐ Deed of Trust	Acknowledgment	Jurat	1	2	3	4
☐ Distrib of Proceeds	Acknowledgment	Jurat	1	2	3	4
☐ E&O Agrmt	Acknowledgment	Jurat	1	2	3	4
☐ Grant Deed	Acknowledgment	Jurat	1	2	3	4
☐ Marital Stat Aff	Acknowledgment	Jurat	1	2	3	4
☐ Mortgage	Acknowledgment	Jurat	1	2	3	4
☐ Occupancy/Fin Aff	Acknowledgment	Jurat	1	2	3	4
☐ Owner's Aff	Acknowledgment	Jurat	1	2	3	4
☐ Payoff Aff	Acknowledgment	Jurat	1	2	3	4
☐ Quit-Claim Deed	Acknowledgment	Jurat	1	2	3	4
☐ Sig/Name Aff	Acknowledgment	Jurat	1	2	3	4
☐ Survey Aff	Acknowledgment	Jurat	1	2	3	4
☐ Warranty Deed	Acknowledgment	Jurat	1	2	3	4

Document	Type				SIGNER			
					1	2	3	4
☐ Minor Medical Consent	Acknowledgment	Jurat			1	2	3	4
☐ Minor Passport Consent	Acknowledgment	Jurat	Copy	Oath SW	1	2	3	4
☐ Minor Travel Consent	Acknowledgment	Jurat			1	2	3	4
☐ Vehicle Duplicate Title	Acknowledgment	Jurat			1	2	3	4
☐ Vehicle Lein Release	Acknowledgment	Jurat	Copy	Oath SW	1	2	3	4
☐ Vehicle Odom/Vin Ver	Acknowledgment	Jurat			1	2	3	4
☐ Vehicle Title Transfer	Acknowledgment	Jurat	Copy	Oath SW	1	2	3	4
☐ Adv Health Care Dir	Acknowledgment	Jurat			1	2	3	4
☐ Assign of Digital Assets	Acknowledgment	Jurat	Copy	Oath SW	1	2	3	4
☐ Assign of Personal Prop	Acknowledgment	Jurat			1	2	3	4
☐ HIPAA Release	Acknowledgment	Jurat			1	2	3	4
☐ Living Trust	Acknowledgment	Jurat	Copy	Oath SW	1	2	3	4
☐ Last Will & Testament	Acknowledgment	Jurat			1	2	3	4
☐ POA	Acknowledgment	Jurat			1	2	3	4
☐ Trust Certification	Acknowledgment	Jurat	Copy	Oath SW	1	2	3	4

SIGNING ADDRESS	OTHERS IN ATTENDANCE	CLIENT / SIGNING SERVICE	FEE
		LENDER / LOAN NUMBER	

NOTES

	ADDRESS	PHONE	EMAIL	SIGNATURE	INITIAL IF OATH/AFF TAKEN	RIGHT THUMB PRINT
1						
2						
3						
4						

Entries 1–4

For each entry (1, 2, 3, 4):

FORMAT
- ☐ Paper
- ☐ Electronic
- ☐ RON

WILLINGNESS & COMPETENCE
- ☐ Expressed willingness
- ☐ Mentally alert
- ☐ Indicated understanding

IDENTITY VERIFIED
- ☐ D.L. ☐ Passport ☐ Credible Witness
- ☐ Other

NAME ☐ Signer ☐ Witness

DATE ___ **TIME** ___

DOCUMENT(S) SIGNED

Document	Type		SIGNER			
☐ Borrower's Aff	Acknowledgment	Jurat	1	2	3	4
☐ Compliance Agrmt	Acknowledgment	Jurat	1	2	3	4
☐ Correction Agrmt	Acknowledgment	Jurat	1	2	3	4
☐ Debts/Leins Aff	Acknowledgment	Jurat	1	2	3	4
☐ Deed of Trust	Acknowledgment	Jurat	1	2	3	4
☐ Distrib of Proceeds	Acknowledgment	Jurat	1	2	3	4
☐ E&O Agrmt	Acknowledgment	Jurat	1	2	3	4
☐ Grant Deed	Acknowledgment	Jurat	1	2	3	4
☐ Marital Stat Aff	Acknowledgment	Jurat	1	2	3	4
☐ Mortgage	Acknowledgment	Jurat	1	2	3	4
☐ Occupancy/Fin Aff	Acknowledgment	Jurat	1	2	3	4
☐ Owner's Aff	Acknowledgment	Jurat	1	2	3	4
☐ Payoff Aff	Acknowledgment	Jurat	1	2	3	4
☐ Quit-Claim Deed	Acknowledgment	Jurat	1	2	3	4
☐ Sig/Name Aff	Acknowledgment	Jurat	1	2	3	4
☐ Survey Aff	Acknowledgment	Jurat	1	2	3	4
☐ Warranty Deed	Acknowledgment	Jurat	1	2	3	4

Document	Type			SIGNER			
☐ Minor Medical Consent	Acknowledgment	Jurat		1	2	3	4
☐ Minor Passport Consent	Acknowledgment	Jurat		1	2	3	4
☐ Minor Travel Consent	Acknowledgment	Jurat		1	2	3	4
☐ Vehicle Duplicate Title	Acknowledgment	Jurat		1	2	3	4
☐ Vehicle Lein Release	Acknowledgment	Jurat		1	2	3	4
☐ Vehicle Odom/Vin Ver	Acknowledgment	Jurat		1	2	3	4
☐ Vehicle Title Transfer	Acknowledgment	Jurat		1	2	3	4
☐ Adv Health Care Dir	Acknowledgment	Jurat		1	2	3	4
☐ Assign of Digital Assets	Acknowledgment	Jurat		1	2	3	4
☐ Assign of Personal Prop	Acknowledgment	Jurat		1	2	3	4
☐ HIPAA Release	Acknowledgment	Jurat		1	2	3	4
☐ Living Trust	Acknowledgment	Jurat		1	2	3	4
☐ Last Will & Testament	Acknowledgment	Jurat		1	2	3	4
☐ POA ___	Acknowledgment	Jurat		1	2	3	4
☐ Trust Certification	Acknowledgment	Jurat		1	2	3	4

The following documents include additional options (Copy, Oath, SW):

Document		SIGNER			
Acknowledgment Jurat Copy Oath SW		1	2	3	4
Acknowledgment Jurat Copy Oath SW		1	2	3	4
Acknowledgment Jurat Copy Oath SW		1	2	3	4
Acknowledgment Jurat Copy Oath SW		1	2	3	4
Acknowledgment Jurat Copy Oath SW		1	2	3	4

Signing Address	Others in Attendance	Client / Signing Service / Lender / Loan Number	Fee

Notes

_____

	Address	Phone / Email	Signature	Initial if Oath/Aff Taken	Right Thumb Print
1		Phone / Email			
2		Phone / Email			
3		Phone / Email			
4		Phone / Email			

Entry Records (1–4)

Each numbered entry (1, 2, 3, 4) contains the following fields:

Entry [1 / 2 / 3 / 4]

- **DATE:** ____
- **TIME:** ____
- **NAME:** ☐ Signer ☐ Witness
- **IDENTITY VERIFIED:** ☐ D.L. ☐ Passport ☐ Credible Witness ☐ Other
- **WILLINGNESS & COMPETENCE:** ☐ Expressed willingness ☐ Mentally alert ☐ Indicated understanding
- **FORMAT:** ☐ Paper ☐ Electronic ☐ RON

DOCUMENT(S) SIGNED

☐ Document	Acts				SIGNER			
					1	2	3	4
☐ Borrower's Aff	Acknowledgment	Jurat			1	2	3	4
☐ Compliance Agrmt	Acknowledgment	Jurat			1	2	3	4
☐ Correction Agrmt	Acknowledgment	Jurat			1	2	3	4
☐ Debts/Leins Aff	Acknowledgment	Jurat			1	2	3	4
☐ Deed of Trust	Acknowledgment	Jurat			1	2	3	4
☐ Distrib of Proceeds	Acknowledgment	Jurat			1	2	3	4
☐ E&O Agrmt	Acknowledgment	Jurat			1	2	3	4
☐ Grant Deed	Acknowledgment	Jurat			1	2	3	4
☐ Marital Stat Aff	Acknowledgment	Jurat			1	2	3	4
☐ Mortgage	Acknowledgment	Jurat			1	2	3	4
☐ Occupancy/Fin Aff	Acknowledgment	Jurat			1	2	3	4
☐ Owner's Aff	Acknowledgment	Jurat			1	2	3	4
☐ Payoff Aff	Acknowledgment	Jurat			1	2	3	4
☐ Quit-Claim Deed	Acknowledgment	Jurat			1	2	3	4
☐ Sig/Name Aff	Acknowledgment	Jurat			1	2	3	4
☐ Survey Aff	Acknowledgment	Jurat			1	2	3	4
☐ Warranty Deed	Acknowledgment	Jurat			1	2	3	4

☐ Document	Acts					SIGNER			
						1	2	3	4
☐ Minor Medical Consent	Acknowledgment	Acknowledgment	Jurat	Copy	Oath	SW	1	2	3	4
☐ Minor Passport Consent	Acknowledgment	Jurat				1	2	3	4
☐ Minor Travel Consent	Acknowledgment	Jurat				1	2	3	4
☐ Vehicle Duplicate Title	Acknowledgment	Acknowledgment	Jurat	Copy	Oath	SW	1	2	3	4
☐ Vehicle Lein Release	Acknowledgment	Jurat				1	2	3	4
☐ Vehicle Odom/Vin Ver	Acknowledgment	Jurat				1	2	3	4
☐ Vehicle Title Transfer	Acknowledgment	Acknowledgment	Jurat	Copy	Oath	SW	1	2	3	4
☐ Adv Health Care Dir	Acknowledgment	Jurat				1	2	3	4
☐ Assign of Digital Assets	Acknowledgment	Acknowledgment	Jurat	Copy	Oath	SW	1	2	3	4
☐ Assign of Personal Prop	Acknowledgment	Jurat				1	2	3	4
☐ HIPAA Release	Acknowledgment	Jurat				1	2	3	4
☐ Living Trust	Acknowledgment	Acknowledgment	Jurat	Copy	Oath	SW	1	2	3	4
☐ Last Will & Testament	Acknowledgment	Jurat				1	2	3	4
☐ POA	Acknowledgment	Jurat				1	2	3	4
☐ Trust Certification	Acknowledgment	Acknowledgment	Jurat	Copy	Oath	SW	1	2	3	4

SIGNING ADDRESS	OTHERS IN ATTENDANCE	CLIENT / SIGNING SERVICE	FEE
		LENDER / LOAN NUMBER	

NOTES

_____
_____
_____
_____
_____
_____
_____
_____
_____
_____
_____
_____

#	ADDRESS / PHONE / EMAIL	SIGNATURE	INITIAL IF OATH/AFF TAKEN	RIGHT THUMB PRINT
1	ADDRESS / PHONE / EMAIL	SIGNATURE	INITIAL IF OATH/AFF TAKEN	RIGHT THUMB PRINT
2	ADDRESS / PHONE / EMAIL	SIGNATURE	INITIAL IF OATH/AFF TAKEN	RIGHT THUMB PRINT
3	ADDRESS / PHONE / EMAIL	SIGNATURE	INITIAL IF OATH/AFF TAKEN	RIGHT THUMB PRINT
4	ADDRESS / PHONE / EMAIL	SIGNATURE	INITIAL IF OATH/AFF TAKEN	RIGHT THUMB PRINT

Signer Entries

1
DATE	
TIME	

NAME □ Signer □ Witness

IDENTITY VERIFIED □ D.L. □ Passport □ Credible Witness
Other ___

WILLINGNESS & COMPETENCE □ Expressed willingness □ Mentally alert □ Indicated understanding

FORMAT □ Paper □ Electronic □ RON

2
DATE	
TIME	

NAME □ Signer □ Witness

IDENTITY VERIFIED □ D.L. □ Passport □ Credible Witness
Other ___

WILLINGNESS & COMPETENCE □ Expressed willingness □ Mentally alert □ Indicated understanding

FORMAT □ Paper □ Electronic □ RON

3
DATE	
TIME	

NAME □ Signer □ Witness

IDENTITY VERIFIED □ D.L. □ Passport □ Credible Witness
Other ___

WILLINGNESS & COMPETENCE □ Expressed willingness □ Mentally alert □ Indicated understanding

FORMAT □ Paper □ Electronic □ RON

4
DATE	
TIME	

NAME □ Signer □ Witness

IDENTITY VERIFIED □ D.L. □ Passport □ Credible Witness
Other ___

WILLINGNESS & COMPETENCE □ Expressed willingness □ Mentally alert □ Indicated understanding

FORMAT □ Paper □ Electronic □ RON

DOCUMENT(S) SIGNED

Document	Type		SIGNER 1	2	3	4
□ Borrower's Aff	Acknowledgment	Jurat ___	1	2	3	4
□ Compliance Agrmt	Acknowledgment	Jurat ___	1	2	3	4
□ Correction Agrmt	Acknowledgment	Jurat ___	1	2	3	4
□ Debts/Leins Aff	Acknowledgment	Jurat ___	1	2	3	4
□ Deed of Trust	Acknowledgment	Jurat ___	1	2	3	4
□ Distrib of Proceeds	Acknowledgment	Jurat ___	1	2	3	4
□ E&O Agrmt	Acknowledgment	Jurat ___	1	2	3	4
□ Grant Deed	Acknowledgment	Jurat ___	1	2	3	4
□ Marital Stat Aff	Acknowledgment	Jurat ___	1	2	3	4
□ Mortgage	Acknowledgment	Jurat ___	1	2	3	4
□ Occupancy/Fin Aff	Acknowledgment	Jurat ___	1	2	3	4
□ Owner's Aff	Acknowledgment	Jurat ___	1	2	3	4
□ Payoff Aff	Acknowledgment	Jurat ___	1	2	3	4
□ Quit-Claim Deed	Acknowledgment	Jurat ___	1	2	3	4
□ Sig/Name Aff	Acknowledgment	Jurat ___	1	2	3	4
□ Survey Aff	Acknowledgment	Jurat ___	1	2	3	4
□ Warranty Deed	Acknowledgment	Jurat ___	1	2	3	4

Document	Type		SIGNER 1	2	3	4
□ Minor Medical Consent	Acknowledgment	Jurat ___	1	2	3	4
□ Minor Passport Consent	Acknowledgment	Jurat ___	1	2	3	4
□ Minor Travel Consent	Acknowledgment	Jurat ___	1	2	3	4
□ Vehicle Duplicate Title	Acknowledgment	Jurat ___	1	2	3	4
□ Vehicle Lein Release	Acknowledgment	Jurat ___	1	2	3	4
□ Vehicle Odom/Vin Ver	Acknowledgment	Jurat ___	1	2	3	4
□ Vehicle Title Transfer	Acknowledgment	Jurat ___	1	2	3	4
□ Adv Health Care Dir	Acknowledgment	Jurat ___	1	2	3	4
□ Assign of Digital Assets	Acknowledgment	Jurat ___	1	2	3	4
□ Assign of Personal Prop	Acknowledgment	Jurat ___	1	2	3	4
□ HIPAA Release	Acknowledgment	Jurat ___	1	2	3	4
□ Living Trust	Acknowledgment	Jurat ___	1	2	3	4
□ Last Will & Testament	Acknowledgment	Jurat ___	1	2	3	4
□ POA ___	Acknowledgment	Jurat ___	1	2	3	4
□ Trust Certification	Acknowledgment	Jurat ___	1	2	3	4

Additional options (right side): □ Copy Oath SW 1 2 3 4 (repeated)

SIGNING ADDRESS	OTHERS IN ATTENDANCE	CLIENT / SIGNING SERVICE	FEE
		LENDER / LOAN NUMBER	

NOTES

#	ADDRESS	PHONE / EMAIL	SIGNATURE	INITIAL IF OATH/AFF TAKEN	RIGHT THUMB PRINT
1		PHONE / EMAIL			
2		PHONE / EMAIL			
3		PHONE / EMAIL			
4		PHONE / EMAIL			

Notary Record Entries

#				FORMAT
1	DATE / TIME	NAME ☐ Signer ☐ Witness	IDENTITY VERIFIED ☐ D.L. ☐ Passport ☐ Credible Witness ☐ Other	WILLINGNESS & COMPETENCE ☐ Expressed willingness ☐ Mentally alert ☐ Indicated understanding	☐ Paper ☐ Electronic ☐ RON
2	DATE / TIME	NAME ☐ Signer ☐ Witness	IDENTITY VERIFIED ☐ D.L. ☐ Passport ☐ Credible Witness ☐ Other	WILLINGNESS & COMPETENCE ☐ Expressed willingness ☐ Mentally alert ☐ Indicated understanding	☐ Paper ☐ Electronic ☐ RON
3	DATE / TIME	NAME ☐ Signer ☐ Witness	IDENTITY VERIFIED ☐ D.L. ☐ Passport ☐ Credible Witness ☐ Other	WILLINGNESS & COMPETENCE ☐ Expressed willingness ☐ Mentally alert ☐ Indicated understanding	☐ Paper ☐ Electronic ☐ RON
4	DATE / TIME	NAME ☐ Signer ☐ Witness	IDENTITY VERIFIED ☐ D.L. ☐ Passport ☐ Credible Witness ☐ Other	WILLINGNESS & COMPETENCE ☐ Expressed willingness ☐ Mentally alert ☐ Indicated understanding	☐ Paper ☐ Electronic ☐ RON

DOCUMENT(S) SIGNED

Document	Type	SIGNER
☐ Borrower's Aff	Acknowledgment Jurat	1 2 3 4
☐ Compliance Agrmt	Acknowledgment Jurat	1 2 3 4
☐ Correction Agrmt	Acknowledgment Jurat	1 2 3 4
☐ Debts/Leins Aff	Acknowledgment Jurat	1 2 3 4
☐ Deed of Trust	Acknowledgment Jurat	1 2 3 4
☐ Distrib of Proceeds	Acknowledgment Jurat	1 2 3 4
☐ E&O Agrmt	Acknowledgment Jurat	1 2 3 4
☐ Grant Deed	Acknowledgment Jurat	1 2 3 4
☐ Marital Stat Aff	Acknowledgment Jurat	1 2 3 4
☐ Mortgage	Acknowledgment Jurat	1 2 3 4
☐ Occupancy/Fin Aff	Acknowledgment Jurat	1 2 3 4
☐ Owner's Aff	Acknowledgment Jurat	1 2 3 4
☐ Payoff Aff	Acknowledgment Jurat	1 2 3 4
☐ Quit-Claim Deed	Acknowledgment Jurat	1 2 3 4
☐ Sig/Name Aff	Acknowledgment Jurat	1 2 3 4
☐ Survey Aff	Acknowledgment Jurat	1 2 3 4
☐ Warranty Deed	Acknowledgment Jurat	1 2 3 4

Document	Type	SIGNER
☐ Minor Medical Consent	Acknowledgment Jurat	1 2 3 4
☐ Minor Passport Consent	Acknowledgment Jurat	1 2 3 4
☐ Minor Travel Consent	Acknowledgment Jurat	1 2 3 4
☐ Vehicle Duplicate Title	Acknowledgment Jurat	1 2 3 4
☐ Vehicle Lein Release	Acknowledgment Jurat	1 2 3 4
☐ Vehicle Odom/Vin Ver	Acknowledgment Jurat	1 2 3 4
☐ Vehicle Title Transfer	Acknowledgment Jurat	1 2 3 4
☐ Adv Health Care Dir	Acknowledgment Jurat	1 2 3 4
☐ Assign of Digital Assets	Acknowledgment Jurat	1 2 3 4
☐ Assign of Personal Prop	Acknowledgment Jurat	1 2 3 4
☐ HIPAA Release	Acknowledgment Jurat	1 2 3 4
☐ Living Trust	Acknowledgment Jurat	1 2 3 4
☐ Last Will & Testament	Acknowledgment Jurat	1 2 3 4
☐ POA	Acknowledgment Jurat	1 2 3 4
☐ Trust Certification	Acknowledgment Jurat	1 2 3 4

SIGNING ADDRESS	OTHERS IN ATTENDANCE	CLIENT / SIGNING SERVICE	FEE
		LENDER / LOAN NUMBER	

NOTES

	ADDRESS	SIGNATURE	RIGHT THUMB PRINT
1	PHONE EMAIL		INITIAL IF OATH/AFF TAKEN
2	ADDRESS PHONE EMAIL	SIGNATURE	RIGHT THUMB PRINT INITIAL IF OATH/AFF TAKEN
3	ADDRESS PHONE EMAIL	SIGNATURE	RIGHT THUMB PRINT INITIAL IF OATH/AFF TAKEN
4	ADDRESS PHONE EMAIL	SIGNATURE	RIGHT THUMB PRINT INITIAL IF OATH/AFF TAKEN

1	DATE TIME	NAME ☐ Signer ☐ Witness	IDENTITY VERIFIED ☐ D.L. ☐ Passport ☐ Credible Witness ☐ Other	WILLINGNESS & COMPETENCE ☐ Expressed willingness ☐ Mentally alert ☐ Indicated understanding	FORMAT ☐ Paper ☐ Electronic ☐ RON
2	DATE TIME	NAME ☐ Signer ☐ Witness	IDENTITY VERIFIED ☐ D.L. ☐ Passport ☐ Credible Witness ☐ Other	WILLINGNESS & COMPETENCE ☐ Expressed willingness ☐ Mentally alert ☐ Indicated understanding	FORMAT ☐ Paper ☐ Electronic ☐ RON
3	DATE TIME	NAME ☐ Signer ☐ Witness	IDENTITY VERIFIED ☐ D.L. ☐ Passport ☐ Credible Witness ☐ Other	WILLINGNESS & COMPETENCE ☐ Expressed willingness ☐ Mentally alert ☐ Indicated understanding	FORMAT ☐ Paper ☐ Electronic ☐ RON
4	DATE TIME	NAME ☐ Signer ☐ Witness	IDENTITY VERIFIED ☐ D.L. ☐ Passport ☐ Credible Witness ☐ Other	WILLINGNESS & COMPETENCE ☐ Expressed willingness ☐ Mentally alert ☐ Indicated understanding	FORMAT ☐ Paper ☐ Electronic ☐ RON

DOCUMENT(S) SIGNED

Document				SIGNER				Document				SIGNER													
☐ Borrower's Aff	Acknowledgment	Jurat	______	1	2	3	4	☐ Minor Medical Consent	Acknowledgment	Jurat	______	1	2	3	4	☐ ______									
☐ Compliance Agrmt	Acknowledgment	Jurat	______	1	2	3	4	☐ Minor Passport Consent	Acknowledgment	Jurat	______	1	2	3	4	Acknowledgment	Jurat	Copy	Oath	SW	1	2	3	4	
☐ Correction Agrmt	Acknowledgment	Jurat	______	1	2	3	4	☐ Minor Travel Consent	Acknowledgment	Jurat	______	1	2	3	4										
☐ Debts/Leins Aff	Acknowledgment	Jurat	______	1	2	3	4									☐ ______									
☐ Deed of Trust	Acknowledgment	Jurat	______	1	2	3	4	☐ Vehicle Duplicate Title	Acknowledgment	Jurat	______	1	2	3	4	Acknowledgment	Jurat	Copy	Oath	SW	1	2	3	4	
☐ Distrib of Proceeds	Acknowledgment	Jurat	______	1	2	3	4	☐ Vehicle Lein Release	Acknowledgment	Jurat	______	1	2	3	4										
☐ E&O Agrmt	Acknowledgment	Jurat	______	1	2	3	4	☐ Vehicle Odom/Vin Ver	Acknowledgment	Jurat	______	1	2	3	4	☐ ______									
☐ Grant Deed	Acknowledgment	Jurat	______	1	2	3	4	☐ Vehicle Title Transfer	Acknowledgment	Jurat	______	1	2	3	4	Acknowledgment	Jurat	Copy	Oath	SW	1	2	3	4	
☐ Marital Stat Aff	Acknowledgment	Jurat	______	1	2	3	4																		
☐ Mortgage	Acknowledgment	Jurat	______	1	2	3	4	☐ Adv Health Care Dir	Acknowledgment	Jurat	______	1	2	3	4	☐ ______									
☐ Occupancy/Fin Aff	Acknowledgment	Jurat	______	1	2	3	4	☐ Assign of Digital Assets	Acknowledgment	Jurat	______	1	2	3	4	Acknowledgment	Jurat	Copy	Oath	SW	1	2	3	4	
☐ Owner's Aff	Acknowledgment	Jurat	______	1	2	3	4	☐ Assign of Personal Prop	Acknowledgment	Jurat	______	1	2	3	4										
☐ Payoff Aff	Acknowledgment	Jurat	______	1	2	3	4	☐ HIPAA Release	Acknowledgment	Jurat	______	1	2	3	4	☐ ______									
☐ Quit-Claim Deed	Acknowledgment	Jurat	______	1	2	3	4	☐ Living Trust ______	Acknowledgment	Jurat	______	1	2	3	4	Acknowledgment	Jurat	Copy	Oath	SW	1	2	3	4	
☐ Sig/Name Aff	Acknowledgment	Jurat	______	1	2	3	4	☐ Last Will & Testament	Acknowledgment	Jurat	______	1	2	3	4										
☐ Survey Aff	Acknowledgment	Jurat	______	1	2	3	4	☐ POA ______	Acknowledgment	Jurat	______	1	2	3	4	☐ ______									
☐ Warranty Deed	Acknowledgment	Jurat	______	1	2	3	4	☐ Trust Certification	Acknowledgment	Jurat	______	1	2	3	4	Acknowledgment	Jurat	Copy	Oath	SW	1	2	3	4	

SIGNING ADDRESS	OTHERS IN ATTENDANCE	CLIENT / SIGNING SERVICE	FEE
		LENDER / LOAN NUMBER	

NOTES

	ADDRESS	SIGNATURE	PHONE	EMAIL	INITIAL IF OATH/AFF TAKEN	RIGHT THUMB PRINT
1						
2						
3						
4						

#	Date / Time	Name	Identity Verified	Willingness & Competence	Format
1	DATE TIME	NAME ❑ Signer ❑ Witness	IDENTITY VERIFIED ❑ D.L. ❑ Passport ❑ Credible Witness ❑ Other	WILLINGNESS & COMPETENCE ❑ Expressed willingness ❑ Mentally alert ❑ Indicated understanding	FORMAT ❑ Paper ❑ Electronic ❑ RON
2	DATE TIME	NAME ❑ Signer ❑ Witness	IDENTITY VERIFIED ❑ D.L. ❑ Passport ❑ Credible Witness ❑ Other	WILLINGNESS & COMPETENCE ❑ Expressed willingness ❑ Mentally alert ❑ Indicated understanding	FORMAT ❑ Paper ❑ Electronic ❑ RON
3	DATE TIME	NAME ❑ Signer ❑ Witness	IDENTITY VERIFIED ❑ D.L. ❑ Passport ❑ Credible Witness ❑ Other	WILLINGNESS & COMPETENCE ❑ Expressed willingness ❑ Mentally alert ❑ Indicated understanding	FORMAT ❑ Paper ❑ Electronic ❑ RON
4	DATE TIME	NAME ❑ Signer ❑ Witness	IDENTITY VERIFIED ❑ D.L. ❑ Passport ❑ Credible Witness ❑ Other	WILLINGNESS & COMPETENCE ❑ Expressed willingness ❑ Mentally alert ❑ Indicated understanding	FORMAT ❑ Paper ❑ Electronic ❑ RON

DOCUMENT(S) SIGNED			SIGNER				
❑ Borrower's Aff	Acknowledgment Jurat ______ 1 2 3 4	❑ Minor Medical Consent	Acknowledgment Jurat ______ 1 2 3 4	❑ ______
❑ Compliance Agrmt	Acknowledgment Jurat ______ 1 2 3 4	❑ Minor Passport Consent	Acknowledgment Jurat ______ 1 2 3 4	Acknowledgment Jurat Copy Oath SW 1 2 3 4
❑ Correction Agrmt	Acknowledgment Jurat ______ 1 2 3 4	❑ Minor Travel Consent	Acknowledgment Jurat ______ 1 2 3 4	
❑ Debts/Leins Aff	Acknowledgment Jurat ______ 1 2 3 4			❑ ______
❑ Deed of Trust	Acknowledgment Jurat ______ 1 2 3 4	❑ Vehicle Duplicate Title	Acknowledgment Jurat ______ 1 2 3 4	Acknowledgment Jurat Copy Oath SW 1 2 3 4
❑ Distrib of Proceeds	Acknowledgment Jurat ______ 1 2 3 4	❑ Vehicle Lein Release	Acknowledgment Jurat ______ 1 2 3 4	
❑ E&O Agrmt	Acknowledgment Jurat ______ 1 2 3 4	❑ Vehicle Odom/Vin Ver	Acknowledgment Jurat ______ 1 2 3 4	❑ ______
❑ Grant Deed	Acknowledgment Jurat ______ 1 2 3 4	❑ Vehicle Title Transfer	Acknowledgment Jurat ______ 1 2 3 4	Acknowledgment Jurat Copy Oath SW 1 2 3 4
❑ Marital Stat Aff	Acknowledgment Jurat ______ 1 2 3 4			
❑ Mortgage	Acknowledgment Jurat ______ 1 2 3 4	❑ Adv Health Care Dir	Acknowledgment Jurat ______ 1 2 3 4	❑ ______
❑ Occupancy/Fin Aff	Acknowledgment Jurat ______ 1 2 3 4	❑ Assign of Digital Assets	Acknowledgment Jurat ______ 1 2 3 4	Acknowledgment Jurat Copy Oath SW 1 2 3 4
❑ Owner's Aff	Acknowledgment Jurat ______ 1 2 3 4	❑ Assign of Personal Prop	Acknowledgment Jurat ______ 1 2 3 4	
❑ Payoff Aff	Acknowledgment Jurat ______ 1 2 3 4	❑ HIPAA Release	Acknowledgment Jurat ______ 1 2 3 4	❑ ______
❑ Quit-Claim Deed	Acknowledgment Jurat ______ 1 2 3 4	❑ Living Trust ______	Acknowledgment Jurat ______ 1 2 3 4	Acknowledgment Jurat Copy Oath SW 1 2 3 4
❑ Sig/Name Aff	Acknowledgment Jurat ______ 1 2 3 4	❑ Last Will & Testament	Acknowledgment Jurat ______ 1 2 3 4	
❑ Survey Aff	Acknowledgment Jurat ______ 1 2 3 4	❑ POA ______	Acknowledgment Jurat ______ 1 2 3 4	❑ ______
❑ Warranty Deed	Acknowledgment Jurat ______ 1 2 3 4	❑ Trust Certification	Acknowledgment Jurat ______ 1 2 3 4	Acknowledgment Jurat Copy Oath SW 1 2 3 4

	SIGNING ADDRESS	OTHERS IN ATTENDANCE	CLIENT / SIGNING SERVICE	FEE
			LENDER / LOAN NUMBER	

NOTES

		ADDRESS		SIGNATURE		RIGHT THUMB PRINT
1	PHONE				INITIAL IF OATH/AFF TAKEN	
	EMAIL					
2	PHONE	ADDRESS		SIGNATURE	INITIAL IF OATH/AFF TAKEN	RIGHT THUMB PRINT
	EMAIL					
3	PHONE	ADDRESS		SIGNATURE	INITIAL IF OATH/AFF TAKEN	RIGHT THUMB PRINT
	EMAIL					
4	PHONE	ADDRESS		SIGNATURE	INITIAL IF OATH/AFF TAKEN	RIGHT THUMB PRINT
	EMAIL					

Entry 1

DATE	
TIME	

NAME ☐ Signer ☐ Witness

IDENTITY VERIFIED ☐ D.L. ☐ Passport ☐ Credible Witness ☐ Other

WILLINGNESS & COMPETENCE ☐ Expressed willingness ☐ Mentally alert ☐ Indicated understanding

FORMAT ☐ Paper ☐ Electronic ☐ RON

Entry 2

DATE	
TIME	

NAME ☐ Signer ☐ Witness

IDENTITY VERIFIED ☐ D.L. ☐ Passport ☐ Credible Witness ☐ Other

WILLINGNESS & COMPETENCE ☐ Expressed willingness ☐ Mentally alert ☐ Indicated understanding

FORMAT ☐ Paper ☐ Electronic ☐ RON

Entry 3

DATE	
TIME	

NAME ☐ Signer ☐ Witness

IDENTITY VERIFIED ☐ D.L. ☐ Passport ☐ Credible Witness ☐ Other

WILLINGNESS & COMPETENCE ☐ Expressed willingness ☐ Mentally alert ☐ Indicated understanding

FORMAT ☐ Paper ☐ Electronic ☐ RON

Entry 4

DATE	
TIME	

NAME ☐ Signer ☐ Witness

IDENTITY VERIFIED ☐ D.L. ☐ Passport ☐ Credible Witness ☐ Other

WILLINGNESS & COMPETENCE ☐ Expressed willingness ☐ Mentally alert ☐ Indicated understanding

FORMAT ☐ Paper ☐ Electronic ☐ RON

DOCUMENT(S) SIGNED

Document	Act			SIGNER 1	2	3	4
☐ Borrower's Aff	Acknowledgment	Jurat		1	2	3	4
☐ Compliance Agrmt	Acknowledgment	Jurat		1	2	3	4
☐ Correction Agrmt	Acknowledgment	Jurat		1	2	3	4
☐ Debts/Leins Aff	Acknowledgment	Jurat		1	2	3	4
☐ Deed of Trust	Acknowledgment	Jurat		1	2	3	4
☐ Distrib of Proceeds	Acknowledgment	Jurat		1	2	3	4
☐ E&O Agrmt	Acknowledgment	Jurat		1	2	3	4
☐ Grant Deed	Acknowledgment	Jurat		1	2	3	4
☐ Marital Stat Aff	Acknowledgment	Jurat		1	2	3	4
☐ Mortgage	Acknowledgment	Jurat		1	2	3	4
☐ Occupancy/Fin Aff	Acknowledgment	Jurat		1	2	3	4
☐ Owner's Aff	Acknowledgment	Jurat		1	2	3	4
☐ Payoff Aff	Acknowledgment	Jurat		1	2	3	4
☐ Quit-Claim Deed	Acknowledgment	Jurat		1	2	3	4
☐ Sig/Name Aff	Acknowledgment	Jurat		1	2	3	4
☐ Survey Aff	Acknowledgment	Jurat		1	2	3	4
☐ Warranty Deed	Acknowledgment	Jurat		1	2	3	4

Document	Act					SIGNER 1	2	3	4
☐ Minor Medical Consent	Acknowledgment	Jurat				1	2	3	4
☐ Minor Passport Consent	Acknowledgment	Jurat	Copy	Oath	SW	1	2	3	4
☐ Minor Travel Consent	Acknowledgment	Jurat				1	2	3	4
☐ Vehicle Duplicate Title	Acknowledgment	Jurat				1	2	3	4
☐ Vehicle Lein Release	Acknowledgment	Jurat	Copy	Oath	SW	1	2	3	4
☐ Vehicle Odom/Vin Ver	Acknowledgment	Jurat				1	2	3	4
☐ Vehicle Title Transfer	Acknowledgment	Jurat	Copy	Oath	SW	1	2	3	4
☐ Adv Health Care Dir	Acknowledgment	Jurat				1	2	3	4
☐ Assign of Digital Assets	Acknowledgment	Jurat	Copy	Oath	SW	1	2	3	4
☐ Assign of Personal Prop	Acknowledgment	Jurat				1	2	3	4
☐ HIPAA Release	Acknowledgment	Jurat				1	2	3	4
☐ Living Trust	Acknowledgment	Jurat	Copy	Oath	SW	1	2	3	4
☐ Last Will & Testament	Acknowledgment	Jurat				1	2	3	4
☐ POA	Acknowledgment	Jurat				1	2	3	4
☐ Trust Certification	Acknowledgment	Jurat	Copy	Oath	SW	1	2	3	4

SIGNING ADDRESS	OTHERS IN ATTENDANCE	CLIENT / SIGNING SERVICE	FEE
		LENDER / LOAN NUMBER	

NOTES

	ADDRESS	PHONE	EMAIL	SIGNATURE	INITIAL IF OATH/AFF TAKEN	RIGHT THUMB PRINT
1						
2						
3						
4						

Notary Journal Entries

Entry 1
DATE		
TIME		

NAME: ☐ Signer ☐ Witness

IDENTITY VERIFIED: ☐ D.L. ☐ Passport ☐ Credible Witness ☐ Other

WILLINGNESS & COMPETENCE: ☐ Expressed willingness ☐ Mentally alert ☐ Indicated understanding

FORMAT: ☐ Paper ☐ Electronic ☐ RON

Entry 2
DATE		
TIME		

NAME: ☐ Signer ☐ Witness

IDENTITY VERIFIED: ☐ D.L. ☐ Passport ☐ Credible Witness ☐ Other

WILLINGNESS & COMPETENCE: ☐ Expressed willingness ☐ Mentally alert ☐ Indicated understanding

FORMAT: ☐ Paper ☐ Electronic ☐ RON

Entry 3
DATE		
TIME		

NAME: ☐ Signer ☐ Witness

IDENTITY VERIFIED: ☐ D.L. ☐ Passport ☐ Credible Witness ☐ Other

WILLINGNESS & COMPETENCE: ☐ Expressed willingness ☐ Mentally alert ☐ Indicated understanding

FORMAT: ☐ Paper ☐ Electronic ☐ RON

Entry 4
DATE		
TIME		

NAME: ☐ Signer ☐ Witness

IDENTITY VERIFIED: ☐ D.L. ☐ Passport ☐ Credible Witness ☐ Other

WILLINGNESS & COMPETENCE: ☐ Expressed willingness ☐ Mentally alert ☐ Indicated understanding

FORMAT: ☐ Paper ☐ Electronic ☐ RON

DOCUMENT(S) SIGNED

Document	Type	SIGNER 1	2	3	4
☐ Borrower's Aff	Acknowledgment Jurat	1	2	3	4
☐ Compliance Agrmt	Acknowledgment Jurat	1	2	3	4
☐ Correction Agrmt	Acknowledgment Jurat	1	2	3	4
☐ Debts/Leins Aff	Acknowledgment Jurat	1	2	3	4
☐ Deed of Trust	Acknowledgment Jurat	1	2	3	4
☐ Distrib of Proceeds	Acknowledgment Jurat	1	2	3	4
☐ E&O Agrmt	Acknowledgment Jurat	1	2	3	4
☐ Grant Deed	Acknowledgment Jurat	1	2	3	4
☐ Marital Stat Aff	Acknowledgment Jurat	1	2	3	4
☐ Mortgage	Acknowledgment Jurat	1	2	3	4
☐ Occupancy/Fin Aff	Acknowledgment Jurat	1	2	3	4
☐ Owner's Aff	Acknowledgment Jurat	1	2	3	4
☐ Payoff Aff	Acknowledgment Jurat	1	2	3	4
☐ Quit-Claim Deed	Acknowledgment Jurat	1	2	3	4
☐ Sig/Name Aff	Acknowledgment Jurat	1	2	3	4
☐ Survey Aff	Acknowledgment Jurat	1	2	3	4
☐ Warranty Deed	Acknowledgment Jurat	1	2	3	4

Document	Type	SIGNER 1	2	3	4			
☐ Minor Medical Consent	Acknowledgment Jurat	1	2	3	4			
☐ Minor Passport Consent	Acknowledgment Jurat	1	2	3	4			
☐ Minor Travel Consent	Acknowledgment Jurat	1	2	3	4			
☐ Vehicle Duplicate Title	Acknowledgment Jurat Copy Oath SW	1	2	3	4			
☐ Vehicle Lein Release	Acknowledgment Jurat	1	2	3	4			
☐ Vehicle Odom/Vin Ver	Acknowledgment Jurat	1	2	3	4			
☐ Vehicle Title Transfer	Acknowledgment Jurat Copy Oath SW	1	2	3	4			
☐ Adv Health Care Dir	Acknowledgment Jurat	1	2	3	4			
☐ Assign of Digital Assets	Acknowledgment Jurat Copy Oath SW	1	2	3	4			
☐ Assign of Personal Prop	Acknowledgment Jurat	1	2	3	4			
☐ HIPAA Release	Acknowledgment Jurat	1	2	3	4			
☐ Living Trust	Acknowledgment Jurat Copy Oath SW	1	2	3	4			
☐ Last Will & Testament	Acknowledgment Jurat	1	2	3	4			
☐ POA	Acknowledgment Jurat	1	2	3	4			
☐ Trust Certification	Acknowledgment Jurat Copy Oath SW	1	2	3	4			

SIGNING ADDRESS	OTHERS IN ATTENDANCE	CLIENT / SIGNING SERVICE	FEE
		LENDER / LOAN NUMBER	

NOTES

	ADDRESS	PHONE	SIGNATURE	INITIAL IF OATH/AFF TAKEN	RIGHT THUMB PRINT
1		EMAIL			
2	ADDRESS	PHONE / EMAIL	SIGNATURE	INITIAL IF OATH/AFF TAKEN	RIGHT THUMB PRINT
3	ADDRESS	PHONE / EMAIL	SIGNATURE	INITIAL IF OATH/AFF TAKEN	RIGHT THUMB PRINT
4	ADDRESS	PHONE / EMAIL	SIGNATURE	INITIAL IF OATH/AFF TAKEN	RIGHT THUMB PRINT

Notary Record Entries

#	DATE / TIME	NAME	IDENTITY VERIFIED	WILLINGNESS & COMPETENCE	FORMAT
1	DATE ____ / TIME ____	☐ Signer ☐ Witness	☐ D.L. ☐ Passport ☐ Credible Witness ☐ Other	☐ Expressed willingness ☐ Mentally alert ☐ Indicated understanding	☐ Paper ☐ Electronic ☐ RON
2	DATE ____ / TIME ____	☐ Signer ☐ Witness	☐ D.L. ☐ Passport ☐ Credible Witness ☐ Other	☐ Expressed willingness ☐ Mentally alert ☐ Indicated understanding	☐ Paper ☐ Electronic ☐ RON
3	DATE ____ / TIME ____	☐ Signer ☐ Witness	☐ D.L. ☐ Passport ☐ Credible Witness ☐ Other	☐ Expressed willingness ☐ Mentally alert ☐ Indicated understanding	☐ Paper ☐ Electronic ☐ RON
4	DATE ____ / TIME ____	☐ Signer ☐ Witness	☐ D.L. ☐ Passport ☐ Credible Witness ☐ Other	☐ Expressed willingness ☐ Mentally alert ☐ Indicated understanding	☐ Paper ☐ Electronic ☐ RON

DOCUMENT(S) SIGNED

	Notarial Act		SIGNER			
			1	2	3	4
☐ Borrower's Aff	Acknowledgment	Jurat ____	1	2	3	4
☐ Compliance Agrmt	Acknowledgment	Jurat ____	1	2	3	4
☐ Correction Agrmt	Acknowledgment	Jurat ____	1	2	3	4
☐ Debts/Leins Aff	Acknowledgment	Jurat ____	1	2	3	4
☐ Deed of Trust	Acknowledgment	Jurat ____	1	2	3	4
☐ Distrib of Proceeds	Acknowledgment	Jurat ____	1	2	3	4
☐ E&O Agrmt	Acknowledgment	Jurat ____	1	2	3	4
☐ Grant Deed	Acknowledgment	Jurat ____	1	2	3	4
☐ Marital Stat Aff	Acknowledgment	Jurat ____	1	2	3	4
☐ Mortgage	Acknowledgment	Jurat ____	1	2	3	4
☐ Occupancy/Fin Aff	Acknowledgment	Jurat ____	1	2	3	4
☐ Owner's Aff	Acknowledgment	Jurat ____	1	2	3	4
☐ Payoff Aff	Acknowledgment	Jurat ____	1	2	3	4
☐ Quit-Claim Deed	Acknowledgment	Jurat ____	1	2	3	4
☐ Sig/Name Aff	Acknowledgment	Jurat ____	1	2	3	4
☐ Survey Aff	Acknowledgment	Jurat ____	1	2	3	4
☐ Warranty Deed	Acknowledgment	Jurat ____	1	2	3	4

	Notarial Act					SIGNER			
						1	2	3	4
☐ Minor Medical Consent	Acknowledgment	Jurat				1	2	3	4
☐ Minor Passport Consent	Acknowledgment	Jurat	Copy	Oath	SW	1	2	3	4
☐ Minor Travel Consent	Acknowledgment	Jurat				1	2	3	4
☐ Vehicle Duplicate Title	Acknowledgment	Jurat				1	2	3	4
☐ Vehicle Lein Release	Acknowledgment	Jurat	Copy	Oath	SW	1	2	3	4
☐ Vehicle Odom/Vin Ver	Acknowledgment	Jurat				1	2	3	4
☐ Vehicle Title Transfer	Acknowledgment	Jurat	Copy	Oath	SW	1	2	3	4
☐ Adv Health Care Dir	Acknowledgment	Jurat				1	2	3	4
☐ Assign of Digital Assets	Acknowledgment	Jurat	Copy	Oath	SW	1	2	3	4
☐ Assign of Personal Prop	Acknowledgment	Jurat				1	2	3	4
☐ HIPAA Release	Acknowledgment	Jurat				1	2	3	4
☐ Living Trust	Acknowledgment	Jurat ____	Copy	Oath	SW	1	2	3	4
☐ Last Will & Testament	Acknowledgment	Jurat	Copy	Oath	SW	1	2	3	4
☐ POA ____	Acknowledgment	Jurat				1	2	3	4
☐ Trust Certification	Acknowledgment	Jurat ____	Copy	Oath	SW	1	2	3	4

SIGNING ADDRESS	OTHERS IN ATTENDANCE	CLIENT / SIGNING SERVICE	FEE
		LENDER / LOAN NUMBER	

NOTES

_____
_____
_____
_____
_____
_____
_____
_____
_____
_____
_____

	ADDRESS	SIGNATURE	PHONE	INITIAL IF OATH/AFF TAKEN	RIGHT THUMB PRINT
1			EMAIL		
2	ADDRESS	SIGNATURE	PHONE / EMAIL	INITIAL IF OATH/AFF TAKEN	RIGHT THUMB PRINT
3	ADDRESS	SIGNATURE	PHONE / EMAIL	INITIAL IF OATH/AFF TAKEN	RIGHT THUMB PRINT
4	ADDRESS	SIGNATURE	PHONE / EMAIL	INITIAL IF OATH/AFF TAKEN	RIGHT THUMB PRINT

Signer Entries

1
- **DATE:**
- **TIME:**
- **NAME:** ☐ Signer ☐ Witness
- **IDENTITY VERIFIED:** ☐ D.L. ☐ Passport ☐ Credible Witness ☐ Other
- **WILLINGNESS & COMPETENCE:** ☐ Expressed willingness ☐ Mentally alert ☐ Indicated understanding
- **FORMAT:** ☐ Paper ☐ Electronic ☐ RON

2
- **DATE:**
- **TIME:**
- **NAME:** ☐ Signer ☐ Witness
- **IDENTITY VERIFIED:** ☐ D.L. ☐ Passport ☐ Credible Witness ☐ Other
- **WILLINGNESS & COMPETENCE:** ☐ Expressed willingness ☐ Mentally alert ☐ Indicated understanding
- **FORMAT:** ☐ Paper ☐ Electronic ☐ RON

3
- **DATE:**
- **TIME:**
- **NAME:** ☐ Signer ☐ Witness
- **IDENTITY VERIFIED:** ☐ D.L. ☐ Passport ☐ Credible Witness ☐ Other
- **WILLINGNESS & COMPETENCE:** ☐ Expressed willingness ☐ Mentally alert ☐ Indicated understanding
- **FORMAT:** ☐ Paper ☐ Electronic ☐ RON

4
- **DATE:**
- **TIME:**
- **NAME:** ☐ Signer ☐ Witness
- **IDENTITY VERIFIED:** ☐ D.L. ☐ Passport ☐ Credible Witness ☐ Other
- **WILLINGNESS & COMPETENCE:** ☐ Expressed willingness ☐ Mentally alert ☐ Indicated understanding
- **FORMAT:** ☐ Paper ☐ Electronic ☐ RON

DOCUMENT(S) SIGNED

Document	Notarial Act		SIGNER 1	2	3	4
☐ Borrower's Aff	Acknowledgment	Jurat	1	2	3	4
☐ Compliance Agrmt	Acknowledgment	Jurat	1	2	3	4
☐ Correction Agrmt	Acknowledgment	Jurat	1	2	3	4
☐ Debts/Leins Aff	Acknowledgment	Jurat	1	2	3	4
☐ Deed of Trust	Acknowledgment	Jurat	1	2	3	4
☐ Distrib of Proceeds	Acknowledgment	Jurat	1	2	3	4
☐ E&O Agrmt	Acknowledgment	Jurat	1	2	3	4
☐ Grant Deed	Acknowledgment	Jurat	1	2	3	4
☐ Marital Stat Aff	Acknowledgment	Jurat	1	2	3	4
☐ Mortgage	Acknowledgment	Jurat	1	2	3	4
☐ Occupancy/Fin Aff	Acknowledgment	Jurat	1	2	3	4
☐ Owner's Aff	Acknowledgment	Jurat	1	2	3	4
☐ Payoff Aff	Acknowledgment	Jurat	1	2	3	4
☐ Quit-Claim Deed	Acknowledgment	Jurat	1	2	3	4
☐ Sig/Name Aff	Acknowledgment	Jurat	1	2	3	4
☐ Survey Aff	Acknowledgment	Jurat	1	2	3	4
☐ Warranty Deed	Acknowledgment	Jurat	1	2	3	4

Document	Notarial Act				SIGNER 1	2	3	4
☐ Minor Medical Consent	Acknowledgment	Jurat			1	2	3	4
☐ Minor Passport Consent	Acknowledgment	Jurat	Copy	Oath SW	1	2	3	4
☐ Minor Travel Consent	Acknowledgment	Jurat			1	2	3	4
☐ Vehicle Duplicate Title	Acknowledgment	Jurat			1	2	3	4
☐ Vehicle Lein Release	Acknowledgment	Jurat	Copy	Oath SW	1	2	3	4
☐ Vehicle Odom/Vin Ver	Acknowledgment	Jurat			1	2	3	4
☐ Vehicle Title Transfer	Acknowledgment	Jurat	Copy	Oath SW	1	2	3	4
☐ Adv Health Care Dir	Acknowledgment	Jurat			1	2	3	4
☐ Assign of Digital Assets	Acknowledgment	Jurat	Copy	Oath SW	1	2	3	4
☐ Assign of Personal Prop	Acknowledgment	Jurat			1	2	3	4
☐ HIPAA Release	Acknowledgment	Jurat			1	2	3	4
☐ Living Trust _____	Acknowledgment	Jurat	Copy	Oath SW	1	2	3	4
☐ Last Will & Testament	Acknowledgment	Jurat			1	2	3	4
☐ POA	Acknowledgment	Jurat			1	2	3	4
☐ Trust Certification	Acknowledgment	Jurat	Copy	Oath SW	1	2	3	4

SIGNING ADDRESS	OTHERS IN ATTENDANCE	CLIENT / SIGNING SERVICE	FEE
		LENDER / LOAN NUMBER	

NOTES

_____
_____
_____
_____
_____
_____
_____
_____
_____
_____
_____
_____

	ADDRESS	PHONE	EMAIL	SIGNATURE	INITIAL IF OATH/AFF TAKEN	RIGHT THUMB PRINT
1						
2						
3						
4						

Notary Journal Entries

#	DATE / TIME	NAME	IDENTITY VERIFIED	WILLINGNESS & COMPETENCE	FORMAT
1	DATE _____ TIME _____	☐ Signer ☐ Witness	☐ D.L. ☐ Passport ☐ Credible Witness ☐ Other	☐ Expressed willingness ☐ Mentally alert ☐ Indicated understanding	☐ Paper ☐ Electronic ☐ RON
2	DATE _____ TIME _____	☐ Signer ☐ Witness	☐ D.L. ☐ Passport ☐ Credible Witness ☐ Other	☐ Expressed willingness ☐ Mentally alert ☐ Indicated understanding	☐ Paper ☐ Electronic ☐ RON
3	DATE _____ TIME _____	☐ Signer ☐ Witness	☐ D.L. ☐ Passport ☐ Credible Witness ☐ Other	☐ Expressed willingness ☐ Mentally alert ☐ Indicated understanding	☐ Paper ☐ Electronic ☐ RON
4	DATE _____ TIME _____	☐ Signer ☐ Witness	☐ D.L. ☐ Passport ☐ Credible Witness ☐ Other	☐ Expressed willingness ☐ Mentally alert ☐ Indicated understanding	☐ Paper ☐ Electronic ☐ RON

DOCUMENT(S) SIGNED

Document	Act Type	SIGNER
☐ Borrower's Aff	Acknowledgment Jurat _____	1 2 3 4
☐ Compliance Agrmt	Acknowledgment Jurat _____	1 2 3 4
☐ Correction Agrmt	Acknowledgment Jurat _____	1 2 3 4
☐ Debts/Leins Aff	Acknowledgment Jurat _____	1 2 3 4
☐ Deed of Trust	Acknowledgment Jurat _____	1 2 3 4
☐ Distrib of Proceeds	Acknowledgment Jurat _____	1 2 3 4
☐ E&O Agrmt	Acknowledgment Jurat _____	1 2 3 4
☐ Grant Deed	Acknowledgment Jurat _____	1 2 3 4
☐ Marital Stat Aff	Acknowledgment Jurat _____	1 2 3 4
☐ Mortgage	Acknowledgment Jurat _____	1 2 3 4
☐ Occupancy/Fin Aff	Acknowledgment Jurat _____	1 2 3 4
☐ Owner's Aff	Acknowledgment Jurat _____	1 2 3 4
☐ Payoff Aff	Acknowledgment Jurat _____	1 2 3 4
☐ Quit-Claim Deed	Acknowledgment Jurat _____	1 2 3 4
☐ Sig/Name Aff	Acknowledgment Jurat _____	1 2 3 4
☐ Survey Aff	Acknowledgment Jurat _____	1 2 3 4
☐ Warranty Deed	Acknowledgment Jurat _____	1 2 3 4

Document	Act Type	SIGNER
☐ Minor Medical Consent	Acknowledgment Jurat _____	1 2 3 4
☐ Minor Passport Consent	Acknowledgment Jurat _____	1 2 3 4
☐ Minor Travel Consent	Acknowledgment Jurat _____	1 2 3 4
☐	Acknowledgment Jurat Copy Oath SW	1 2 3 4
☐ Vehicle Duplicate Title	Acknowledgment Jurat _____	1 2 3 4
☐ Vehicle Lein Release	Acknowledgment Jurat _____	1 2 3 4
☐ Vehicle Odom/Vin Ver	Acknowledgment Jurat _____	1 2 3 4
☐ Vehicle Title Transfer	Acknowledgment Jurat _____	1 2 3 4
☐	Acknowledgment Jurat Copy Oath SW	1 2 3 4
☐ Adv Health Care Dir	Acknowledgment Jurat _____	1 2 3 4
☐ Assign of Digital Assets	Acknowledgment Jurat _____	1 2 3 4
☐	Acknowledgment Jurat Copy Oath SW	1 2 3 4
☐ Assign of Personal Prop	Acknowledgment Jurat _____	1 2 3 4
☐ HIPAA Release	Acknowledgment Jurat _____	1 2 3 4
☐	Acknowledgment Jurat Copy Oath SW	1 2 3 4
☐ Living Trust _____	Acknowledgment Jurat _____	1 2 3 4
☐ Last Will & Testament	Acknowledgment Jurat _____	1 2 3 4
☐	Acknowledgment Jurat Copy Oath SW	1 2 3 4
☐ POA _____	Acknowledgment Jurat _____	1 2 3 4
☐ Trust Certification	Acknowledgment Jurat Copy Oath SW	1 2 3 4

SIGNING ADDRESS	OTHERS IN ATTENDANCE	CLIENT / SIGNING SERVICE	FEE
		LENDER / LOAN NUMBER	

NOTES

	ADDRESS	PHONE / EMAIL	SIGNATURE	INITIAL IF OATH/AFF TAKEN	RIGHT THUMB PRINT
1		PHONE / EMAIL			RIGHT THUMB PRINT
2		PHONE / EMAIL			RIGHT THUMB PRINT
3		PHONE / EMAIL			RIGHT THUMB PRINT
4		PHONE / EMAIL			RIGHT THUMB PRINT

1	DATE TIME	NAME ☐ Signer ☐ Witness	IDENTITY VERIFIED ☐ D.L. ☐ Passport ☐ Credible Witness ☐ Other	WILLINGNESS & COMPETENCE ☐ Expressed willingness ☐ Mentally alert ☐ Indicated understanding	FORMAT ☐ Paper ☐ Electronic ☐ RON
2	DATE TIME	NAME ☐ Signer ☐ Witness	IDENTITY VERIFIED ☐ D.L. ☐ Passport ☐ Credible Witness ☐ Other	WILLINGNESS & COMPETENCE ☐ Expressed willingness ☐ Mentally alert ☐ Indicated understanding	FORMAT ☐ Paper ☐ Electronic ☐ RON
3	DATE TIME	NAME ☐ Signer ☐ Witness	IDENTITY VERIFIED ☐ D.L. ☐ Passport ☐ Credible Witness ☐ Other	WILLINGNESS & COMPETENCE ☐ Expressed willingness ☐ Mentally alert ☐ Indicated understanding	FORMAT ☐ Paper ☐ Electronic ☐ RON
4	DATE TIME	NAME ☐ Signer ☐ Witness	IDENTITY VERIFIED ☐ D.L. ☐ Passport ☐ Credible Witness ☐ Other	WILLINGNESS & COMPETENCE ☐ Expressed willingness ☐ Mentally alert ☐ Indicated understanding	FORMAT ☐ Paper ☐ Electronic ☐ RON

DOCUMENT(S) SIGNED

Document			Signer			
☐ Borrower's Aff	Acknowledgment	Jurat ______	1	2	3	4
☐ Compliance Agrmt	Acknowledgment	Jurat ______	1	2	3	4
☐ Correction Agrmt	Acknowledgment	Jurat ______	1	2	3	4
☐ Debts/Leins Aff	Acknowledgment	Jurat ______	1	2	3	4
☐ Deed of Trust	Acknowledgment	Jurat ______	1	2	3	4
☐ Distrib of Proceeds	Acknowledgment	Jurat ______	1	2	3	4
☐ E&O Agrmt	Acknowledgment	Jurat ______	1	2	3	4
☐ Grant Deed	Acknowledgment	Jurat ______	1	2	3	4
☐ Marital Stat Aff	Acknowledgment	Jurat ______	1	2	3	4
☐ Mortgage	Acknowledgment	Jurat ______	1	2	3	4
☐ Occupancy/Fin Aff	Acknowledgment	Jurat ______	1	2	3	4
☐ Owner's Aff	Acknowledgment	Jurat ______	1	2	3	4
☐ Payoff Aff	Acknowledgment	Jurat ______	1	2	3	4
☐ Quit-Claim Deed	Acknowledgment	Jurat ______	1	2	3	4
☐ Sig/Name Aff	Acknowledgment	Jurat ______	1	2	3	4
☐ Survey Aff	Acknowledgment	Jurat ______	1	2	3	4
☐ Warranty Deed	Acknowledgment	Jurat ______	1	2	3	4

Document			Signer			
☐ Minor Medical Consent	Acknowledgment	Jurat ______	1	2	3	4
☐ Minor Passport Consent	Acknowledgment	Jurat ______	1	2	3	4
☐ Minor Travel Consent	Acknowledgment	Jurat ______	1	2	3	4
☐ Vehicle Duplicate Title	Acknowledgment	Jurat ______	1	2	3	4
☐ Vehicle Lein Release	Acknowledgment	Jurat ______	1	2	3	4
☐ Vehicle Odom/Vin Ver	Acknowledgment	Jurat ______	1	2	3	4
☐ Vehicle Title Transfer	Acknowledgment	Jurat ______	1	2	3	4
☐ Adv Health Care Dir	Acknowledgment	Jurat ______	1	2	3	4
☐ Assign of Digital Assets	Acknowledgment	Jurat ______	1	2	3	4
☐ Assign of Personal Prop	Acknowledgment	Jurat ______	1	2	3	4
☐ HIPAA Release	Acknowledgment	Jurat ______	1	2	3	4
☐ Living Trust ______	Acknowledgment	Jurat ______	1	2	3	4
☐ Last Will & Testament	Acknowledgment	Jurat ______	1	2	3	4
☐ POA ______	Acknowledgment	Jurat ______	1	2	3	4
☐ Trust Certification	Acknowledgment	Jurat ______	1	2	3	4

☐ ______								
Acknowledgment	Jurat	Copy	Oath	SW	1	2	3	4
☐ ______								
Acknowledgment	Jurat	Copy	Oath	SW	1	2	3	4
☐ ______								
Acknowledgment	Jurat	Copy	Oath	SW	1	2	3	4
☐ ______								
Acknowledgment	Jurat	Copy	Oath	SW	1	2	3	4
☐ ______								
Acknowledgment	Jurat	Copy	Oath	SW	1	2	3	4
☐ ______								
Acknowledgment	Jurat	Copy	Oath	SW	1	2	3	4

SIGNING ADDRESS	OTHERS IN ATTENDANCE	CLIENT / SIGNING SERVICE	FEE
		LENDER / LOAN NUMBER	

NOTES

#				SIGNATURE	INITIAL IF OATH/AFF TAKEN	RIGHT THUMB PRINT
1	ADDRESS	PHONE	EMAIL	SIGNATURE	INITIAL IF OATH/AFF TAKEN	RIGHT THUMB PRINT
2	ADDRESS	PHONE	EMAIL	SIGNATURE	INITIAL IF OATH/AFF TAKEN	RIGHT THUMB PRINT
3	ADDRESS	PHONE	EMAIL	SIGNATURE	INITIAL IF OATH/AFF TAKEN	RIGHT THUMB PRINT
4	ADDRESS	PHONE	EMAIL	SIGNATURE	INITIAL IF OATH/AFF TAKEN	RIGHT THUMB PRINT

Notary Journal Entries

Entry 1
Field	Details
DATE	
TIME	
NAME	☐ Signer ☐ Witness
IDENTITY VERIFIED	☐ D.L. ☐ Passport ☐ Credible Witness ☐ Other
WILLINGNESS & COMPETENCE	☐ Expressed willingness ☐ Mentally alert ☐ Indicated understanding
FORMAT	☐ Paper ☐ Electronic ☐ RON

Entry 2
Field	Details
DATE	
TIME	
NAME	☐ Signer ☐ Witness
IDENTITY VERIFIED	☐ D.L. ☐ Passport ☐ Credible Witness ☐ Other
WILLINGNESS & COMPETENCE	☐ Expressed willingness ☐ Mentally alert ☐ Indicated understanding
FORMAT	☐ Paper ☐ Electronic ☐ RON

Entry 3
Field	Details
DATE	
TIME	
NAME	☐ Signer ☐ Witness
IDENTITY VERIFIED	☐ D.L. ☐ Passport ☐ Credible Witness ☐ Other
WILLINGNESS & COMPETENCE	☐ Expressed willingness ☐ Mentally alert ☐ Indicated understanding
FORMAT	☐ Paper ☐ Electronic ☐ RON

Entry 4
Field	Details
DATE	
TIME	
NAME	☐ Signer ☐ Witness
IDENTITY VERIFIED	☐ D.L. ☐ Passport ☐ Credible Witness ☐ Other
WILLINGNESS & COMPETENCE	☐ Expressed willingness ☐ Mentally alert ☐ Indicated understanding
FORMAT	☐ Paper ☐ Electronic ☐ RON

DOCUMENT(S) SIGNED

Document	Options	SIGNER
☐ Borrower's Aff	Acknowledgment Jurat	1 2 3 4
☐ Compliance Agrmt	Acknowledgment Jurat	1 2 3 4
☐ Correction Agrmt	Acknowledgment Jurat	1 2 3 4
☐ Debts/Leins Aff	Acknowledgment Jurat	1 2 3 4
☐ Deed of Trust	Acknowledgment Jurat	1 2 3 4
☐ Distrib of Proceeds	Acknowledgment Jurat	1 2 3 4
☐ E&O Agrmt	Acknowledgment Jurat	1 2 3 4
☐ Grant Deed	Acknowledgment Jurat	1 2 3 4
☐ Marital Stat Aff	Acknowledgment Jurat	1 2 3 4
☐ Mortgage	Acknowledgment Jurat	1 2 3 4
☐ Occupancy/Fin Aff	Acknowledgment Jurat	1 2 3 4
☐ Owner's Aff	Acknowledgment Jurat	1 2 3 4
☐ Payoff Aff	Acknowledgment Jurat	1 2 3 4
☐ Quit-Claim Deed	Acknowledgment Jurat	1 2 3 4
☐ Sig/Name Aff	Acknowledgment Jurat	1 2 3 4
☐ Survey Aff	Acknowledgment Jurat	1 2 3 4
☐ Warranty Deed	Acknowledgment Jurat	1 2 3 4
☐ Minor Medical Consent	Acknowledgment Jurat	1 2 3 4
☐ Minor Passport Consent	Acknowledgment Jurat Copy Oath SW	1 2 3 4
☐ Minor Travel Consent	Acknowledgment Jurat	1 2 3 4
☐ Vehicle Duplicate Title	Acknowledgment Jurat	1 2 3 4
☐ Vehicle Lein Release	Acknowledgment Jurat Copy Oath SW	1 2 3 4
☐ Vehicle Odom/Vin Ver	Acknowledgment Jurat	1 2 3 4
☐ Vehicle Title Transfer	Acknowledgment Jurat	1 2 3 4
☐ Adv Health Care Dir	Acknowledgment Jurat	1 2 3 4
☐ Assign of Digital Assets	Acknowledgment Jurat Copy Oath SW	1 2 3 4
☐ Assign of Personal Prop	Acknowledgment Jurat	1 2 3 4
☐ HIPAA Release	Acknowledgment Jurat	1 2 3 4
☐ Living Trust	Acknowledgment Jurat	1 2 3 4
☐ Last Will & Testament	Acknowledgment Jurat	1 2 3 4
☐ POA	Acknowledgment Jurat	1 2 3 4
☐ Trust Certification	Acknowledgment Jurat Copy Oath SW	1 2 3 4

SIGNING ADDRESS	OTHERS IN ATTENDANCE	CLIENT / SIGNING SERVICE	FEE
		LENDER / LOAN NUMBER	

NOTES

_____
_____
_____
_____
_____
_____
_____
_____
_____
_____
_____
_____

	ADDRESS	PHONE	SIGNATURE	INITIAL IF OATH/AFF TAKEN	RIGHT THUMB PRINT
1		PHONE / EMAIL	SIGNATURE		RIGHT THUMB PRINT
2		PHONE / EMAIL	SIGNATURE		RIGHT THUMB PRINT
3		PHONE / EMAIL	SIGNATURE		RIGHT THUMB PRINT
4		PHONE / EMAIL	SIGNATURE		RIGHT THUMB PRINT

Notary Entries

Entry 1
- **DATE:**
- **TIME:**
- **NAME:** ☐ Signer ☐ Witness
- **IDENTITY VERIFIED:** ☐ D.L. ☐ Passport ☐ Credible Witness ☐ Other
- **WILLINGNESS & COMPETENCE:** ☐ Expressed willingness ☐ Mentally alert ☐ Indicated understanding
- **FORMAT:** ☐ Paper ☐ Electronic ☐ RON

Entry 2
- **DATE:**
- **TIME:**
- **NAME:** ☐ Signer ☐ Witness
- **IDENTITY VERIFIED:** ☐ D.L. ☐ Passport ☐ Credible Witness ☐ Other
- **WILLINGNESS & COMPETENCE:** ☐ Expressed willingness ☐ Mentally alert ☐ Indicated understanding
- **FORMAT:** ☐ Paper ☐ Electronic ☐ RON

Entry 3
- **DATE:**
- **TIME:**
- **NAME:** ☐ Signer ☐ Witness
- **IDENTITY VERIFIED:** ☐ D.L. ☐ Passport ☐ Credible Witness ☐ Other
- **WILLINGNESS & COMPETENCE:** ☐ Expressed willingness ☐ Mentally alert ☐ Indicated understanding
- **FORMAT:** ☐ Paper ☐ Electronic ☐ RON

Entry 4
- **DATE:**
- **TIME:**
- **NAME:** ☐ Signer ☐ Witness
- **IDENTITY VERIFIED:** ☐ D.L. ☐ Passport ☐ Credible Witness ☐ Other
- **WILLINGNESS & COMPETENCE:** ☐ Expressed willingness ☐ Mentally alert ☐ Indicated understanding
- **FORMAT:** ☐ Paper ☐ Electronic ☐ RON

DOCUMENT(S) SIGNED

Document	Type	Type	Signer 1	2	3	4
☐ Borrower's Aff	Acknowledgment	Jurat	1	2	3	4
☐ Compliance Agrmt	Acknowledgment	Jurat	1	2	3	4
☐ Correction Agrmt	Acknowledgment	Jurat	1	2	3	4
☐ Debts/Leins Aff	Acknowledgment	Jurat	1	2	3	4
☐ Deed of Trust	Acknowledgment	Jurat	1	2	3	4
☐ Distrib of Proceeds	Acknowledgment	Jurat	1	2	3	4
☐ E&O Agrmt	Acknowledgment	Jurat	1	2	3	4
☐ Grant Deed	Acknowledgment	Jurat	1	2	3	4
☐ Marital Stat Aff	Acknowledgment	Jurat	1	2	3	4
☐ Mortgage	Acknowledgment	Jurat	1	2	3	4
☐ Occupancy/Fin Aff	Acknowledgment	Jurat	1	2	3	4
☐ Owner's Aff	Acknowledgment	Jurat	1	2	3	4
☐ Payoff Aff	Acknowledgment	Jurat	1	2	3	4
☐ Quit-Claim Deed	Acknowledgment	Jurat	1	2	3	4
☐ Sig/Name Aff	Acknowledgment	Jurat	1	2	3	4
☐ Survey Aff	Acknowledgment	Jurat	1	2	3	4
☐ Warranty Deed	Acknowledgment	Jurat	1	2	3	4

Document	Type	Type	Type	Signer 1	2	3	4
☐ Minor Medical Consent	Acknowledgment	Jurat		1	2	3	4
☐ Minor Passport Consent	Acknowledgment	Jurat		1	2	3	4
☐ Minor Travel Consent	Acknowledgment	Jurat		1	2	3	4
☐ Vehicle Duplicate Title	Acknowledgment	Jurat		1	2	3	4
☐ Vehicle Lein Release	Acknowledgment	Jurat		1	2	3	4
☐ Vehicle Odom/Vin Ver	Acknowledgment	Jurat		1	2	3	4
☐ Vehicle Title Transfer	Acknowledgment	Jurat		1	2	3	4
☐ Adv Health Care Dir	Acknowledgment	Jurat		1	2	3	4
☐ Assign of Digital Assets	Acknowledgment	Jurat		1	2	3	4
☐ Assign of Personal Prop	Acknowledgment	Jurat		1	2	3	4
☐ HIPAA Release	Acknowledgment	Jurat		1	2	3	4
☐ Living Trust ____	Acknowledgment	Jurat	Copy Oath SW	1	2	3	4
☐ Last Will & Testament	Acknowledgment	Jurat		1	2	3	4
☐ POA ____	Acknowledgment	Jurat	Copy Oath SW	1	2	3	4
☐ Trust Certification	Acknowledgment	Jurat	Copy Oath SW	1	2	3	4

Signing Address	Others in Attendance	Client / Signing Service Lender / Loan Number	Fee

Notes

1	Address	Phone Email	Signature	Initial if oath/aff taken	Right Thumb Print
2	Address	Phone Email	Signature	Initial if oath/aff taken	Right Thumb Print
3	Address	Phone Email	Signature	Initial if oath/aff taken	Right Thumb Print
4	Address	Phone Email	Signature	Initial if oath/aff taken	Right Thumb Print

#	DATE / TIME	NAME	IDENTITY VERIFIED	WILLINGNESS & COMPETENCE	FORMAT
1	DATE ___ TIME ___	☐ Signer ☐ Witness	☐ D.L. ☐ Passport ☐ Credible Witness ☐ Other	☐ Expressed willingness ☐ Mentally alert ☐ Indicated understanding	☐ Paper ☐ Electronic ☐ RON
2	DATE ___ TIME ___	☐ Signer ☐ Witness	☐ D.L. ☐ Passport ☐ Credible Witness ☐ Other	☐ Expressed willingness ☐ Mentally alert ☐ Indicated understanding	☐ Paper ☐ Electronic ☐ RON
3	DATE ___ TIME ___	☐ Signer ☐ Witness	☐ D.L. ☐ Passport ☐ Credible Witness ☐ Other	☐ Expressed willingness ☐ Mentally alert ☐ Indicated understanding	☐ Paper ☐ Electronic ☐ RON
4	DATE ___ TIME ___	☐ Signer ☐ Witness	☐ D.L. ☐ Passport ☐ Credible Witness ☐ Other	☐ Expressed willingness ☐ Mentally alert ☐ Indicated understanding	☐ Paper ☐ Electronic ☐ RON

DOCUMENT(S) SIGNED

Document	Type	SIGNER 1 2 3 4
☐ Borrower's Aff	Acknowledgment Jurat	1 2 3 4
☐ Compliance Agrmt	Acknowledgment Jurat	1 2 3 4
☐ Correction Agrmt	Acknowledgment Jurat	1 2 3 4
☐ Debts/Leins Aff	Acknowledgment Jurat	1 2 3 4
☐ Deed of Trust	Acknowledgment Jurat	1 2 3 4
☐ Distrib of Proceeds	Acknowledgment Jurat	1 2 3 4
☐ E&O Agrmt	Acknowledgment Jurat	1 2 3 4
☐ Grant Deed	Acknowledgment Jurat	1 2 3 4
☐ Marital Stat Aff	Acknowledgment Jurat	1 2 3 4
☐ Mortgage	Acknowledgment Jurat	1 2 3 4
☐ Occupancy/Fin Aff	Acknowledgment Jurat	1 2 3 4
☐ Owner's Aff	Acknowledgment Jurat	1 2 3 4
☐ Payoff Aff	Acknowledgment Jurat	1 2 3 4
☐ Quit-Claim Deed	Acknowledgment Jurat	1 2 3 4
☐ Sig/Name Aff	Acknowledgment Jurat	1 2 3 4
☐ Survey Aff	Acknowledgment Jurat	1 2 3 4
☐ Warranty Deed	Acknowledgment Jurat	1 2 3 4

Document	Type	SIGNER 1 2 3 4
☐ Minor Medical Consent	Acknowledgment Jurat	1 2 3 4
☐ Minor Passport Consent	Acknowledgment Jurat	1 2 3 4
☐ Minor Travel Consent	Acknowledgment Jurat	1 2 3 4
☐	Acknowledgment Jurat Copy Oath SW	1 2 3 4
☐ Vehicle Duplicate Title	Acknowledgment Jurat	1 2 3 4
☐ Vehicle Lein Release	Acknowledgment Jurat	1 2 3 4
☐ Vehicle Odom/Vin Ver	Acknowledgment Jurat	1 2 3 4
☐ Vehicle Title Transfer	Acknowledgment Jurat	1 2 3 4
☐	Acknowledgment Jurat Copy Oath SW	1 2 3 4
☐ Adv Health Care Dir	Acknowledgment Jurat	1 2 3 4
☐ Assign of Digital Assets	Acknowledgment Jurat	1 2 3 4
☐ Assign of Personal Prop	Acknowledgment Jurat	1 2 3 4
☐ HIPAA Release	Acknowledgment Jurat	1 2 3 4
☐	Acknowledgment Jurat Copy Oath SW	1 2 3 4
☐ Living Trust ___	Acknowledgment Jurat	1 2 3 4
☐ Last Will & Testament	Acknowledgment Jurat	1 2 3 4
☐ POA ___	Acknowledgment Jurat	1 2 3 4
☐ Trust Certification	Acknowledgment Jurat Copy Oath SW	1 2 3 4

SIGNING ADDRESS	OTHERS IN ATTENDANCE	CLIENT / SIGNING SERVICE	FEE
		LENDER / LOAN NUMBER	

NOTES

_____

#	ADDRESS	PHONE / EMAIL	SIGNATURE	INITIAL IF OATH/AFF TAKEN	RIGHT THUMB PRINT
1	ADDRESS	PHONE / EMAIL	SIGNATURE	INITIAL IF OATH/AFF TAKEN	RIGHT THUMB PRINT
2	ADDRESS	PHONE / EMAIL	SIGNATURE	INITIAL IF OATH/AFF TAKEN	RIGHT THUMB PRINT
3	ADDRESS	PHONE / EMAIL	SIGNATURE	INITIAL IF OATH/AFF TAKEN	RIGHT THUMB PRINT
4	ADDRESS	PHONE / EMAIL	SIGNATURE	INITIAL IF OATH/AFF TAKEN	RIGHT THUMB PRINT

Signer Entries

Entry 1
- **DATE:** _____
- **TIME:** _____
- **NAME:** _____ ☐ Signer ☐ Witness
- **IDENTITY VERIFIED:** ☐ D.L. ☐ Passport ☐ Credible Witness ☐ Other
- **WILLINGNESS & COMPETENCE:** ☐ Expressed willingness ☐ Mentally alert ☐ Indicated understanding
- **FORMAT:** ☐ Paper ☐ Electronic ☐ RON

Entry 2
- **DATE:** _____
- **TIME:** _____
- **NAME:** _____ ☐ Signer ☐ Witness
- **IDENTITY VERIFIED:** ☐ D.L. ☐ Passport ☐ Credible Witness ☐ Other
- **WILLINGNESS & COMPETENCE:** ☐ Expressed willingness ☐ Mentally alert ☐ Indicated understanding
- **FORMAT:** ☐ Paper ☐ Electronic ☐ RON

Entry 3
- **DATE:** _____
- **TIME:** _____
- **NAME:** _____ ☐ Signer ☐ Witness
- **IDENTITY VERIFIED:** ☐ D.L. ☐ Passport ☐ Credible Witness ☐ Other
- **WILLINGNESS & COMPETENCE:** ☐ Expressed willingness ☐ Mentally alert ☐ Indicated understanding
- **FORMAT:** ☐ Paper ☐ Electronic ☐ RON

Entry 4
- **DATE:** _____
- **TIME:** _____
- **NAME:** _____ ☐ Signer ☐ Witness
- **IDENTITY VERIFIED:** ☐ D.L. ☐ Passport ☐ Credible Witness ☐ Other
- **WILLINGNESS & COMPETENCE:** ☐ Expressed willingness ☐ Mentally alert ☐ Indicated understanding
- **FORMAT:** ☐ Paper ☐ Electronic ☐ RON

DOCUMENT(S) SIGNED

Document	Type		SIGNER			
☐ Borrower's Aff	Acknowledgment	Jurat	1	2	3	4
☐ Compliance Agrmt	Acknowledgment	Jurat	1	2	3	4
☐ Correction Agrmt	Acknowledgment	Jurat	1	2	3	4
☐ Debts/Leins Aff	Acknowledgment	Jurat	1	2	3	4
☐ Deed of Trust	Acknowledgment	Jurat	1	2	3	4
☐ Distrib of Proceeds	Acknowledgment	Jurat	1	2	3	4
☐ E&O Agrmt	Acknowledgment	Jurat	1	2	3	4
☐ Grant Deed	Acknowledgment	Jurat	1	2	3	4
☐ Marital Stat Aff	Acknowledgment	Jurat	1	2	3	4
☐ Mortgage	Acknowledgment	Jurat	1	2	3	4
☐ Occupancy/Fin Aff	Acknowledgment	Jurat	1	2	3	4
☐ Owner's Aff	Acknowledgment	Jurat	1	2	3	4
☐ Payoff Aff	Acknowledgment	Jurat	1	2	3	4
☐ Quit-Claim Deed	Acknowledgment	Jurat	1	2	3	4
☐ Sig/Name Aff	Acknowledgment	Jurat	1	2	3	4
☐ Survey Aff	Acknowledgment	Jurat	1	2	3	4
☐ Warranty Deed	Acknowledgment	Jurat	1	2	3	4

Document	Type		SIGNER			
☐ Minor Medical Consent	Acknowledgment	Jurat	1	2	3	4
☐ Minor Passport Consent	Acknowledgment	Jurat	1	2	3	4
☐ Minor Travel Consent	Acknowledgment	Jurat	1	2	3	4
☐ Vehicle Duplicate Title	Acknowledgment	Jurat	1	2	3	4
☐ Vehicle Lein Release	Acknowledgment	Jurat	1	2	3	4
☐ Vehicle Odom/Vin Ver	Acknowledgment	Jurat	1	2	3	4
☐ Vehicle Title Transfer	Acknowledgment	Jurat	1	2	3	4
☐ Adv Health Care Dir	Acknowledgment	Jurat	1	2	3	4
☐ Assign of Digital Assets	Acknowledgment	Jurat	1	2	3	4
☐ Assign of Personal Prop	Acknowledgment	Jurat	1	2	3	4
☐ HIPAA Release	Acknowledgment	Jurat	1	2	3	4
☐ Living Trust _____	Acknowledgment	Jurat	1	2	3	4
☐ Last Will & Testament	Acknowledgment	Jurat	1	2	3	4
☐ POA _____	Acknowledgment	Jurat	1	2	3	4
☐ Trust Certification	Acknowledgment	Jurat	1	2	3	4

Additional entries (right side): ☐ Acknowledgment Jurat Copy Oath SW 1 2 3 4 (repeated blank rows)

SIGNING ADDRESS	OTHERS IN ATTENDANCE	CLIENT / SIGNING SERVICE	FEE
		LENDER / LOAN NUMBER	

NOTES

	ADDRESS	SIGNATURE	RIGHT THUMB PRINT
	PHONE	INITIAL IF OATH/AFF TAKEN	
1	EMAIL		
	ADDRESS	SIGNATURE	RIGHT THUMB PRINT
	PHONE	INITIAL IF OATH/AFF TAKEN	
2	EMAIL		
	ADDRESS	SIGNATURE	RIGHT THUMB PRINT
	PHONE	INITIAL IF OATH/AFF TAKEN	
3	EMAIL		
	ADDRESS	SIGNATURE	RIGHT THUMB PRINT
	PHONE	INITIAL IF OATH/AFF TAKEN	
4	EMAIL		

Entries 1–4

1
- DATE / TIME
- NAME: ☐ Signer ☐ Witness
- IDENTITY VERIFIED: ☐ D.L. ☐ Passport ☐ Credible Witness ☐ Other
- WILLINGNESS & COMPETENCE: ☐ Expressed willingness ☐ Mentally alert ☐ Indicated understanding
- FORMAT: ☐ Paper ☐ Electronic ☐ RON

2
- DATE / TIME
- NAME: ☐ Signer ☐ Witness
- IDENTITY VERIFIED: ☐ D.L. ☐ Passport ☐ Credible Witness ☐ Other
- WILLINGNESS & COMPETENCE: ☐ Expressed willingness ☐ Mentally alert ☐ Indicated understanding
- FORMAT: ☐ Paper ☐ Electronic ☐ RON

3
- DATE / TIME
- NAME: ☐ Signer ☐ Witness
- IDENTITY VERIFIED: ☐ D.L. ☐ Passport ☐ Credible Witness ☐ Other
- WILLINGNESS & COMPETENCE: ☐ Expressed willingness ☐ Mentally alert ☐ Indicated understanding
- FORMAT: ☐ Paper ☐ Electronic ☐ RON

4
- DATE / TIME
- NAME: ☐ Signer ☐ Witness
- IDENTITY VERIFIED: ☐ D.L. ☐ Passport ☐ Credible Witness ☐ Other
- WILLINGNESS & COMPETENCE: ☐ Expressed willingness ☐ Mentally alert ☐ Indicated understanding
- FORMAT: ☐ Paper ☐ Electronic ☐ RON

DOCUMENT(S) SIGNED

Document			SIGNER			
☐ Borrower's Aff	Acknowledgment	Jurat	1	2	3	4
☐ Compliance Agrmt	Acknowledgment	Jurat	1	2	3	4
☐ Correction Agrmt	Acknowledgment	Jurat	1	2	3	4
☐ Debts/Leins Aff	Acknowledgment	Jurat	1	2	3	4
☐ Deed of Trust	Acknowledgment	Jurat	1	2	3	4
☐ Distrib of Proceeds	Acknowledgment	Jurat	1	2	3	4
☐ E&O Agrmt	Acknowledgment	Jurat	1	2	3	4
☐ Grant Deed	Acknowledgment	Jurat	1	2	3	4
☐ Marital Stat Aff	Acknowledgment	Jurat	1	2	3	4
☐ Mortgage	Acknowledgment	Jurat	1	2	3	4
☐ Occupancy/Fin Aff	Acknowledgment	Jurat	1	2	3	4
☐ Owner's Aff	Acknowledgment	Jurat	1	2	3	4
☐ Payoff Aff	Acknowledgment	Jurat	1	2	3	4
☐ Qui-Claim Deed	Acknowledgment	Jurat	1	2	3	4
☐ Sig/Name Aff	Acknowledgment	Jurat	1	2	3	4
☐ Survey Aff	Acknowledgment	Jurat	1	2	3	4
☐ Warranty Deed	Acknowledgment	Jurat	1	2	3	4

Document					SIGNER			
☐ Minor Medical Consent	Acknowledgment	Jurat			1	2	3	4
☐ Minor Passport Consent	Acknowledgment	Jurat	Copy	Oath	SW 1	2	3	4
☐ Minor Travel Consent	Acknowledgment	Jurat			1	2	3	4
☐ Vehicle Duplicate Title	Acknowledgment	Jurat			1	2	3	4
☐ Vehicle Lein Release	Acknowledgment	Jurat	Copy	Oath	SW 1	2	3	4
☐ Vehicle Odom/Vin Ver	Acknowledgment	Jurat			1	2	3	4
☐ Vehicle Title Transfer	Acknowledgment	Jurat	Copy	Oath	SW 1	2	3	4
☐ Adv Health Care Dir	Acknowledgment	Jurat			1	2	3	4
☐ Assign of Digital Assets	Acknowledgment	Jurat	Copy	Oath	SW 1	2	3	4
☐ Assign of Personal Prop	Acknowledgment	Jurat			1	2	3	4
☐ HIPAA Release	Acknowledgment	Jurat			1	2	3	4
☐ Living Trust	Acknowledgment	Jurat	Copy	Oath	SW 1	2	3	4
☐ Last Will & Testament	Acknowledgment	Jurat			1	2	3	4
☐ POA	Acknowledgment	Jurat			1	2	3	4
☐ Trust Certification	Acknowledgment	Jurat	Copy	Oath	SW 1	2	3	4

SIGNING ADDRESS	OTHERS IN ATTENDANCE	CLIENT / SIGNING SERVICE	FEE
		LENDER / LOAN NUMBER	

NOTES

	ADDRESS	PHONE	EMAIL	SIGNATURE	INITIAL IF OATH/AFF TAKEN	RIGHT THUMB PRINT
1						
2						
3						
4						

Left Section — Journal Entries (1–4)

Entry 1
- DATE: _____
- TIME: _____
- NAME: ☐ Signer ☐ Witness
- IDENTITY VERIFIED: ☐ D.L. ☐ Passport ☐ Credible Witness ☐ Other
- WILLINGNESS & COMPETENCE: ☐ Expressed willingness ☐ Mentally alert ☐ Indicated understanding
- FORMAT: ☐ Paper ☐ Electronic ☐ RON

Entry 2
- DATE: _____
- TIME: _____
- NAME: ☐ Signer ☐ Witness
- IDENTITY VERIFIED: ☐ D.L. ☐ Passport ☐ Credible Witness ☐ Other
- WILLINGNESS & COMPETENCE: ☐ Expressed willingness ☐ Mentally alert ☐ Indicated understanding
- FORMAT: ☐ Paper ☐ Electronic ☐ RON

Entry 3
- DATE: _____
- TIME: _____
- NAME: ☐ Signer ☐ Witness
- IDENTITY VERIFIED: ☐ D.L. ☐ Passport ☐ Credible Witness ☐ Other
- WILLINGNESS & COMPETENCE: ☐ Expressed willingness ☐ Mentally alert ☐ Indicated understanding
- FORMAT: ☐ Paper ☐ Electronic ☐ RON

Entry 4
- DATE: _____
- TIME: _____
- NAME: ☐ Signer ☐ Witness
- IDENTITY VERIFIED: ☐ D.L. ☐ Passport ☐ Credible Witness ☐ Other
- WILLINGNESS & COMPETENCE: ☐ Expressed willingness ☐ Mentally alert ☐ Indicated understanding
- FORMAT: ☐ Paper ☐ Electronic ☐ RON

Right Section — DOCUMENT(S) SIGNED

Upper list (with Acknowledgment / Jurat / Copy / Oath / SW and SIGNER 1 2 3 4)

Document	Acknowledgment	Jurat	Copy	Oath	SW	1	2	3	4
☐ Minor Medical Consent	Acknowledgment	Jurat							
☐ Minor Passport Consent	Acknowledgment	Jurat	Copy	Oath	SW	1	2	3	4
☐ Minor Travel Consent	Acknowledgment	Jurat				1	2	3	4
☐ Vehicle Duplicate Title	Acknowledgment	Jurat	Copy	Oath	SW	1	2	3	4
☐ Vehicle Lein Release	Acknowledgment	Jurat							4
☐ Vehicle Odom/Vin Ver	Acknowledgment	Jurat						3	4
☐ Vehicle Title Transfer	Acknowledgment	Jurat	Copy	Oath	SW	1	2	3	4
☐ Adv Health Care Dir	Acknowledgment	Jurat						3	4
☐ Assign of Digital Assets	Acknowledgment	Jurat	Copy	Oath	SW	1	2	3	4
☐ Assign of Personal Prop	Acknowledgment	Jurat						3	4
☐ HIPAA Release	Acknowledgment	Jurat							4
☐ Living Trust _____	Acknowledgment	Jurat	Copy	Oath	SW	1	2	3	4
☐ Last Will & Testament	Acknowledgment	Jurat							
☐ POA _____	Acknowledgment	Jurat							
☐ Trust Certification	Acknowledgment	Jurat	Copy	Oath	SW	1	2	3	4

Lower list (Acknowledgment / Jurat and SIGNER 1 2 3 4)

Document	Acknowledgment	Jurat	1	2	3	4
☐ Borrower's Aff	Acknowledgment	Jurat	1	2	3	4
☐ Compliance Agrmt	Acknowledgment	Jurat _____	1	2	3	4
☐ Correction Agrmt	Acknowledgment	Jurat _____	1	2	3	4
☐ Debts/Leins Aff	Acknowledgment	Jurat	1	2	3	4
☐ Deed of Trust	Acknowledgment	Jurat	1	2	3	4
☐ Distrib of Proceeds	Acknowledgment	Jurat	1	2	3	4
☐ E&O Agrmt	Acknowledgment	Jurat	1	2	3	4
☐ Grant Deed	Acknowledgment	Jurat	1	2	3	4
☐ Marital Stat Aff	Acknowledgment	Jurat	1	2	3	4
☐ Mortgage	Acknowledgment	Jurat	1	2	3	4
☐ Occupancy/Fin Aff	Acknowledgment	Jurat _____	1	2	3	4
☐ Owner's Aff	Acknowledgment	Jurat	1	2	3	4
☐ Payoff Aff	Acknowledgment	Jurat	1	2	3	4
☐ Quit-Claim Deed	Acknowledgment	Jurat	1	2	3	4
☐ Sig/Name Aff	Acknowledgment	Jurat	1	2	3	4
☐ Survey Aff	Acknowledgment	Jurat _____	1	2	3	4
☐ Warranty Deed	Acknowledgment	Jurat	1	2	3	4

SIGNING ADDRESS	OTHERS IN ATTENDANCE	CLIENT / SIGNING SERVICE	FEE
		LENDER / LOAN NUMBER	

NOTES

#	ADDRESS	PHONE	EMAIL	SIGNATURE	INITIAL IF OATH/AFF TAKEN	RIGHT THUMB PRINT
1						
2						
3						
4						

1	DATE TIME	NAME ❑ Signer ❑ Witness	IDENTITY VERIFIED ❑ D.L. ❑ Passport ❑ Credible Witness ❑ Other	WILLINGNESS & COMPETENCE ❑ Expressed willingness ❑ Mentally alert ❑ Indicated understanding	FORMAT ❑ Paper ❑ Electronic ❑ RON
2	DATE TIME	NAME ❑ Signer ❑ Witness	IDENTITY VERIFIED ❑ D.L. ❑ Passport ❑ Credible Witness ❑ Other	WILLINGNESS & COMPETENCE ❑ Expressed willingness ❑ Mentally alert ❑ Indicated understanding	FORMAT ❑ Paper ❑ Electronic ❑ RON
3	DATE TIME	NAME ❑ Signer ❑ Witness	IDENTITY VERIFIED ❑ D.L. ❑ Passport ❑ Credible Witness ❑ Other	WILLINGNESS & COMPETENCE ❑ Expressed willingness ❑ Mentally alert ❑ Indicated understanding	FORMAT ❑ Paper ❑ Electronic ❑ RON
4	DATE TIME	NAME ❑ Signer ❑ Witness	IDENTITY VERIFIED ❑ D.L. ❑ Passport ❑ Credible Witness ❑ Other	WILLINGNESS & COMPETENCE ❑ Expressed willingness ❑ Mentally alert ❑ Indicated understanding	FORMAT ❑ Paper ❑ Electronic ❑ RON

DOCUMENT(S) SIGNED

Document			SIGNER	Document			SIGNER	
❑ Borrower's Aff	Acknowledgment	Jurat ______	1 2 3 4	❑ Minor Medical Consent	Acknowledgment	Jurat ______	1 2 3 4	❑ ______
❑ Compliance Agrmt	Acknowledgment	Jurat ______	1 2 3 4	❑ Minor Passport Consent	Acknowledgment	Jurat ______	1 2 3 4	Acknowledgment Jurat Copy Oath SW 1 2 3 4
❑ Correction Agrmt	Acknowledgment	Jurat ______	1 2 3 4	❑ Minor Travel Consent	Acknowledgment	Jurat ______	1 2 3 4	
❑ Debts/Leins Aff	Acknowledgment	Jurat ______	1 2 3 4					❑ ______
❑ Deed of Trust	Acknowledgment	Jurat ______	1 2 3 4	❑ Vehicle Duplicate Title	Acknowledgment	Jurat ______	1 2 3 4	Acknowledgment Jurat Copy Oath SW 1 2 3 4
❑ Distrib of Proceeds	Acknowledgment	Jurat ______	1 2 3 4	❑ Vehicle Lein Release	Acknowledgment	Jurat ______	1 2 3 4	
❑ E&O Agrmt	Acknowledgment	Jurat ______	1 2 3 4	❑ Vehicle Odom/Vin Ver	Acknowledgment	Jurat ______	1 2 3 4	❑ ______
❑ Grant Deed	Acknowledgment	Jurat ______	1 2 3 4	❑ Vehicle Title Transfer	Acknowledgment	Jurat ______	1 2 3 4	Acknowledgment Jurat Copy Oath SW 1 2 3 4
❑ Marital Stat Aff	Acknowledgment	Jurat ______	1 2 3 4					
❑ Mortgage	Acknowledgment	Jurat ______	1 2 3 4	❑ Adv Health Care Dir	Acknowledgment	Jurat ______	1 2 3 4	❑ ______
❑ Occupancy/Fin Aff	Acknowledgment	Jurat ______	1 2 3 4	❑ Assign of Digital Assets	Acknowledgment	Jurat ______	1 2 3 4	Acknowledgment Jurat Copy Oath SW 1 2 3 4
❑ Owner's Aff	Acknowledgment	Jurat ______	1 2 3 4	❑ Assign of Personal Prop	Acknowledgment	Jurat ______	1 2 3 4	
❑ Payoff Aff	Acknowledgment	Jurat ______	1 2 3 4	❑ HIPAA Release	Acknowledgment	Jurat ______	1 2 3 4	❑ ______
❑ Quit-Claim Deed	Acknowledgment	Jurat ______	1 2 3 4	❑ Living Trust ______	Acknowledgment	Jurat ______	1 2 3 4	Acknowledgment Jurat Copy Oath SW 1 2 3 4
❑ Sig/Name Aff	Acknowledgment	Jurat ______	1 2 3 4	❑ Last Will & Testament	Acknowledgment	Jurat ______	1 2 3 4	
❑ Survey Aff	Acknowledgment	Jurat ______	1 2 3 4	❑ POA ______	Acknowledgment	Jurat ______	1 2 3 4	❑ ______
❑ Warranty Deed	Acknowledgment	Jurat ______	1 2 3 4	❑ Trust Certification	Acknowledgment	Jurat ______	1 2 3 4	Acknowledgment Jurat Copy Oath SW 1 2 3 4

SIGNING ADDRESS	OTHERS IN ATTENDANCE	CLIENT / SIGNING SERVICE	FEE
		LENDER / LOAN NUMBER	

NOTES

	ADDRESS	PHONE	SIGNATURE	INITIAL IF OATH/AFF TAKEN	RIGHT THUMB PRINT
1		EMAIL			
2	ADDRESS	PHONE EMAIL	SIGNATURE	INITIAL IF OATH/AFF TAKEN	RIGHT THUMB PRINT
3	ADDRESS	PHONE EMAIL	SIGNATURE	INITIAL IF OATH/AFF TAKEN	RIGHT THUMB PRINT
4	ADDRESS	PHONE EMAIL	SIGNATURE	INITIAL IF OATH/AFF TAKEN	RIGHT THUMB PRINT

Notary Journal Entries

#			NAME	IDENTITY VERIFIED	WILLINGNESS & COMPETENCE	FORMAT
1	DATE		☐ Signer ☐ Witness	☐ D.L. ☐ Passport ☐ Credible Witness ☐ Other	☐ Expressed willingness ☐ Mentally alert ☐ Indicated understanding	☐ Paper ☐ Electronic ☐ RON
	TIME					
2	DATE		☐ Signer ☐ Witness	☐ D.L. ☐ Passport ☐ Credible Witness ☐ Other	☐ Expressed willingness ☐ Mentally alert ☐ Indicated understanding	☐ Paper ☐ Electronic ☐ RON
	TIME					
3	DATE		☐ Signer ☐ Witness	☐ D.L. ☐ Passport ☐ Credible Witness ☐ Other	☐ Expressed willingness ☐ Mentally alert ☐ Indicated understanding	☐ Paper ☐ Electronic ☐ RON
	TIME					
4	DATE		☐ Signer ☐ Witness	☐ D.L. ☐ Passport ☐ Credible Witness ☐ Other	☐ Expressed willingness ☐ Mentally alert ☐ Indicated understanding	☐ Paper ☐ Electronic ☐ RON
	TIME					

DOCUMENT(S) SIGNED

Document	Type	SIGNER 1	2	3	4
☐ Borrower's Aff	Acknowledgment Jurat	1	2	3	4
☐ Compliance Agrmt	Acknowledgment Jurat	1	2	3	4
☐ Correction Agrmt	Acknowledgment Jurat	1	2	3	4
☐ Debts/Leins Aff	Acknowledgment Jurat	1	2	3	4
☐ Deed of Trust	Acknowledgment Jurat	1	2	3	4
☐ Distrib of Proceeds	Acknowledgment Jurat	1	2	3	4
☐ E&O Agrmt	Acknowledgment Jurat	1	2	3	4
☐ Grant Deed	Acknowledgment Jurat	1	2	3	4
☐ Marital Stat Aff	Acknowledgment Jurat	1	2	3	4
☐ Mortgage	Acknowledgment Jurat	1	2	3	4
☐ Occupancy/Fin Aff	Acknowledgment Jurat	1	2	3	4
☐ Owner's Aff	Acknowledgment Jurat	1	2	3	4
☐ Payoff Aff	Acknowledgment Jurat	1	2	3	4
☐ Quit-Claim Deed	Acknowledgment Jurat	1	2	3	4
☐ Sig/Name Aff	Acknowledgment Jurat	1	2	3	4
☐ Survey Aff	Acknowledgment Jurat	1	2	3	4
☐ Warranty Deed	Acknowledgment Jurat	1	2	3	4

Document	Type	SIGNER 1	2	3	4
☐ Minor Medical Consent	Acknowledgment Jurat	1	2	3	4
☐ Minor Passport Consent	Acknowledgment Jurat	1	2	3	4
☐ Minor Travel Consent	Acknowledgment Jurat	1	2	3	4
☐ Vehicle Duplicate Title	Acknowledgment Jurat	1	2	3	4
☐ Vehicle Lein Release	Acknowledgment Jurat	1	2	3	4
☐ Vehicle Odom/Vin Ver	Acknowledgment Jurat	1	2	3	4
☐ Vehicle Title Transfer	Acknowledgment Jurat	1	2	3	4
☐ Adv Health Care Dir	Acknowledgment Jurat	1	2	3	4
☐ Assign of Digital Assets	Acknowledgment Jurat	1	2	3	4
☐ Assign of Personal Prop	Acknowledgment Jurat	1	2	3	4
☐ HIPAA Release	Acknowledgment Jurat	1	2	3	4
☐ Living Trust	Acknowledgment Jurat	1	2	3	4
☐ Last Will & Testament	Acknowledgment Jurat	1	2	3	4
☐ POA	Acknowledgment Jurat	1	2	3	4
☐ Trust Certification	Acknowledgment Jurat	1	2	3	4

☐ Acknowledgment Jurat Copy Oath SW 1 2 3 4

☐ Acknowledgment Jurat Copy Oath SW 1 2 3 4

☐ Acknowledgment Jurat Copy Oath SW 1 2 3 4

☐ Acknowledgment Jurat Copy Oath SW 1 2 3 4

☐ Acknowledgment Jurat Copy Oath SW 1 2 3 4

☐ Acknowledgment Jurat Copy Oath SW 1 2 3 4

SIGNING ADDRESS	OTHERS IN ATTENDANCE	CLIENT / SIGNING SERVICE	FEE
		LENDER / LOAN NUMBER	

NOTES

_____
_____
_____
_____
_____
_____
_____
_____
_____
_____
_____
_____
_____

	ADDRESS	PHONE	SIGNATURE	INITIAL IF OATH/AFF TAKEN	RIGHT THUMB PRINT
1		PHONE / EMAIL	SIGNATURE	INITIAL IF OATH/AFF TAKEN	RIGHT THUMB PRINT
2	ADDRESS	PHONE / EMAIL	SIGNATURE	INITIAL IF OATH/AFF TAKEN	RIGHT THUMB PRINT
3	ADDRESS	PHONE / EMAIL	SIGNATURE	INITIAL IF OATH/AFF TAKEN	RIGHT THUMB PRINT
4	ADDRESS	PHONE / EMAIL	SIGNATURE	INITIAL IF OATH/AFF TAKEN	RIGHT THUMB PRINT

Entry 1

FORMAT	☐ Paper ☐ Electronic ☐ RON
WILLINGNESS & COMPETENCE	☐ Expressed willingness ☐ Mentally alert ☐ Indicated understanding
IDENTITY VERIFIED	☐ D.L. ☐ Passport ☐ Credible Witness ☐ Other
NAME	☐ Signer ☐ Witness
DATE	
TIME	

Entry 2

FORMAT	☐ Paper ☐ Electronic ☐ RON
WILLINGNESS & COMPETENCE	☐ Expressed willingness ☐ Mentally alert ☐ Indicated understanding
IDENTITY VERIFIED	☐ D.L. ☐ Passport ☐ Credible Witness ☐ Other
NAME	☐ Signer ☐ Witness
DATE	
TIME	

Entry 3

FORMAT	☐ Paper ☐ Electronic ☐ RON
WILLINGNESS & COMPETENCE	☐ Expressed willingness ☐ Mentally alert ☐ Indicated understanding
IDENTITY VERIFIED	☐ D.L. ☐ Passport ☐ Credible Witness ☐ Other
NAME	☐ Signer ☐ Witness
DATE	
TIME	

Entry 4

FORMAT	☐ Paper ☐ Electronic ☐ RON
WILLINGNESS & COMPETENCE	☐ Expressed willingness ☐ Mentally alert ☐ Indicated understanding
IDENTITY VERIFIED	☐ D.L. ☐ Passport ☐ Credible Witness ☐ Other
NAME	☐ Signer ☐ Witness
DATE	
TIME	

DOCUMENT(S) SIGNED

Document	Type	SIGNER
☐ Borrower's Aff	Acknowledgment Jurat ___	1 2 3 4
☐ Compliance Agrmt	Acknowledgment Jurat ___	1 2 3 4
☐ Correction Agrmt	Acknowledgment Jurat ___	1 2 3 4
☐ Debts/Leins Aff	Acknowledgment Jurat ___	1 2 3 4
☐ Deed of Trust	Acknowledgment Jurat ___	1 2 3 4
☐ Distrib of Proceeds	Acknowledgment Jurat ___	1 2 3 4
☐ E&O Agrmt	Acknowledgment Jurat ___	1 2 3 4
☐ Grant Deed	Acknowledgment Jurat ___	1 2 3 4
☐ Marital Stat Aff	Acknowledgment Jurat ___	1 2 3 4
☐ Mortgage	Acknowledgment Jurat ___	1 2 3 4
☐ Occupancy/Fin Aff	Acknowledgment Jurat ___	1 2 3 4
☐ Owner's Aff	Acknowledgment Jurat ___	1 2 3 4
☐ Payoff Aff	Acknowledgment Jurat ___	1 2 3 4
☐ Quit-Claim Deed	Acknowledgment Jurat ___	1 2 3 4
☐ Sig/Name Aff	Acknowledgment Jurat ___	1 2 3 4
☐ Survey Aff	Acknowledgment Jurat ___	1 2 3 4
☐ Warranty Deed	Acknowledgment Jurat ___	1 2 3 4

Document	Type	SIGNER	Notarial
☐ Minor Medical Consent	Acknowledgment Jurat ___	1 2 3 4	
☐ Minor Passport Consent	Acknowledgment Jurat ___	1 2 3 4	Acknowledgment Jurat Copy Oath SW 1 2 3 4
☐ Minor Travel Consent	Acknowledgment Jurat ___	1 2 3 4	
☐ Vehicle Duplicate Title	Acknowledgment Jurat ___	1 2 3 4	Acknowledgment Jurat Copy Oath SW 1 2 3 4
☐ Vehicle Lein Release	Acknowledgment Jurat ___	1 2 3 4	
☐ Vehicle Odom/Vin Ver	Acknowledgment Jurat ___	1 2 3 4	☐
☐ Vehicle Title Transfer	Acknowledgment Jurat ___	1 2 3 4	Acknowledgment Jurat Copy Oath SW 1 2 3 4
☐ Adv Health Care Dir	Acknowledgment Jurat ___	1 2 3 4	☐
☐ Assign of Digital Assets	Acknowledgment Jurat ___	1 2 3 4	Acknowledgment Jurat Copy Oath SW 1 2 3 4
☐ Assign of Personal Prop	Acknowledgment Jurat ___	1 2 3 4	☐
☐ HIPAA Release	Acknowledgment Jurat ___	1 2 3 4	
☐ Living Trust	Acknowledgment Jurat ___	1 2 3 4	Acknowledgment Jurat Copy Oath SW 1 2 3 4
☐ Last Will & Testament	Acknowledgment Jurat ___	1 2 3 4	
☐ POA _____	Acknowledgment Jurat ___	1 2 3 4	☐
☐ Trust Certification	Acknowledgment Jurat ___	1 2 3 4	Acknowledgment Jurat Copy Oath SW 1 2 3 4

SIGNING ADDRESS	OTHERS IN ATTENDANCE	CLIENT / SIGNING SERVICE	FEE
		LENDER / LOAN NUMBER	

NOTES

_____
_____
_____
_____
_____
_____
_____
_____
_____
_____
_____
_____

	ADDRESS	SIGNATURE	PHONE	INITIAL IF OATH/AFF TAKEN	RIGHT THUMB PRINT
1			EMAIL		
2	ADDRESS	SIGNATURE	PHONE	INITIAL IF OATH/AFF TAKEN	RIGHT THUMB PRINT
			EMAIL		
3	ADDRESS	SIGNATURE	PHONE	INITIAL IF OATH/AFF TAKEN	RIGHT THUMB PRINT
			EMAIL		
4	ADDRESS	SIGNATURE	PHONE	INITIAL IF OATH/AFF TAKEN	RIGHT THUMB PRINT
			EMAIL		

Notary Journal Entry Form

Entries 1–4

#				
1	DATE ___ / TIME ___	NAME: ☐ Signer ☐ Witness	IDENTITY VERIFIED: ☐ D.L. ☐ Passport ☐ Credible Witness ☐ Other	WILLINGNESS & COMPETENCE: ☐ Expressed willingness ☐ Mentally alert ☐ Indicated understanding	FORMAT: ☐ Paper ☐ Electronic ☐ RON
2	DATE ___ / TIME ___	NAME: ☐ Signer ☐ Witness	IDENTITY VERIFIED: ☐ D.L. ☐ Passport ☐ Credible Witness ☐ Other	WILLINGNESS & COMPETENCE: ☐ Expressed willingness ☐ Mentally alert ☐ Indicated understanding	FORMAT: ☐ Paper ☐ Electronic ☐ RON
3	DATE ___ / TIME ___	NAME: ☐ Signer ☐ Witness	IDENTITY VERIFIED: ☐ D.L. ☐ Passport ☐ Credible Witness ☐ Other	WILLINGNESS & COMPETENCE: ☐ Expressed willingness ☐ Mentally alert ☐ Indicated understanding	FORMAT: ☐ Paper ☐ Electronic ☐ RON
4	DATE ___ / TIME ___	NAME: ☐ Signer ☐ Witness	IDENTITY VERIFIED: ☐ D.L. ☐ Passport ☐ Credible Witness ☐ Other	WILLINGNESS & COMPETENCE: ☐ Expressed willingness ☐ Mentally alert ☐ Indicated understanding	FORMAT: ☐ Paper ☐ Electronic ☐ RON

Document(s) Signed

Document	Notarial Act	Signer
☐ Borrower's Aff	Acknowledgment Jurat	1 2 3 4
☐ Compliance Agrmt	Acknowledgment Jurat	1 2 3 4
☐ Correction Agrmt	Acknowledgment Jurat	1 2 3 4
☐ Debts/Leins Aff	Acknowledgment Jurat	1 2 3 4
☐ Deed of Trust	Acknowledgment Jurat	1 2 3 4
☐ Distrib of Proceeds	Acknowledgment Jurat	1 2 3 4
☐ E&O Agrmt	Acknowledgment Jurat	1 2 3 4
☐ Grant Deed	Acknowledgment Jurat	1 2 3 4
☐ Marital Stat Aff	Acknowledgment Jurat	1 2 3 4
☐ Mortgage	Acknowledgment Jurat	1 2 3 4
☐ Occupancy/Fin Aff	Acknowledgment Jurat	1 2 3 4
☐ Owner's Aff	Acknowledgment Jurat	1 2 3 4
☐ Payoff Aff	Acknowledgment Jurat	1 2 3 4
☐ Quit-Claim Deed	Acknowledgment Jurat	1 2 3 4
☐ Sig/Name Aff	Acknowledgment Jurat	1 2 3 4
☐ Survey Aff	Acknowledgment Jurat	1 2 3 4
☐ Warranty Deed	Acknowledgment Jurat	1 2 3 4

Document	Notarial Act	Signer
☐ Minor Medical Consent	Acknowledgment Jurat	1 2 3 4
☐ Minor Passport Consent	Acknowledgment Jurat	1 2 3 4
☐ Minor Travel Consent	Acknowledgment Jurat	1 2 3 4
☐ Vehicle Duplicate Title	Acknowledgment Jurat	1 2 3 4
☐ Vehicle Lein Release	Acknowledgment Jurat	1 2 3 4
☐ Vehicle Odom/Vin Ver	Acknowledgment Jurat	1 2 3 4
☐ Vehicle Title Transfer	Acknowledgment Jurat	1 2 3 4
☐ Adv Health Care Dir	Acknowledgment Jurat	1 2 3 4
☐ Assign of Digital Assets	Acknowledgment Jurat	1 2 3 4
☐ Assign of Personal Prop	Acknowledgment Jurat	1 2 3 4
☐ HIPAA Release	Acknowledgment Jurat	1 2 3 4
☐ Living Trust ____	Acknowledgment Jurat	1 2 3 4
☐ Last Will & Testament	Acknowledgment Jurat	1 2 3 4
☐ POA ____	Acknowledgment Jurat	1 2 3 4
☐ Trust Certification	Acknowledgment Jurat	1 2 3 4

Other notarial acts: ☐ Acknowledgment Jurat Copy Oath SW 1 2 3 4

	SIGNING ADDRESS	OTHERS IN ATTENDANCE	CLIENT / SIGNING SERVICE	FEE
			LENDER / LOAN NUMBER	

NOTES

#	ADDRESS / PHONE / EMAIL	SIGNATURE	INITIAL IF OATH/AFF TAKEN	RIGHT THUMB PRINT
1	ADDRESS / PHONE / EMAIL	SIGNATURE	INITIAL IF OATH/AFF TAKEN	RIGHT THUMB PRINT
2	ADDRESS / PHONE / EMAIL	SIGNATURE	INITIAL IF OATH/AFF TAKEN	RIGHT THUMB PRINT
3	ADDRESS / PHONE / EMAIL	SIGNATURE	INITIAL IF OATH/AFF TAKEN	RIGHT THUMB PRINT
4	ADDRESS / PHONE / EMAIL	SIGNATURE	INITIAL IF OATH/AFF TAKEN	RIGHT THUMB PRINT

Notary Journal Entry

#	DATE / TIME	NAME	IDENTITY VERIFIED	WILLINGNESS & COMPETENCE	FORMAT
1	DATE: TIME:	☐ Signer ☐ Witness	☐ D.L. ☐ Passport ☐ Credible Witness ☐ Other	☐ Expressed willingness ☐ Mentally alert ☐ Indicated understanding	☐ Paper ☐ Electronic ☐ RON
2	DATE: TIME:	☐ Signer ☐ Witness	☐ D.L. ☐ Passport ☐ Credible Witness ☐ Other	☐ Expressed willingness ☐ Mentally alert ☐ Indicated understanding	☐ Paper ☐ Electronic ☐ RON
3	DATE: TIME:	☐ Signer ☐ Witness	☐ D.L. ☐ Passport ☐ Credible Witness ☐ Other	☐ Expressed willingness ☐ Mentally alert ☐ Indicated understanding	☐ Paper ☐ Electronic ☐ RON
4	DATE: TIME:	☐ Signer ☐ Witness	☐ D.L. ☐ Passport ☐ Credible Witness ☐ Other	☐ Expressed willingness ☐ Mentally alert ☐ Indicated understanding	☐ Paper ☐ Electronic ☐ RON

DOCUMENT(S) SIGNED

Document	Type	SIGNER
☐ Borrower's Aff	Acknowledgment / Jurat	1 2 3 4
☐ Compliance Agrmt	Acknowledgment / Jurat	1 2 3 4
☐ Correction Agrmt	Acknowledgment / Jurat	1 2 3 4
☐ Debts/Leins Aff	Acknowledgment / Jurat	1 2 3 4
☐ Deed of Trust	Acknowledgment / Jurat	1 2 3 4
☐ Distrib of Proceeds	Acknowledgment / Jurat	1 2 3 4
☐ E&O Agrmt	Acknowledgment / Jurat	1 2 3 4
☐ Grant Deed	Acknowledgment / Jurat	1 2 3 4
☐ Marital Stat Aff	Acknowledgment / Jurat	1 2 3 4
☐ Mortgage	Acknowledgment / Jurat	1 2 3 4
☐ Occupancy/Fin Aff	Acknowledgment / Jurat	1 2 3 4
☐ Owner's Aff	Acknowledgment / Jurat	1 2 3 4
☐ Payoff Aff	Acknowledgment / Jurat	1 2 3 4
☐ Quit-Claim Deed	Acknowledgment / Jurat	1 2 3 4
☐ Sig/Name Aff	Acknowledgment / Jurat	1 2 3 4
☐ Survey Aff	Acknowledgment / Jurat	1 2 3 4
☐ Warranty Deed	Acknowledgment / Jurat	1 2 3 4
☐ Minor Medical Consent	Acknowledgment / Jurat	1 2 3 4
☐ Minor Passport Consent	Acknowledgment / Jurat	1 2 3 4
☐ Minor Travel Consent	Acknowledgment / Jurat	1 2 3 4
☐ Vehicle Duplicate Title	Acknowledgment / Jurat	1 2 3 4
☐ Vehicle Lein Release	Acknowledgment / Jurat	1 2 3 4
☐ Vehicle Odom/Vin Ver	Acknowledgment / Jurat	1 2 3 4
☐ Vehicle Title Transfer	Acknowledgment / Jurat	1 2 3 4
☐ Adv Health Care Dir	Acknowledgment / Jurat	1 2 3 4
☐ Assign of Digital Assets	Acknowledgment / Jurat	1 2 3 4
☐ Assign of Personal Prop	Acknowledgment / Jurat	1 2 3 4
☐ HIPAA Release	Acknowledgment / Jurat	1 2 3 4
☐ Living Trust	Acknowledgment / Jurat	1 2 3 4
☐ Last Will & Testament	Acknowledgment / Jurat	1 2 3 4
☐ POA	Acknowledgment / Jurat	1 2 3 4
☐ Trust Certification	Acknowledgment / Jurat	1 2 3 4

Additional columns (right side): Acknowledgment | Jurat | Copy | Oath | SW — 1 2 3 4

SIGNING ADDRESS	OTHERS IN ATTENDANCE	CLIENT / SIGNING SERVICE	FEE
		LENDER / LOAN NUMBER	

NOTES

	ADDRESS	PHONE / EMAIL	SIGNATURE	INITIAL IF OATH/AFF TAKEN	RIGHT THUMB PRINT
1		PHONE / EMAIL			
2		PHONE / EMAIL			
3		PHONE / EMAIL			
4		PHONE / EMAIL			

#	DATE / TIME	NAME	IDENTITY VERIFIED	WILLINGNESS & COMPETENCE	FORMAT
1	DATE ___ / TIME ___	☐ Signer ☐ Witness	☐ D.L. ☐ Passport ☐ Credible Witness ☐ Other	☐ Expressed willingness ☐ Mentally alert ☐ Indicated understanding	☐ Paper ☐ Electronic ☐ RON
2	DATE ___ / TIME ___	☐ Signer ☐ Witness	☐ D.L. ☐ Passport ☐ Credible Witness ☐ Other	☐ Expressed willingness ☐ Mentally alert ☐ Indicated understanding	☐ Paper ☐ Electronic ☐ RON
3	DATE ___ / TIME ___	☐ Signer ☐ Witness	☐ D.L. ☐ Passport ☐ Credible Witness ☐ Other	☐ Expressed willingness ☐ Mentally alert ☐ Indicated understanding	☐ Paper ☐ Electronic ☐ RON
4	DATE ___ / TIME ___	☐ Signer ☐ Witness	☐ D.L. ☐ Passport ☐ Credible Witness ☐ Other	☐ Expressed willingness ☐ Mentally alert ☐ Indicated understanding	☐ Paper ☐ Electronic ☐ RON

DOCUMENT(S) SIGNED

Document	Type	SIGNER 1	2	3	4
☐ Borrower's Aff	Acknowledgment / Jurat	1	2	3	4
☐ Compliance Agrmt	Acknowledgment / Jurat	1	2	3	4
☐ Correction Agrmt	Acknowledgment / Jurat	1	2	3	4
☐ Debts/Leins Aff	Acknowledgment / Jurat	1	2	3	4
☐ Deed of Trust	Acknowledgment / Jurat	1	2	3	4
☐ Distrib of Proceeds	Acknowledgment / Jurat	1	2	3	4
☐ E&O Agrmt	Acknowledgment / Jurat	1	2	3	4
☐ Grant Deed	Acknowledgment / Jurat	1	2	3	4
☐ Marital Stat Aff	Acknowledgment / Jurat	1	2	3	4
☐ Mortgage	Acknowledgment / Jurat	1	2	3	4
☐ Occupancy/Fin Aff	Acknowledgment / Jurat	1	2	3	4
☐ Owner's Aff	Acknowledgment / Jurat	1	2	3	4
☐ Payoff Aff	Acknowledgment / Jurat	1	2	3	4
☐ Quit-Claim Deed	Acknowledgment / Jurat	1	2	3	4
☐ Sig/Name Aff	Acknowledgment / Jurat	1	2	3	4
☐ Survey Aff	Acknowledgment / Jurat	1	2	3	4
☐ Warranty Deed	Acknowledgment / Jurat	1	2	3	4

Document	Type	SIGNER 1	2	3	4
☐ Minor Medical Consent	Acknowledgment / Jurat	1	2	3	4
☐ Minor Passport Consent	Acknowledgment / Jurat	1	2	3	4
☐ Minor Travel Consent	Acknowledgment / Jurat	1	2	3	4
☐ Vehicle Duplicate Title	Acknowledgment / Jurat	1	2	3	4
☐ Vehicle Lein Release	Acknowledgment / Jurat	1	2	3	4
☐ Vehicle Odom/Vin Ver	Acknowledgment / Jurat	1	2	3	4
☐ Vehicle Title Transfer	Acknowledgment / Jurat	1	2	3	4
☐ Adv Health Care Dir	Acknowledgment / Jurat	1	2	3	4
☐ Assign of Digital Assets	Acknowledgment / Jurat	1	2	3	4
☐ Assign of Personal Prop	Acknowledgment / Jurat	1	2	3	4
☐ HIPAA Release	Acknowledgment / Jurat	1	2	3	4
☐ Living Trust	Acknowledgment / Jurat	1	2	3	4
☐ Last Will & Testament	Acknowledgment / Jurat	1	2	3	4
☐ POA	Acknowledgment / Jurat	1	2	3	4
☐ Trust Certification	Acknowledgment / Jurat	1	2	3	4

Additional notarial acts (per signer, checkbox column): Acknowledgment / Jurat / Copy / Oath / SW — Signer 1 2 3 4

SIGNING ADDRESS	OTHERS IN ATTENDANCE	CLIENT / SIGNING SERVICE	FEE
		LENDER / LOAN NUMBER	

NOTES

	ADDRESS / PHONE / EMAIL	SIGNATURE	INITIAL IF OATH/AFF TAKEN	RIGHT THUMB PRINT
1	ADDRESS / PHONE / EMAIL	SIGNATURE	INITIAL IF OATH/AFF TAKEN	RIGHT THUMB PRINT
2	ADDRESS / PHONE / EMAIL	SIGNATURE	INITIAL IF OATH/AFF TAKEN	RIGHT THUMB PRINT
3	ADDRESS / PHONE / EMAIL	SIGNATURE	INITIAL IF OATH/AFF TAKEN	RIGHT THUMB PRINT
4	ADDRESS / PHONE / EMAIL	SIGNATURE	INITIAL IF OATH/AFF TAKEN	RIGHT THUMB PRINT

Notary Journal Entries

Entry 1
- **DATE:**
- **TIME:**
- **NAME:** ☐ Signer ☐ Witness
- **IDENTITY VERIFIED:** ☐ D.L. ☐ Passport ☐ Credible Witness ☐ Other
- **WILLINGNESS & COMPETENCE:** ☐ Expressed willingness ☐ Mentally alert ☐ Indicated understanding
- **FORMAT:** ☐ Paper ☐ Electronic ☐ RON

Entry 2
- **DATE:**
- **TIME:**
- **NAME:** ☐ Signer ☐ Witness
- **IDENTITY VERIFIED:** ☐ D.L. ☐ Passport ☐ Credible Witness ☐ Other
- **WILLINGNESS & COMPETENCE:** ☐ Expressed willingness ☐ Mentally alert ☐ Indicated understanding
- **FORMAT:** ☐ Paper ☐ Electronic ☐ RON

Entry 3
- **DATE:**
- **TIME:**
- **NAME:** ☐ Signer ☐ Witness
- **IDENTITY VERIFIED:** ☐ D.L. ☐ Passport ☐ Credible Witness ☐ Other
- **WILLINGNESS & COMPETENCE:** ☐ Expressed willingness ☐ Mentally alert ☐ Indicated understanding
- **FORMAT:** ☐ Paper ☐ Electronic ☐ RON

Entry 4
- **DATE:**
- **TIME:**
- **NAME:** ☐ Signer ☐ Witness
- **IDENTITY VERIFIED:** ☐ D.L. ☐ Passport ☐ Credible Witness ☐ Other
- **WILLINGNESS & COMPETENCE:** ☐ Expressed willingness ☐ Mentally alert ☐ Indicated understanding
- **FORMAT:** ☐ Paper ☐ Electronic ☐ RON

Document(s) Signed

Document	Notarial Act			Signer
☐ Borrower's Aff	Acknowledgment	Jurat	_____	1 2 3 4
☐ Compliance Agrmt	Acknowledgment	Jurat	_____	1 2 3 4
☐ Correction Agrmt	Acknowledgment	Jurat	_____	1 2 3 4
☐ Debts/Leins Aff	Acknowledgment	Jurat	_____	1 2 3 4
☐ Deed of Trust	Acknowledgment	Jurat	_____	1 2 3 4
☐ Distrib of Proceeds	Acknowledgment	Jurat	_____	1 2 3 4
☐ E&O Agrmt	Acknowledgment	Jurat	_____	1 2 3 4
☐ Grant Deed	Acknowledgment	Jurat	_____	1 2 3 4
☐ Marital Stat Aff	Acknowledgment	Jurat	_____	1 2 3 4
☐ Mortgage	Acknowledgment	Jurat	_____	1 2 3 4
☐ Occupancy/Fin Aff	Acknowledgment	Jurat	_____	1 2 3 4
☐ Owner's Aff	Acknowledgment	Jurat	_____	1 2 3 4
☐ Payoff Aff	Acknowledgment	Jurat	_____	1 2 3 4
☐ Quit-Claim Deed	Acknowledgment	Jurat	_____	1 2 3 4
☐ Sig/Name Aff	Acknowledgment	Jurat	_____	1 2 3 4
☐ Survey Aff	Acknowledgment	Jurat	_____	1 2 3 4
☐ Warranty Deed	Acknowledgment	Jurat	_____	1 2 3 4

Document	Notarial Act					Signer
☐ Minor Medical Consent	Acknowledgment	Jurat	Copy	Oath	SW	1 2 3 4
☐ Minor Passport Consent	Acknowledgment	Jurat	Copy	Oath	SW	1 2 3 4
☐ Minor Travel Consent	Acknowledgment	Jurat	Copy	Oath	SW	1 2 3 4
☐ Vehicle Duplicate Title	Acknowledgment	Jurat	Copy	Oath	SW	1 2 3 4
☐ Vehicle Lein Release	Acknowledgment	Jurat	Copy	Oath	SW	1 2 3 4
☐ Vehicle Odom/Vin Ver	Acknowledgment	Jurat	Copy	Oath	SW	1 2 3 4
☐ Vehicle Title Transfer	Acknowledgment	Jurat	Copy	Oath	SW	1 2 3 4
☐ Adv Health Care Dir	Acknowledgment	Jurat	Copy	Oath	SW	1 2 3 4
☐ Assign of Digital Assets	Acknowledgment	Jurat	Copy	Oath	SW	1 2 3 4
☐ Assign of Personal Prop	Acknowledgment	Jurat	Copy	Oath	SW	1 2 3 4
☐ HIPAA Release	Acknowledgment	Jurat	Copy	Oath	SW	1 2 3 4
☐ Living Trust _____	Acknowledgment	Jurat	Copy	Oath	SW	1 2 3 4
☐ Last Will & Testament	Acknowledgment	Jurat	Copy	Oath	SW	1 2 3 4
☐ POA _____	Acknowledgment	Jurat	Copy	Oath	SW	1 2 3 4
☐ Trust Certification	Acknowledgment	Jurat	Copy	Oath	SW	1 2 3 4

SIGNING ADDRESS	OTHERS IN ATTENDANCE	CLIENT / SIGNING SERVICE	FEE
		LENDER / LOAN NUMBER	

NOTES

	ADDRESS	PHONE	SIGNATURE	INITIAL IF OATH/AFF TAKEN	RIGHT THUMB PRINT
1		EMAIL			
2	ADDRESS	PHONE	SIGNATURE	INITIAL IF OATH/AFF TAKEN	RIGHT THUMB PRINT
		EMAIL			
3	ADDRESS	PHONE	SIGNATURE	INITIAL IF OATH/AFF TAKEN	RIGHT THUMB PRINT
		EMAIL			
4	ADDRESS	PHONE	SIGNATURE	INITIAL IF OATH/AFF TAKEN	RIGHT THUMB PRINT
		EMAIL			

Entry 1

DATE			
TIME			

NAME: ☐ Signer ☐ Witness

IDENTITY VERIFIED: ☐ D.L. ☐ Passport ☐ Credible Witness ☐ Other

WILLINGNESS & COMPETENCE: ☐ Expressed willingness ☐ Mentally alert ☐ Indicated understanding

FORMAT: ☐ Paper ☐ Electronic ☐ RON

Entry 2

DATE			
TIME			

NAME: ☐ Signer ☐ Witness

IDENTITY VERIFIED: ☐ D.L. ☐ Passport ☐ Credible Witness ☐ Other

WILLINGNESS & COMPETENCE: ☐ Expressed willingness ☐ Mentally alert ☐ Indicated understanding

FORMAT: ☐ Paper ☐ Electronic ☐ RON

Entry 3

DATE			
TIME			

NAME: ☐ Signer ☐ Witness

IDENTITY VERIFIED: ☐ D.L. ☐ Passport ☐ Credible Witness ☐ Other

WILLINGNESS & COMPETENCE: ☐ Expressed willingness ☐ Mentally alert ☐ Indicated understanding

FORMAT: ☐ Paper ☐ Electronic ☐ RON

Entry 4

DATE			
TIME			

NAME: ☐ Signer ☐ Witness

IDENTITY VERIFIED: ☐ D.L. ☐ Passport ☐ Credible Witness ☐ Other

WILLINGNESS & COMPETENCE: ☐ Expressed willingness ☐ Mentally alert ☐ Indicated understanding

FORMAT: ☐ Paper ☐ Electronic ☐ RON

DOCUMENT(S) SIGNED

Document			SIGNER			
			1	2	3	4
☐ Borrower's Aff	Acknowledgment	Jurat				
☐ Compliance Agrmt	Acknowledgment	Jurat	1	2	3	4
☐ Correction Agrmt	Acknowledgment	Jurat	1	2	3	4
☐ Debts/Leins Aff	Acknowledgment	Jurat	1	2	3	4
☐ Deed of Trust	Acknowledgment	Jurat	1	2	3	4
☐ Distrib of Proceeds	Acknowledgment	Jurat	1	2	3	4
☐ E&O Agrmt	Acknowledgment	Jurat	1	2	3	4
☐ Grant Deed	Acknowledgment	Jurat	1	2	3	4
☐ Marital Stat Aff	Acknowledgment	Jurat	1	2	3	4
☐ Mortgage	Acknowledgment	Jurat	1	2	3	4
☐ Occupancy/Fin Aff	Acknowledgment	Jurat	1	2	3	4
☐ Owner's Aff	Acknowledgment	Jurat	1	2	3	4
☐ Payoff Aff	Acknowledgment	Jurat	1	2	3	4
☐ Quit-Claim Deed	Acknowledgment	Jurat	1	2	3	4
☐ Sig/Name Aff	Acknowledgment	Jurat	1	2	3	4
☐ Survey Aff	Acknowledgment	Jurat	1	2	3	4
☐ Warranty Deed	Acknowledgment	Jurat	1	2	3	4

Document						SIGNER			
						1	2	3	4
☐ Minor Medical Consent	Acknowledgment	Jurat				1	2	3	4
☐ Minor Passport Consent	Acknowledgment	Jurat	Copy	Oath	SW	1	2	3	4
☐ Minor Travel Consent	Acknowledgment	Jurat				1	2	3	4
☐ Vehicle Duplicate Title	Acknowledgment	Jurat				1	2	3	4
☐ Vehicle Lein Release	Acknowledgment	Jurat	Copy	Oath	SW	1	2	3	4
☐ Vehicle Odom/Vin Ver	Acknowledgment	Jurat				1	2	3	4
☐ Vehicle Title Transfer	Acknowledgment	Jurat	Copy	Oath	SW	1	2	3	4
☐ Adv Health Care Dir	Acknowledgment	Jurat				1	2	3	4
☐ Assign of Digital Assets	Acknowledgment	Jurat	Copy	Oath	SW	1	2	3	4
☐ Assign of Personal Prop	Acknowledgment	Jurat				1	2	3	4
☐ HIPAA Release	Acknowledgment	Jurat				1	2	3	4
☐ Living Trust	Acknowledgment	Jurat	Copy	Oath	SW	1	2	3	4
☐ Last Will & Testament	Acknowledgment	Jurat				1	2	3	4
☐ POA	Acknowledgment	Jurat				1	2	3	4
☐ Trust Certification	Acknowledgment	Jurat	Copy	Oath	SW	1	2	3	4

Signing Address	Others in Attendance	Client / Signing Service	Fee
		Lender / Loan Number	

Notes

	Address	Phone / Email	Signature	Initial if Oath/Aff Taken	Right Thumb Print
1		Phone / Email	Signature		Right Thumb Print
2		Phone / Email	Signature		Right Thumb Print
3		Phone / Email	Signature		Right Thumb Print
4		Phone / Email	Signature		Right Thumb Print

Entry 1

DATE		NAME	IDENTITY VERIFIED	WILLINGNESS & COMPETENCE	FORMAT
1	TIME	☐ Signer ☐ Witness	☐ D.L. ☐ Passport ☐ Credible Witness ☐ Other	☐ Expressed willingness ☐ Mentally alert ☐ Indicated understanding	☐ Paper ☐ Electronic ☐ RON

Entry 2

DATE		NAME	IDENTITY VERIFIED	WILLINGNESS & COMPETENCE	FORMAT
2	TIME	☐ Signer ☐ Witness	☐ D.L. ☐ Passport ☐ Credible Witness ☐ Other	☐ Expressed willingness ☐ Mentally alert ☐ Indicated understanding	☐ Paper ☐ Electronic ☐ RON

Entry 3

DATE		NAME	IDENTITY VERIFIED	WILLINGNESS & COMPETENCE	FORMAT
3	TIME	☐ Signer ☐ Witness	☐ D.L. ☐ Passport ☐ Credible Witness ☐ Other	☐ Expressed willingness ☐ Mentally alert ☐ Indicated understanding	☐ Paper ☐ Electronic ☐ RON

Entry 4

DATE		NAME	IDENTITY VERIFIED	WILLINGNESS & COMPETENCE	FORMAT
4	TIME	☐ Signer ☐ Witness	☐ D.L. ☐ Passport ☐ Credible Witness ☐ Other	☐ Expressed willingness ☐ Mentally alert ☐ Indicated understanding	☐ Paper ☐ Electronic ☐ RON

DOCUMENT(S) SIGNED

Document	Act		SIGNER			
			1	2	3	4
☐ Borrower's Aff	Acknowledgment	Jurat	1	2	3	4
☐ Compliance Agrmt	Acknowledgment	Jurat	1	2	3	4
☐ Correction Agrmt	Acknowledgment	Jurat	1	2	3	4
☐ Debts/Leins Aff	Acknowledgment	Jurat	1	2	3	4
☐ Deed of Trust	Acknowledgment	Jurat	1	2	3	4
☐ Distrib of Proceeds	Acknowledgment	Jurat	1	2	3	4
☐ E&O Agrmt	Acknowledgment	Jurat	1	2	3	4
☐ Grant Deed	Acknowledgment	Jurat	1	2	3	4
☐ Marital Stat Aff	Acknowledgment	Jurat	1	2	3	4
☐ Mortgage	Acknowledgment	Jurat	1	2	3	4
☐ Occupancy/Fin Aff	Acknowledgment	Jurat	1	2	3	4
☐ Owner's Aff	Acknowledgment	Jurat	1	2	3	4
☐ Payoff Aff	Acknowledgment	Jurat	1	2	3	4
☐ Quit-Claim Deed	Acknowledgment	Jurat	1	2	3	4
☐ Sig/Name Aff	Acknowledgment	Jurat	1	2	3	4
☐ Survey Aff	Acknowledgment	Jurat	1	2	3	4
☐ Warranty Deed	Acknowledgment	Jurat	1	2	3	4

Document	Acknowledgment	Jurat	Copy	Oath	SW	SIGNER 1	2	3	4
☐ Minor Medical Consent	Acknowledgment	Jurat				1	2	3	4
☐ Minor Passport Consent	Acknowledgment	Jurat				1	2	3	4
☐ Minor Travel Consent	Acknowledgment	Jurat				1	2	3	4
☐ Vehicle Duplicate Title	Acknowledgment	Jurat	Copy	Oath	SW	1	2	3	4
☐ Vehicle Lein Release	Acknowledgment	Jurat				1	2	3	4
☐ Vehicle Odom/Vin Ver	Acknowledgment	Jurat				1	2	3	4
☐ Vehicle Title Transfer	Acknowledgment	Jurat	Copy	Oath	SW	1	2	3	4
☐ Adv Health Care Dir	Acknowledgment	Jurat				1	2	3	4
☐ Assign of Digital Assets	Acknowledgment	Jurat	Copy	Oath	SW	1	2	3	4
☐ Assign of Personal Prop	Acknowledgment	Jurat				1	2	3	4
☐ HIPAA Release	Acknowledgment	Jurat				1	2	3	4
☐ Living Trust	Acknowledgment	Jurat	Copy	Oath	SW	1	2	3	4
☐ Last Will & Testament	Acknowledgment	Jurat				1	2	3	4
☐ POA	Acknowledgment	Jurat				1	2	3	4
☐ Trust Certification	Acknowledgment	Jurat	Copy	Oath	SW	1	2	3	4

SIGNING ADDRESS	OTHERS IN ATTENDANCE	CLIENT / SIGNING SERVICE	FEE
		LENDER / LOAN NUMBER	

NOTES

_____
_____
_____
_____
_____
_____
_____
_____
_____
_____
_____
_____
_____

#	ADDRESS	PHONE	EMAIL	SIGNATURE	INITIAL IF OATH/AFF TAKEN	RIGHT THUMB PRINT
1						
2						
3						
4						

- 123 -

Notary Journal Entries

Entry 1

DATE	NAME	IDENTITY VERIFIED	WILLINGNESS & COMPETENCE	FORMAT
	☐ Signer ☐ Witness	☐ D.L. ☐ Passport ☐ Credible Witness	☐ Expressed willingness	☐ Paper
TIME		☐ Other	☐ Mentally alert	☐ Electronic
			☐ Indicated understanding	☐ RON

Entry 2

DATE	NAME	IDENTITY VERIFIED	WILLINGNESS & COMPETENCE	FORMAT
	☐ Signer ☐ Witness	☐ D.L. ☐ Passport ☐ Credible Witness	☐ Expressed willingness	☐ Paper
TIME		☐ Other	☐ Mentally alert	☐ Electronic
			☐ Indicated understanding	☐ RON

Entry 3

DATE	NAME	IDENTITY VERIFIED	WILLINGNESS & COMPETENCE	FORMAT
	☐ Signer ☐ Witness	☐ D.L. ☐ Passport ☐ Credible Witness	☐ Expressed willingness	☐ Paper
TIME		☐ Other	☐ Mentally alert	☐ Electronic
			☐ Indicated understanding	☐ RON

Entry 4

DATE	NAME	IDENTITY VERIFIED	WILLINGNESS & COMPETENCE	FORMAT
	☐ Signer ☐ Witness	☐ D.L. ☐ Passport ☐ Credible Witness	☐ Expressed willingness	☐ Paper
TIME		☐ Other	☐ Mentally alert	☐ Electronic
			☐ Indicated understanding	☐ RON

DOCUMENT(S) SIGNED

Document	Type		SIGNER			
			1	2	3	4
☐ Borrower's Aff	Acknowledgment	Jurat	1	2	3	4
☐ Compliance Agrmt	Acknowledgment	Jurat	1	2	3	4
☐ Correction Agrmt	Acknowledgment	Jurat	1	2	3	4
☐ Debts/Leins Aff	Acknowledgment	Jurat	1	2	3	4
☐ Deed of Trust	Acknowledgment	Jurat	1	2	3	4
☐ Distrib of Proceeds	Acknowledgment	Jurat	1	2	3	4
☐ E&O Agrmt	Acknowledgment	Jurat	1	2	3	4
☐ Grant Deed	Acknowledgment	Jurat	1	2	3	4
☐ Marital Stat Aff	Acknowledgment	Jurat	1	2	3	4
☐ Mortgage	Acknowledgment	Jurat	1	2	3	4
☐ Occupancy/Fin Aff	Acknowledgment	Jurat	1	2	3	4
☐ Owner's Aff	Acknowledgment	Jurat	1	2	3	4
☐ Payoff Aff	Acknowledgment	Jurat	1	2	3	4
☐ Quit-Claim Deed	Acknowledgment	Jurat	1	2	3	4
☐ Sig/Name Aff	Acknowledgment	Jurat	1	2	3	4
☐ Survey Aff	Acknowledgment	Jurat	1	2	3	4
☐ Warranty Deed	Acknowledgment	Jurat	1	2	3	4

Document	Type				SIGNER			
					1	2	3	4
☐ Minor Medical Consent	Acknowledgment	Jurat			1	2	3	4
☐ Minor Passport Consent	Acknowledgment	Jurat	Copy	Oath	SW	1	2	3	4
☐ Minor Travel Consent	Acknowledgment	Jurat			1	2	3	4
☐ Vehicle Duplicate Title	Acknowledgment	Jurat			1	2	3	4
☐ Vehicle Lein Release	Acknowledgment	Jurat	Copy	Oath	SW	1	2	3	4
☐ Vehicle Odom/Vin Ver	Acknowledgment	Jurat			1	2	3	4
☐ Vehicle Title Transfer	Acknowledgment	Jurat	Copy	Oath	SW	1	2	3	4
☐ Adv Health Care Dir	Acknowledgment	Jurat			1	2	3	4
☐ Assign of Digital Assets	Acknowledgment	Jurat	Copy	Oath	SW	1	2	3	4
☐ Assign of Personal Prop	Acknowledgment	Jurat			1	2	3	4
☐ HIPAA Release	Acknowledgment	Jurat			1	2	3	4
☐ Living Trust	Acknowledgment	Jurat	Copy	Oath	SW	1	2	3	4
☐ Last Will & Testament	Acknowledgment	Jurat			1	2	3	4
☐ POA	Acknowledgment	Jurat			1	2	3	4
☐ Trust Certification	Acknowledgment	Jurat	Copy	Oath	SW	1	2	3	4

	SIGNING ADDRESS	OTHERS IN ATTENDANCE	CLIENT / SIGNING SERVICE	FEE
			LENDER / LOAN NUMBER	

NOTES

_____
_____
_____
_____
_____
_____
_____
_____
_____
_____
_____
_____

	ADDRESS	PHONE	EMAIL	SIGNATURE	INITIAL IF OATH/AFF TAKEN	RIGHT THUMB PRINT
1						
2						
3						
4						

Notary Journal Entries

Entry 1
DATE	NAME	IDENTITY VERIFIED	WILLINGNESS & COMPETENCE	FORMAT
TIME	☐ Signer ☐ Witness	☐ D.L. ☐ Passport ☐ Credible Witness ☐ Other	☐ Expressed willingness ☐ Mentally alert ☐ Indicated understanding	☐ Paper ☐ Electronic ☐ RON

Entry 2
DATE	NAME	IDENTITY VERIFIED	WILLINGNESS & COMPETENCE	FORMAT
TIME	☐ Signer ☐ Witness	☐ D.L. ☐ Passport ☐ Credible Witness ☐ Other	☐ Expressed willingness ☐ Mentally alert ☐ Indicated understanding	☐ Paper ☐ Electronic ☐ RON

Entry 3
DATE	NAME	IDENTITY VERIFIED	WILLINGNESS & COMPETENCE	FORMAT
TIME	☐ Signer ☐ Witness	☐ D.L. ☐ Passport ☐ Credible Witness ☐ Other	☐ Expressed willingness ☐ Mentally alert ☐ Indicated understanding	☐ Paper ☐ Electronic ☐ RON

Entry 4
DATE	NAME	IDENTITY VERIFIED	WILLINGNESS & COMPETENCE	FORMAT
TIME	☐ Signer ☐ Witness	☐ D.L. ☐ Passport ☐ Credible Witness ☐ Other	☐ Expressed willingness ☐ Mentally alert ☐ Indicated understanding	☐ Paper ☐ Electronic ☐ RON

DOCUMENT(S) SIGNED

Document	Type	SIGNER
☐ Borrower's Aff	Acknowledgment Jurat	1 2 3 4
☐ Compliance Agrmt	Acknowledgment Jurat	1 2 3 4
☐ Correction Agrmt	Acknowledgment Jurat	1 2 3 4
☐ Debts/Leins Aff	Acknowledgment Jurat	1 2 3 4
☐ Deed of Trust	Acknowledgment Jurat	1 2 3 4
☐ Distrib of Proceeds	Acknowledgment Jurat	1 2 3 4
☐ E&O Agrmt	Acknowledgment Jurat	1 2 3 4
☐ Grant Deed	Acknowledgment Jurat	1 2 3 4
☐ Marital Stat Aff	Acknowledgment Jurat	1 2 3 4
☐ Mortgage	Acknowledgment Jurat	1 2 3 4
☐ Occupancy/Fin Aff	Acknowledgment Jurat	1 2 3 4
☐ Owner's Aff	Acknowledgment Jurat	1 2 3 4
☐ Payoff Aff	Acknowledgment Jurat	1 2 3 4
☐ Quit-Claim Deed	Acknowledgment Jurat	1 2 3 4
☐ Sig/Name Aff	Acknowledgment Jurat	1 2 3 4
☐ Survey Aff	Acknowledgment Jurat	1 2 3 4
☐ Warranty Deed	Acknowledgment Jurat	1 2 3 4

Document	Type	SIGNER
☐ Minor Medical Consent	Acknowledgment Jurat	1 2 3 4
☐ Minor Passport Consent	Acknowledgment Jurat	1 2 3 4
☐ Minor Travel Consent	Acknowledgment Jurat	1 2 3 4
☐ Vehicle Duplicate Title	Acknowledgment Jurat	1 2 3 4
☐ Vehicle Lein Release	Acknowledgment Jurat	1 2 3 4
☐ Vehicle Odom/Vin Ver	Acknowledgment Jurat	1 2 3 4
☐ Vehicle Title Transfer	Acknowledgment Jurat	1 2 3 4
☐ Adv Health Care Dir	Acknowledgment Jurat	1 2 3 4
☐ Assign of Digital Assets	Acknowledgment Jurat	1 2 3 4
☐ Assign of Personal Prop	Acknowledgment Jurat	1 2 3 4
☐ HIPAA Release	Acknowledgment Jurat	1 2 3 4
☐ Living Trust	Acknowledgment Jurat	1 2 3 4
☐ Last Will & Testament	Acknowledgment Jurat	1 2 3 4
☐ POA	Acknowledgment Jurat	1 2 3 4
☐ Trust Certification	Acknowledgment Jurat	1 2 3 4

Acknowledgment Jurat Copy Oath SW — 1 2 3 4

SIGNING ADDRESS	OTHERS IN ATTENDANCE	CLIENT / SIGNING SERVICE	FEE
		LENDER / LOAN NUMBER	

NOTES

_____
_____
_____
_____
_____
_____
_____
_____
_____
_____
_____

	ADDRESS	PHONE	SIGNATURE	INITIAL IF OATH/AFF TAKEN	RIGHT THUMB PRINT
1		EMAIL			
2	ADDRESS	PHONE / EMAIL	SIGNATURE	INITIAL IF OATH/AFF TAKEN	RIGHT THUMB PRINT
3	ADDRESS	PHONE / EMAIL	SIGNATURE	INITIAL IF OATH/AFF TAKEN	RIGHT THUMB PRINT
4	ADDRESS	PHONE / EMAIL	SIGNATURE	INITIAL IF OATH/AFF TAKEN	RIGHT THUMB PRINT

Notary Journal Entries (1–4)

Entry 1
	DATE	NAME ☐ Signer ☐ Witness	IDENTITY VERIFIED ☐ D.L. ☐ Passport ☐ Credible Witness ☐ Other	WILLINGNESS & COMPETENCE ☐ Expressed willingness ☐ Mentally alert ☐ Indicated understanding	FORMAT ☐ Paper ☐ Electronic ☐ RON
	TIME				

Entry 2
	DATE	NAME ☐ Signer ☐ Witness	IDENTITY VERIFIED ☐ D.L. ☐ Passport ☐ Credible Witness ☐ Other	WILLINGNESS & COMPETENCE ☐ Expressed willingness ☐ Mentally alert ☐ Indicated understanding	FORMAT ☐ Paper ☐ Electronic ☐ RON
	TIME				

Entry 3
	DATE	NAME ☐ Signer ☐ Witness	IDENTITY VERIFIED ☐ D.L. ☐ Passport ☐ Credible Witness ☐ Other	WILLINGNESS & COMPETENCE ☐ Expressed willingness ☐ Mentally alert ☐ Indicated understanding	FORMAT ☐ Paper ☐ Electronic ☐ RON
	TIME				

Entry 4
	DATE	NAME ☐ Signer ☐ Witness	IDENTITY VERIFIED ☐ D.L. ☐ Passport ☐ Credible Witness ☐ Other	WILLINGNESS & COMPETENCE ☐ Expressed willingness ☐ Mentally alert ☐ Indicated understanding	FORMAT ☐ Paper ☐ Electronic ☐ RON
	TIME				

DOCUMENT(S) SIGNED

Document	Notarial Act		SIGNER 1 2 3 4
☐ Borrower's Aff	Acknowledgment	Jurat	1 2 3 4
☐ Compliance Agrmt	Acknowledgment	Jurat	1 2 3 4
☐ Correction Agrmt	Acknowledgment	Jurat	1 2 3 4
☐ Debts/Leins Aff	Acknowledgment	Jurat	1 2 3 4
☐ Deed of Trust	Acknowledgment	Jurat	1 2 3 4
☐ Distrib of Proceeds	Acknowledgment	Jurat	1 2 3 4
☐ E&O Agrmt	Acknowledgment	Jurat	1 2 3 4
☐ Grant Deed	Acknowledgment	Jurat	1 2 3 4
☐ Marital Stat Aff	Acknowledgment	Jurat	1 2 3 4
☐ Mortgage	Acknowledgment	Jurat	1 2 3 4
☐ Occupancy/Fin Aff	Acknowledgment	Jurat	1 2 3 4
☐ Owner's Aff	Acknowledgment	Jurat	1 2 3 4
☐ Payoff Aff	Acknowledgment	Jurat	1 2 3 4
☐ Quit-Claim Deed	Acknowledgment	Jurat	1 2 3 4
☐ Sig/Name Aff	Acknowledgment	Jurat	1 2 3 4
☐ Survey Aff	Acknowledgment	Jurat	1 2 3 4
☐ Warranty Deed	Acknowledgment	Jurat	1 2 3 4

Document	Notarial Act					SIGNER 1 2 3 4
☐ Minor Medical Consent	Acknowledgment	Jurat				1 2 3 4
☐ Minor Passport Consent	Acknowledgment	Jurat				1 2 3 4
☐ Minor Travel Consent	Acknowledgment	Jurat				1 2 3 4
☐ Vehicle Duplicate Title	Acknowledgment	Jurat				1 2 3 4
☐ Vehicle Lein Release	Acknowledgment	Jurat				1 2 3 4
☐ Vehicle Odom/Vin Ver	Acknowledgment	Jurat				1 2 3 4
☐ Vehicle Title Transfer	Acknowledgment	Jurat				1 2 3 4
☐ Adv Health Care Dir	Acknowledgment	Jurat				1 2 3 4
☐ Assign of Digital Assets	Acknowledgment	Jurat				1 2 3 4
☐ Assign of Personal Prop	Acknowledgment	Jurat				1 2 3 4
☐ HIPAA Release	Acknowledgment	Jurat				1 2 3 4
☐ Living Trust _____	Acknowledgment	Jurat				1 2 3 4
☐ Last Will & Testament	Acknowledgment	Jurat				1 2 3 4
☐ POA _____	Acknowledgment	Jurat				1 2 3 4
☐ Trust Certification	Acknowledgment	Jurat	Copy	Oath	SW	1 2 3 4

(Columns Copy, Oath, SW with checkbox rows appear at right for additional document entries.)

SIGNING ADDRESS	OTHERS IN ATTENDANCE	CLIENT / SIGNING SERVICE	FEE
		LENDER / LOAN NUMBER	

NOTES

_____
_____
_____
_____
_____
_____
_____
_____
_____
_____
_____

		ADDRESS	PHONE	SIGNATURE	INITIAL IF OATH/AFF TAKEN	RIGHT THUMB PRINT
1			EMAIL			
2		ADDRESS	PHONE	SIGNATURE	INITIAL IF OATH/AFF TAKEN	RIGHT THUMB PRINT
			EMAIL			
3		ADDRESS	PHONE	SIGNATURE	INITIAL IF OATH/AFF TAKEN	RIGHT THUMB PRINT
			EMAIL			
4		ADDRESS	PHONE	SIGNATURE	INITIAL IF OATH/AFF TAKEN	RIGHT THUMB PRINT
			EMAIL			

Notary Journal Entries

#	DATE / TIME	NAME	IDENTITY VERIFIED	WILLINGNESS & COMPETENCE	FORMAT
1	DATE _____ TIME _____	☐ Signer ☐ Witness	☐ D.L. ☐ Passport ☐ Credible Witness ☐ Other	☐ Expressed willingness ☐ Mentally alert ☐ Indicated understanding	☐ Paper ☐ Electronic ☐ RON
2	DATE _____ TIME _____	☐ Signer ☐ Witness	☐ D.L. ☐ Passport ☐ Credible Witness ☐ Other	☐ Expressed willingness ☐ Mentally alert ☐ Indicated understanding	☐ Paper ☐ Electronic ☐ RON
3	DATE _____ TIME _____	☐ Signer ☐ Witness	☐ D.L. ☐ Passport ☐ Credible Witness ☐ Other	☐ Expressed willingness ☐ Mentally alert ☐ Indicated understanding	☐ Paper ☐ Electronic ☐ RON
4	DATE _____ TIME _____	☐ Signer ☐ Witness	☐ D.L. ☐ Passport ☐ Credible Witness ☐ Other	☐ Expressed willingness ☐ Mentally alert ☐ Indicated understanding	☐ Paper ☐ Electronic ☐ RON

DOCUMENT(S) SIGNED

Document	Notarial Act	SIGNER
☐ Borrower's Aff	Acknowledgment Jurat _____	1 2 3 4
☐ Compliance Agrmt	Acknowledgment Jurat _____	1 2 3 4
☐ Correction Agrmt	Acknowledgment Jurat _____	1 2 3 4
☐ Debts/Leins Aff	Acknowledgment Jurat _____	1 2 3 4
☐ Deed of Trust	Acknowledgment Jurat _____	1 2 3 4
☐ Distrib of Proceeds	Acknowledgment Jurat _____	1 2 3 4
☐ E&O Agrmt	Acknowledgment Jurat _____	1 2 3 4
☐ Grant Deed	Acknowledgment Jurat _____	1 2 3 4
☐ Marital Stat Aff	Acknowledgment Jurat _____	1 2 3 4
☐ Mortgage	Acknowledgment Jurat _____	1 2 3 4
☐ Occupancy/Fin Aff	Acknowledgment Jurat _____	1 2 3 4
☐ Owner's Aff	Acknowledgment Jurat _____	1 2 3 4
☐ Payoff Aff	Acknowledgment Jurat _____	1 2 3 4
☐ Quit-Claim Deed	Acknowledgment Jurat _____	1 2 3 4
☐ Sig/Name Aff	Acknowledgment Jurat _____	1 2 3 4
☐ Survey Aff	Acknowledgment Jurat _____	1 2 3 4
☐ Warranty Deed	Acknowledgment Jurat _____	1 2 3 4

Document	Notarial Act	SIGNER
☐ Minor Medical Consent	Acknowledgment Jurat _____	1 2 3 4
☐ Minor Passport Consent	Acknowledgment Jurat Copy Oath SW	1 2 3 4
☐ Minor Travel Consent	Acknowledgment Jurat _____	1 2 3 4
☐ Vehicle Duplicate Title	Acknowledgment Jurat Copy Oath SW	1 2 3 4
☐ Vehicle Lein Release	Acknowledgment Jurat _____	1 2 3 4
☐ Vehicle Odom/Vin Ver	Acknowledgment Jurat _____	1 2 3 4
☐ Vehicle Title Transfer	Acknowledgment Jurat Copy Oath SW	1 2 3 4
☐ Adv Health Care Dir	Acknowledgment Jurat _____	1 2 3 4
☐ Assign of Digital Assets	Acknowledgment Jurat Copy Oath SW	1 2 3 4
☐ Assign of Personal Prop	Acknowledgment Jurat _____	1 2 3 4
☐ HIPAA Release	Acknowledgment Jurat Copy Oath SW	1 2 3 4
☐ Living Trust _____	Acknowledgment Jurat _____	1 2 3 4
☐ Last Will & Testament	Acknowledgment Jurat _____	1 2 3 4
☐ POA _____	Acknowledgment Jurat Copy Oath SW	1 2 3 4
☐ Trust Certification	Acknowledgment Jurat _____	1 2 3 4

SIGNING ADDRESS	OTHERS IN ATTENDANCE	CLIENT / SIGNING SERVICE	FEE
		LENDER / LOAN NUMBER	

NOTES

	ADDRESS	PHONE	EMAIL	SIGNATURE	INITIAL IF OATH/AFF TAKEN	RIGHT THUMB PRINT
1						
2						
3						
4						

Signer Entries

#	DATE / TIME	NAME	IDENTITY VERIFIED	WILLINGNESS & COMPETENCE	FORMAT
1	DATE ___ / TIME ___	☐ Signer ☐ Witness	☐ D.L. ☐ Passport ☐ Credible Witness ☐ Other	☐ Expressed willingness ☐ Mentally alert ☐ Indicated understanding	☐ Paper ☐ Electronic ☐ RON
2	DATE ___ / TIME ___	☐ Signer ☐ Witness	☐ D.L. ☐ Passport ☐ Credible Witness ☐ Other	☐ Expressed willingness ☐ Mentally alert ☐ Indicated understanding	☐ Paper ☐ Electronic ☐ RON
3	DATE ___ / TIME ___	☐ Signer ☐ Witness	☐ D.L. ☐ Passport ☐ Credible Witness ☐ Other	☐ Expressed willingness ☐ Mentally alert ☐ Indicated understanding	☐ Paper ☐ Electronic ☐ RON
4	DATE ___ / TIME ___	☐ Signer ☐ Witness	☐ D.L. ☐ Passport ☐ Credible Witness ☐ Other	☐ Expressed willingness ☐ Mentally alert ☐ Indicated understanding	☐ Paper ☐ Electronic ☐ RON

DOCUMENT(S) SIGNED

Document	Type	SIGNER
☐ Borrower's Aff	Acknowledgment Jurat ___	1 2 3 4
☐ Compliance Agrmt	Acknowledgment Jurat ___	1 2 3 4
☐ Correction Agrmt	Acknowledgment Jurat ___	1 2 3 4
☐ Debts/Leins Aff	Acknowledgment Jurat ___	1 2 3 4
☐ Deed of Trust	Acknowledgment Jurat ___	1 2 3 4
☐ Distrib of Proceeds	Acknowledgment Jurat ___	1 2 3 4
☐ E&O Agrmt	Acknowledgment Jurat ___	1 2 3 4
☐ Grant Deed	Acknowledgment Jurat ___	1 2 3 4
☐ Marital Stat Aff	Acknowledgment Jurat ___	1 2 3 4
☐ Mortgage	Acknowledgment Jurat ___	1 2 3 4
☐ Occupancy/Fin Aff	Acknowledgment Jurat ___	1 2 3 4
☐ Owner's Aff	Acknowledgment Jurat ___	1 2 3 4
☐ Payoff Aff	Acknowledgment Jurat ___	1 2 3 4
☐ Quit-Claim Deed	Acknowledgment Jurat ___	1 2 3 4
☐ Sig/Name Aff	Acknowledgment Jurat ___	1 2 3 4
☐ Survey Aff	Acknowledgment Jurat ___	1 2 3 4
☐ Warranty Deed	Acknowledgment Jurat ___	1 2 3 4

Document	Type	SIGNER
☐ Minor Medical Consent	Acknowledgment Jurat ___	1 2 3 4
☐ Minor Passport Consent	Acknowledgment Jurat ___	1 2 3 4
☐ Minor Travel Consent	Acknowledgment Jurat ___	1 2 3 4
☐ Vehicle Duplicate Title	Acknowledgment Jurat ___	1 2 3 4
☐ Vehicle Lein Release	Acknowledgment Jurat ___	1 2 3 4
☐ Vehicle Odom/Vin Ver	Acknowledgment Jurat ___	1 2 3 4
☐ Vehicle Title Transfer	Acknowledgment Jurat ___	1 2 3 4
☐ Adv Health Care Dir	Acknowledgment Jurat ___	1 2 3 4
☐ Assign of Digital Assets	Acknowledgment Jurat ___	1 2 3 4
☐ Assign of Personal Prop	Acknowledgment Jurat ___	1 2 3 4
☐ HIPAA Release	Acknowledgment Jurat ___	1 2 3 4
☐ Living Trust	Acknowledgment Jurat ___	1 2 3 4
☐ Last Will & Testament	Acknowledgment Jurat ___	1 2 3 4
☐ POA	Acknowledgment Jurat ___	1 2 3 4
☐ Trust Certification	Acknowledgment Jurat Copy Oath SW	1 2 3 4

Additional type columns (Acknowledgment · Jurat · Copy · Oath · SW) appear for: Minor Passport Consent, Minor Travel Consent, Vehicle Lein Release, Vehicle Odom/Vin Ver, Vehicle Title Transfer, Assign of Digital Assets, Assign of Personal Prop, Last Will & Testament, Trust Certification.

SIGNING ADDRESS	OTHERS IN ATTENDANCE	CLIENT / SIGNING SERVICE	FEE
		LENDER / LOAN NUMBER	

NOTES

_____
_____
_____
_____
_____
_____
_____
_____
_____
_____
_____
_____

#	ADDRESS / PHONE / EMAIL	SIGNATURE	INITIAL IF OATH/AFF TAKEN	RIGHT THUMB PRINT
1	ADDRESS / PHONE / EMAIL	SIGNATURE		RIGHT THUMB PRINT
2	ADDRESS / PHONE / EMAIL	SIGNATURE		RIGHT THUMB PRINT
3	ADDRESS / PHONE / EMAIL	SIGNATURE		RIGHT THUMB PRINT
4	ADDRESS / PHONE / EMAIL	SIGNATURE		RIGHT THUMB PRINT

Notary Journal Entry

Entries 1–4

#	DATE / TIME	NAME	IDENTITY VERIFIED	WILLINGNESS & COMPETENCE	FORMAT
1	DATE _____ / TIME _____	☐ Signer ☐ Witness	☐ D.L. ☐ Passport ☐ Credible Witness ☐ Other	☐ Expressed willingness ☐ Mentally alert ☐ Indicated understanding	☐ Paper ☐ Electronic ☐ RON
2	DATE _____ / TIME _____	☐ Signer ☐ Witness	☐ D.L. ☐ Passport ☐ Credible Witness ☐ Other	☐ Expressed willingness ☐ Mentally alert ☐ Indicated understanding	☐ Paper ☐ Electronic ☐ RON
3	DATE _____ / TIME _____	☐ Signer ☐ Witness	☐ D.L. ☐ Passport ☐ Credible Witness ☐ Other	☐ Expressed willingness ☐ Mentally alert ☐ Indicated understanding	☐ Paper ☐ Electronic ☐ RON
4	DATE _____ / TIME _____	☐ Signer ☐ Witness	☐ D.L. ☐ Passport ☐ Credible Witness ☐ Other	☐ Expressed willingness ☐ Mentally alert ☐ Indicated understanding	☐ Paper ☐ Electronic ☐ RON

DOCUMENT(S) SIGNED

Document	Act	SIGNER
☐ Borrower's Aff	Acknowledgment Jurat	1 2 3 4
☐ Compliance Agrmt	Acknowledgment Jurat	1 2 3 4
☐ Correction Agrmt	Acknowledgment Jurat	1 2 3 4
☐ Debts/Leins Aff	Acknowledgment Jurat	1 2 3 4
☐ Deed of Trust	Acknowledgment Jurat	1 2 3 4
☐ Distrib of Proceeds	Acknowledgment Jurat	1 2 3 4
☐ E&O Agrmt	Acknowledgment Jurat	1 2 3 4
☐ Grant Deed	Acknowledgment Jurat	1 2 3 4
☐ Marital Stat Aff	Acknowledgment Jurat	1 2 3 4
☐ Mortgage	Acknowledgment Jurat	1 2 3 4
☐ Occupancy/Fin Aff	Acknowledgment Jurat	1 2 3 4
☐ Owner's Aff	Acknowledgment Jurat	1 2 3 4
☐ Payoff Aff	Acknowledgment Jurat	1 2 3 4
☐ Quit-Claim Deed	Acknowledgment Jurat	1 2 3 4
☐ Sig/Name Aff	Acknowledgment Jurat	1 2 3 4
☐ Survey Aff	Acknowledgment Jurat	1 2 3 4
☐ Warranty Deed	Acknowledgment Jurat	1 2 3 4

Document	Act	SIGNER
☐ Minor Medical Consent	Acknowledgment Jurat Copy Oath SW	1 2 3 4
☐ Minor Passport Consent	Acknowledgment Jurat	1 2 3 4
☐ Minor Travel Consent	Acknowledgment Jurat	1 2 3 4
☐ Vehicle Duplicate Title	Acknowledgment Jurat Copy Oath SW	1 2 3 4
☐ Vehicle Lein Release	Acknowledgment Jurat	1 2 3 4
☐ Vehicle Odom/Vin Ver	Acknowledgment Jurat	1 2 3 4
☐ Vehicle Title Transfer	Acknowledgment Jurat Copy Oath SW	1 2 3 4
☐ Adv Health Care Dir	Acknowledgment Jurat	1 2 3 4
☐ Assign of Digital Assets	Acknowledgment Jurat Copy Oath SW	1 2 3 4
☐ Assign of Personal Prop	Acknowledgment Jurat	1 2 3 4
☐ HIPAA Release	Acknowledgment Jurat	1 2 3 4
☐ Living Trust	Acknowledgment Jurat Copy Oath SW	1 2 3 4
☐ Last Will & Testament	Acknowledgment Jurat	1 2 3 4
☐ POA _____	Acknowledgment Jurat	1 2 3 4
☐ Trust Certification	Acknowledgment Jurat	1 2 3 4

SIGNING ADDRESS	OTHERS IN ATTENDANCE	CLIENT / SIGNING SERVICE	FEE
		LENDER / LOAN NUMBER	

NOTES

_____
_____
_____
_____
_____
_____
_____
_____
_____
_____
_____
_____

	ADDRESS	PHONE	SIGNATURE	INITIAL IF OATH/AFF TAKEN	RIGHT THUMB PRINT
1		EMAIL			
2	ADDRESS	PHONE	SIGNATURE	INITIAL IF OATH/AFF TAKEN	RIGHT THUMB PRINT
		EMAIL			
3	ADDRESS	PHONE	SIGNATURE	INITIAL IF OATH/AFF TAKEN	RIGHT THUMB PRINT
		EMAIL			
4	ADDRESS	PHONE	SIGNATURE	INITIAL IF OATH/AFF TAKEN	RIGHT THUMB PRINT
		EMAIL			

Notary Journal Entries

#	DATE / TIME	NAME	IDENTITY VERIFIED	WILLINGNESS & COMPETENCE	FORMAT
1	DATE ___ / TIME ___	□ Signer □ Witness	□ D.L. □ Passport □ Credible Witness □ Other	□ Expressed willingness □ Mentally alert □ Indicated understanding	□ Paper □ Electronic □ RON
2	DATE ___ / TIME ___	□ Signer □ Witness	□ D.L. □ Passport □ Credible Witness □ Other	□ Expressed willingness □ Mentally alert □ Indicated understanding	□ Paper □ Electronic □ RON
3	DATE ___ / TIME ___	□ Signer □ Witness	□ D.L. □ Passport □ Credible Witness □ Other	□ Expressed willingness □ Mentally alert □ Indicated understanding	□ Paper □ Electronic □ RON
4	DATE ___ / TIME ___	□ Signer □ Witness	□ D.L. □ Passport □ Credible Witness □ Other	□ Expressed willingness □ Mentally alert □ Indicated understanding	□ Paper □ Electronic □ RON

DOCUMENT(S) SIGNED

Document	Type	SIGNER
□ Borrower's Aff	Acknowledgment Jurat	1 2 3 4
□ Compliance Agrmt	Acknowledgment Jurat	1 2 3 4
□ Correction Agrmt	Acknowledgment Jurat	1 2 3 4
□ Debts/Leins Aff	Acknowledgment Jurat	1 2 3 4
□ Deed of Trust	Acknowledgment Jurat	1 2 3 4
□ Distrib of Proceeds	Acknowledgment Jurat	1 2 3 4
□ E&O Agrmt	Acknowledgment Jurat	1 2 3 4
□ Grant Deed	Acknowledgment Jurat	1 2 3 4
□ Marital Stat Aff	Acknowledgment Jurat	1 2 3 4
□ Mortgage	Acknowledgment Jurat	1 2 3 4
□ Occupancy/Fin Aff	Acknowledgment Jurat	1 2 3 4
□ Owner's Aff	Acknowledgment Jurat	1 2 3 4
□ Payoff Aff	Acknowledgment Jurat	1 2 3 4
□ Quit-Claim Deed	Acknowledgment Jurat	1 2 3 4
□ Sig/Name Aff	Acknowledgment Jurat	1 2 3 4
□ Survey Aff	Acknowledgment Jurat	1 2 3 4
□ Warranty Deed	Acknowledgment Jurat	1 2 3 4

Document	Type	SIGNER
□ Minor Medical Consent	Acknowledgment Jurat	1 2 3 4
□ Minor Passport Consent	Acknowledgment Jurat	1 2 3 4
□ Minor Travel Consent	Acknowledgment Jurat	1 2 3 4
□ Vehicle Duplicate Title	Acknowledgment Jurat	1 2 3 4
□ Vehicle Lein Release	Acknowledgment Jurat	1 2 3 4
□ Vehicle Odom/Vin Ver	Acknowledgment Jurat	1 2 3 4
□ Vehicle Title Transfer	Acknowledgment Jurat	1 2 3 4
□ Adv Health Care Dir	Acknowledgment Jurat	1 2 3 4
□ Assign of Digital Assets	Acknowledgment Jurat	1 2 3 4
□ Assign of Personal Prop	Acknowledgment Jurat	1 2 3 4
□ HIPAA Release	Acknowledgment Jurat	1 2 3 4
□ Living Trust _____	Acknowledgment Jurat	1 2 3 4
□ Last Will & Testament	Acknowledgment Jurat	1 2 3 4
□ POA _____	Acknowledgment Jurat	1 2 3 4
□ Trust Certification	Acknowledgment Jurat	1 2 3 4

The following checkbox options appear with each document entry in the right-hand column:
□ Acknowledgment Jurat Copy Oath SW 1 2 3 4

SIGNING ADDRESS	OTHERS IN ATTENDANCE	CLIENT / SIGNING SERVICE	FEE
		LENDER / LOAN NUMBER	

NOTES

	ADDRESS	SIGNATURE	PHONE	INITIAL IF OATH/AFF TAKEN	RIGHT THUMB PRINT
1			EMAIL		
2	ADDRESS	SIGNATURE	PHONE	INITIAL IF OATH/AFF TAKEN	RIGHT THUMB PRINT
			EMAIL		
3	ADDRESS	SIGNATURE	PHONE	INITIAL IF OATH/AFF TAKEN	RIGHT THUMB PRINT
			EMAIL		
4	ADDRESS	SIGNATURE	PHONE	INITIAL IF OATH/AFF TAKEN	RIGHT THUMB PRINT
			EMAIL		

Notary Journal Entries

Entry 1
Field	Details
DATE	
TIME	
NAME	☐ Signer ☐ Witness
IDENTITY VERIFIED	☐ D.L. ☐ Passport ☐ Credible Witness ☐ Other
WILLINGNESS & COMPETENCE	☐ Expressed willingness ☐ Mentally alert ☐ Indicated understanding
FORMAT	☐ Paper ☐ Electronic ☐ RON

Entry 2
Field	Details
DATE	
TIME	
NAME	☐ Signer ☐ Witness
IDENTITY VERIFIED	☐ D.L. ☐ Passport ☐ Credible Witness ☐ Other
WILLINGNESS & COMPETENCE	☐ Expressed willingness ☐ Mentally alert ☐ Indicated understanding
FORMAT	☐ Paper ☐ Electronic ☐ RON

Entry 3
Field	Details
DATE	
TIME	
NAME	☐ Signer ☐ Witness
IDENTITY VERIFIED	☐ D.L. ☐ Passport ☐ Credible Witness ☐ Other
WILLINGNESS & COMPETENCE	☐ Expressed willingness ☐ Mentally alert ☐ Indicated understanding
FORMAT	☐ Paper ☐ Electronic ☐ RON

Entry 4
Field	Details
DATE	
TIME	
NAME	☐ Signer ☐ Witness
IDENTITY VERIFIED	☐ D.L. ☐ Passport ☐ Credible Witness ☐ Other
WILLINGNESS & COMPETENCE	☐ Expressed willingness ☐ Mentally alert ☐ Indicated understanding
FORMAT	☐ Paper ☐ Electronic ☐ RON

DOCUMENT(S) SIGNED

Document	Notarial Act	SIGNER
☐ Borrower's Aff	Acknowledgment Jurat	1 2 3 4
☐ Compliance Agrmt	Acknowledgment Jurat	1 2 3 4
☐ Correction Agrmt	Acknowledgment Jurat	1 2 3 4
☐ Debts/Leins Aff	Acknowledgment Jurat	1 2 3 4
☐ Deed of Trust	Acknowledgment Jurat	1 2 3 4
☐ Distrib of Proceeds	Acknowledgment Jurat	1 2 3 4
☐ E&O Agrmt	Acknowledgment Jurat	1 2 3 4
☐ Grant Deed	Acknowledgment Jurat	1 2 3 4
☐ Marital Stat Aff	Acknowledgment Jurat	1 2 3 4
☐ Mortgage	Acknowledgment Jurat	1 2 3 4
☐ Occupancy/Fin Aff	Acknowledgment Jurat	1 2 3 4
☐ Owner's Aff	Acknowledgment Jurat	1 2 3 4
☐ Payoff Aff	Acknowledgment Jurat	1 2 3 4
☐ Quit-Claim Deed	Acknowledgment Jurat	1 2 3 4
☐ Sig/Name Aff	Acknowledgment Jurat	1 2 3 4
☐ Survey Aff	Acknowledgment Jurat	1 2 3 4
☐ Warranty Deed	Acknowledgment Jurat	1 2 3 4

Document	Notarial Act	SIGNER
☐ Minor Medical Consent	Acknowledgment Jurat	1 2 3 4
☐ Minor Passport Consent	Acknowledgment Jurat	1 2 3 4
☐ Minor Travel Consent	Acknowledgment Jurat	1 2 3 4
☐ Vehicle Duplicate Title	Acknowledgment Jurat	1 2 3 4
☐ Vehicle Lein Release	Acknowledgment Jurat	1 2 3 4
☐ Vehicle Odom/Vin Ver	Acknowledgment Jurat	1 2 3 4
☐ Vehicle Title Transfer	Acknowledgment Jurat	1 2 3 4
☐ Adv Health Care Dir	Acknowledgment Jurat	1 2 3 4
☐ Assign of Digital Assets	Acknowledgment Jurat	1 2 3 4
☐ Assign of Personal Prop	Acknowledgment Jurat	1 2 3 4
☐ HIPAA Release	Acknowledgment Jurat	1 2 3 4
☐ Living Trust	Acknowledgment Jurat	1 2 3 4
☐ Last Will & Testament	Acknowledgment Jurat	1 2 3 4
☐ POA	Acknowledgment Jurat	1 2 3 4
☐ Trust Certification	Acknowledgment Jurat	1 2 3 4

☐ Acknowledgment Jurat Copy Oath SW 1 2 3 4

SIGNING ADDRESS	OTHERS IN ATTENDANCE	CLIENT / SIGNING SERVICE	FEE
		LENDER / LOAN NUMBER	

NOTES

	ADDRESS	PHONE	SIGNATURE	INITIAL IF OATH/AFF TAKEN	RIGHT THUMB PRINT
1		EMAIL			
2	ADDRESS	PHONE	SIGNATURE	INITIAL IF OATH/AFF TAKEN	RIGHT THUMB PRINT
		EMAIL			
3	ADDRESS	PHONE	SIGNATURE	INITIAL IF OATH/AFF TAKEN	RIGHT THUMB PRINT
		EMAIL			
4	ADDRESS	PHONE	SIGNATURE	INITIAL IF OATH/AFF TAKEN	RIGHT THUMB PRINT
		EMAIL			

Notary Journal Entries

Entry 1
DATE		NAME ☐ Signer ☐ Witness
TIME		

IDENTITY VERIFIED ☐ D.L. ☐ Passport ☐ Credible Witness ☐ Other

WILLINGNESS & COMPETENCE ☐ Expressed willingness ☐ Mentally alert ☐ Indicated understanding

FORMAT ☐ Paper ☐ Electronic ☐ RON

Entry 2
DATE		NAME ☐ Signer ☐ Witness
TIME		

IDENTITY VERIFIED ☐ D.L. ☐ Passport ☐ Credible Witness ☐ Other

WILLINGNESS & COMPETENCE ☐ Expressed willingness ☐ Mentally alert ☐ Indicated understanding

FORMAT ☐ Paper ☐ Electronic ☐ RON

Entry 3
DATE		NAME ☐ Signer ☐ Witness
TIME		

IDENTITY VERIFIED ☐ D.L. ☐ Passport ☐ Credible Witness ☐ Other

WILLINGNESS & COMPETENCE ☐ Expressed willingness ☐ Mentally alert ☐ Indicated understanding

FORMAT ☐ Paper ☐ Electronic ☐ RON

Entry 4
DATE		NAME ☐ Signer ☐ Witness
TIME		

IDENTITY VERIFIED ☐ D.L. ☐ Passport ☐ Credible Witness ☐ Other

WILLINGNESS & COMPETENCE ☐ Expressed willingness ☐ Mentally alert ☐ Indicated understanding

FORMAT ☐ Paper ☐ Electronic ☐ RON

DOCUMENT(S) SIGNED

Document	Act		SIGNER 1 2 3 4
☐ Borrower's Aff	Acknowledgment	Jurat	1 2 3 4
☐ Compliance Agrmt	Acknowledgment	Jurat	1 2 3 4
☐ Correction Agrmt	Acknowledgment	Jurat	1 2 3 4
☐ Debts/Leins Aff	Acknowledgment	Jurat	1 2 3 4
☐ Deed of Trust	Acknowledgment	Jurat	1 2 3 4
☐ Distrib of Proceeds	Acknowledgment	Jurat	1 2 3 4
☐ E&O Agrmt	Acknowledgment	Jurat	1 2 3 4
☐ Grant Deed	Acknowledgment	Jurat	1 2 3 4
☐ Marital Stat Aff	Acknowledgment	Jurat	1 2 3 4
☐ Mortgage	Acknowledgment	Jurat	1 2 3 4
☐ Occupancy/Fin Aff	Acknowledgment	Jurat	1 2 3 4
☐ Owner's Aff	Acknowledgment	Jurat	1 2 3 4
☐ Payoff Aff	Acknowledgment	Jurat	1 2 3 4
☐ Quit-Claim Deed	Acknowledgment	Jurat	1 2 3 4
☐ Sig/Name Aff	Acknowledgment	Jurat	1 2 3 4
☐ Survey Aff	Acknowledgment	Jurat	1 2 3 4
☐ Warranty Deed	Acknowledgment	Jurat	1 2 3 4

Document	Act		SIGNER 1 2 3 4	Notarial Act					1 2 3 4
☐ Minor Medical Consent	Acknowledgment	Jurat	1 2 3 4	☐					
☐ Minor Passport Consent	Acknowledgment	Jurat	1 2 3 4		Acknowledgment	Jurat	Copy	Oath SW	1 2 3 4
☐ Minor Travel Consent	Acknowledgment	Jurat	1 2 3 4		Acknowledgment	Jurat	Copy	Oath SW	1 2 3 4
☐ Vehicle Duplicate Title	Acknowledgment	Jurat	1 2 3 4	☐					
☐ Vehicle Lein Release	Acknowledgment	Jurat	1 2 3 4		Acknowledgment	Jurat	Copy	Oath SW	1 2 3 4
☐ Vehicle Odom/Vin Ver	Acknowledgment	Jurat	1 2 3 4		Acknowledgment	Jurat	Copy	Oath SW	1 2 3 4
☐ Vehicle Title Transfer	Acknowledgment	Jurat	1 2 3 4	☐					
☐ Adv Health Care Dir	Acknowledgment	Jurat	1 2 3 4		Acknowledgment	Jurat	Copy	Oath SW	1 2 3 4
☐ Assign of Digital Assets	Acknowledgment	Jurat	1 2 3 4	☐					
☐ Assign of Personal Prop	Acknowledgment	Jurat	1 2 3 4		Acknowledgment	Jurat	Copy	Oath SW	1 2 3 4
☐ HIPAA Release	Acknowledgment	Jurat	1 2 3 4	☐					
☐ Living Trust _____	Acknowledgment	Jurat	1 2 3 4		Acknowledgment	Jurat	Copy	Oath SW	1 2 3 4
☐ Last Will & Testament	Acknowledgment	Jurat	1 2 3 4	☐					
☐ POA _____	Acknowledgment	Jurat	1 2 3 4		Acknowledgment	Jurat	Copy	Oath SW	1 2 3 4
☐ Trust Certification	Acknowledgment	Jurat	1 2 3 4		Acknowledgment	Jurat	Copy	Oath SW	1 2 3 4

SIGNING ADDRESS	OTHERS IN ATTENDANCE	CLIENT / SIGNING SERVICE	FEE
		LENDER / LOAN NUMBER	

NOTES

_____
_____
_____
_____
_____
_____
_____
_____
_____
_____
_____

#	ADDRESS	PHONE	EMAIL	SIGNATURE	INITIAL IF OATH/AFF TAKEN	RIGHT THUMB PRINT
1						
2						
3						
4						

Entry 1

DATE	
TIME	

NAME ☐ Signer ☐ Witness

IDENTITY VERIFIED ☐ D.L. ☐ Passport ☐ Credible Witness ☐ Other

WILLINGNESS & COMPETENCE ☐ Expressed willingness ☐ Mentally alert ☐ Indicated understanding

FORMAT ☐ Paper ☐ Electronic ☐ RON

Entry 2

DATE	
TIME	

NAME ☐ Signer ☐ Witness

IDENTITY VERIFIED ☐ D.L. ☐ Passport ☐ Credible Witness ☐ Other

WILLINGNESS & COMPETENCE ☐ Expressed willingness ☐ Mentally alert ☐ Indicated understanding

FORMAT ☐ Paper ☐ Electronic ☐ RON

Entry 3

DATE	
TIME	

NAME ☐ Signer ☐ Witness

IDENTITY VERIFIED ☐ D.L. ☐ Passport ☐ Credible Witness ☐ Other

WILLINGNESS & COMPETENCE ☐ Expressed willingness ☐ Mentally alert ☐ Indicated understanding

FORMAT ☐ Paper ☐ Electronic ☐ RON

Entry 4

DATE	
TIME	

NAME ☐ Signer ☐ Witness

IDENTITY VERIFIED ☐ D.L. ☐ Passport ☐ Credible Witness ☐ Other

WILLINGNESS & COMPETENCE ☐ Expressed willingness ☐ Mentally alert ☐ Indicated understanding

FORMAT ☐ Paper ☐ Electronic ☐ RON

DOCUMENT(S) SIGNED

Document	Act	Act	SIGNER 1	2	3	4
☐ Borrower's Aff	Acknowledgment	Jurat	1	2	3	4
☐ Compliance Agrmt	Acknowledgment	Jurat	1	2	3	4
☐ Correction Agrmt	Acknowledgment	Jurat	1	2	3	4
☐ Debts/Leins Aff	Acknowledgment	Jurat	1	2	3	4
☐ Deed of Trust	Acknowledgment	Jurat	1	2	3	4
☐ Distrib of Proceeds	Acknowledgment	Jurat	1	2	3	4
☐ E&O Agrmt	Acknowledgment	Jurat	1	2	3	4
☐ Grant Deed	Acknowledgment	Jurat	1	2	3	4
☐ Marital Stat Aff	Acknowledgment	Jurat	1	2	3	4
☐ Mortgage	Acknowledgment	Jurat	1	2	3	4
☐ Occupancy/Fin Aff	Acknowledgment	Jurat	1	2	3	4
☐ Owner's Aff	Acknowledgment	Jurat	1	2	3	4
☐ Payoff Aff	Acknowledgment	Jurat	1	2	3	4
☐ Quit-Claim Deed	Acknowledgment	Jurat	1	2	3	4
☐ Sig/Name Aff	Acknowledgment	Jurat	1	2	3	4
☐ Survey Aff	Acknowledgment	Jurat	1	2	3	4
☐ Warranty Deed	Acknowledgment	Jurat	1	2	3	4

Document	Act	Act	Act	Act	Act	SIGNER 1	2	3	4
☐ Minor Medical Consent	Acknowledgment	Jurat				1	2	3	4
☐ Minor Passport Consent	Acknowledgment	Jurat				1	2	3	4
☐ Minor Travel Consent	Acknowledgment	Jurat				1	2	3	4
☐ Vehicle Duplicate Title	Acknowledgment	Jurat				1	2	3	4
☐ Vehicle Lein Release	Acknowledgment	Jurat				1	2	3	4
☐ Vehicle Odom/Vin Ver	Acknowledgment	Jurat				1	2	3	4
☐ Vehicle Title Transfer	Acknowledgment	Jurat				1	2	3	4
☐ Adv Health Care Dir	Acknowledgment	Jurat				1	2	3	4
☐ Assign of Digital Assets	Acknowledgment	Jurat				1	2	3	4
☐ Assign of Personal Prop	Acknowledgment	Jurat				1	2	3	4
☐ HIPAA Release	Acknowledgment	Jurat				1	2	3	4
☐ Living Trust _____	Acknowledgment	Jurat				1	2	3	4
☐ Last Will & Testament	Acknowledgment	Jurat				1	2	3	4
☐ POA _____	Acknowledgment	Jurat				1	2	3	4
☐ Trust Certification	Acknowledgment	Jurat	Copy	Oath	SW	1	2	3	4

Additional acts (Copy, Oath, SW) with ☐ markers appear for:
- Minor Travel Consent — Acknowledgment Jurat Copy Oath SW — 1 2 3 4
- Vehicle Lein Release — Acknowledgment Jurat Copy Oath SW — 1 2 3 4
- Vehicle Title Transfer — Acknowledgment Jurat Copy Oath SW — 1 2 3 4
- Adv Health Care Dir — Acknowledgment Jurat Copy Oath SW — 1 2 3 4
- Assign of Personal Prop — Acknowledgment Jurat Copy Oath SW — 1 2 3 4
- Living Trust — Acknowledgment Jurat Copy Oath SW — 1 2 3 4
- POA — Acknowledgment Jurat Copy Oath SW — 1 2 3 4
- Trust Certification — Acknowledgment Jurat Copy Oath SW — 1 2 3 4

SIGNING ADDRESS	OTHERS IN ATTENDANCE	CLIENT / SIGNING SERVICE	FEE
		LENDER / LOAN NUMBER	

NOTES

	ADDRESS	PHONE	EMAIL	SIGNATURE	INITIAL IF OATH/AFF TAKEN	RIGHT THUMB PRINT
1						
2						
3						
4						

Notary Journal Entry

Entries 1–4

#	DATE / TIME	NAME	IDENTITY VERIFIED	WILLINGNESS & COMPETENCE	FORMAT
1	DATE ____ / TIME ____	☐ Signer ☐ Witness	☐ D.L. ☐ Passport ☐ Credible Witness ☐ Other	☐ Expressed willingness ☐ Mentally alert ☐ Indicated understanding	☐ Paper ☐ Electronic ☐ RON
2	DATE ____ / TIME ____	☐ Signer ☐ Witness	☐ D.L. ☐ Passport ☐ Credible Witness ☐ Other	☐ Expressed willingness ☐ Mentally alert ☐ Indicated understanding	☐ Paper ☐ Electronic ☐ RON
3	DATE ____ / TIME ____	☐ Signer ☐ Witness	☐ D.L. ☐ Passport ☐ Credible Witness ☐ Other	☐ Expressed willingness ☐ Mentally alert ☐ Indicated understanding	☐ Paper ☐ Electronic ☐ RON
4	DATE ____ / TIME ____	☐ Signer ☐ Witness	☐ D.L. ☐ Passport ☐ Credible Witness ☐ Other	☐ Expressed willingness ☐ Mentally alert ☐ Indicated understanding	☐ Paper ☐ Electronic ☐ RON

DOCUMENT(S) SIGNED

Document	Type		SIGNER			
			1	2	3	4
☐ Borrower's Aff	Acknowledgment	Jurat	1	2	3	4
☐ Compliance Agrmt	Acknowledgment	Jurat	1	2	3	4
☐ Correction Agrmt	Acknowledgment	Jurat	1	2	3	4
☐ Debts/Leins Aff	Acknowledgment	Jurat	1	2	3	4
☐ Deed of Trust	Acknowledgment	Jurat	1	2	3	4
☐ Distrib of Proceeds	Acknowledgment	Jurat	1	2	3	4
☐ E&O Agrmt	Acknowledgment	Jurat	1	2	3	4
☐ Grant Deed	Acknowledgment	Jurat	1	2	3	4
☐ Marital Stat Aff	Acknowledgment	Jurat	1	2	3	4
☐ Mortgage	Acknowledgment	Jurat	1	2	3	4
☐ Occupancy/Fin Aff	Acknowledgment	Jurat	1	2	3	4
☐ Owner's Aff	Acknowledgment	Jurat	1	2	3	4
☐ Payoff Aff	Acknowledgment	Jurat	1	2	3	4
☐ Quit-Claim Deed	Acknowledgment	Jurat	1	2	3	4
☐ Sig/Name Aff	Acknowledgment	Jurat	1	2	3	4
☐ Survey Aff	Acknowledgment	Jurat	1	2	3	4
☐ Warranty Deed	Acknowledgment	Jurat	1	2	3	4

Document	Type					SIGNER			
						1	2	3	4
☐ Minor Medical Consent	Acknowledgment	Jurat				1	2	3	4
☐ Minor Passport Consent	Acknowledgment	Jurat				1	2	3	4
☐ Minor Travel Consent	Acknowledgment	Jurat				1	2	3	4
☐ _____	Acknowledgment	Jurat	Copy	Oath	SW	1	2	3	4
☐ Vehicle Duplicate Title	Acknowledgment	Jurat				1	2	3	4
☐ Vehicle Lein Release	Acknowledgment	Jurat				1	2	3	4
☐ Vehicle Odom/Vin Ver	Acknowledgment	Jurat				1	2	3	4
☐ Vehicle Title Transfer	Acknowledgment	Jurat				1	2	3	4
☐ _____	Acknowledgment	Jurat	Copy	Oath	SW	1	2	3	4
☐ Adv Health Care Dir	Acknowledgment	Jurat				1	2	3	4
☐ Assign of Digital Assets	Acknowledgment	Jurat				1	2	3	4
☐ Assign of Personal Prop	Acknowledgment	Jurat				1	2	3	4
☐ HIPAA Release	Acknowledgment	Jurat				1	2	3	4
☐ _____	Acknowledgment	Jurat	Copy	Oath	SW	1	2	3	4
☐ Living Trust	Acknowledgment	Jurat				1	2	3	4
☐ Last Will & Testament	Acknowledgment	Jurat				1	2	3	4
☐ POA	Acknowledgment	Jurat				1	2	3	4
☐ Trust Certification	Acknowledgment	Jurat	Copy	Oath	SW	1	2	3	4

SIGNING ADDRESS	OTHERS IN ATTENDANCE	CLIENT / SIGNING SERVICE	FEE
		LENDER / LOAN NUMBER	

NOTES

_____

	ADDRESS	PHONE / EMAIL	SIGNATURE	INITIAL IF OATH/AFF TAKEN	RIGHT THUMB PRINT
1		PHONE / EMAIL	SIGNATURE	INITIAL IF OATH/AFF TAKEN	RIGHT THUMB PRINT
2	ADDRESS	PHONE / EMAIL	SIGNATURE	INITIAL IF OATH/AFF TAKEN	RIGHT THUMB PRINT
3	ADDRESS	PHONE / EMAIL	SIGNATURE	INITIAL IF OATH/AFF TAKEN	RIGHT THUMB PRINT
4	ADDRESS	PHONE / EMAIL	SIGNATURE	INITIAL IF OATH/AFF TAKEN	RIGHT THUMB PRINT

Notary Journal Entries

Entry 1
- **DATE:** _____
- **TIME:** _____
- **NAME:** ☐ Signer ☐ Witness
- **IDENTITY VERIFIED:** ☐ D.L. ☐ Passport ☐ Credible Witness ☐ Other
- **WILLINGNESS & COMPETENCE:** ☐ Expressed willingness ☐ Mentally alert ☐ Indicated understanding
- **FORMAT:** ☐ Paper ☐ Electronic ☐ RON

Entry 2
- **DATE:** _____
- **TIME:** _____
- **NAME:** ☐ Signer ☐ Witness
- **IDENTITY VERIFIED:** ☐ D.L. ☐ Passport ☐ Credible Witness ☐ Other
- **WILLINGNESS & COMPETENCE:** ☐ Expressed willingness ☐ Mentally alert ☐ Indicated understanding
- **FORMAT:** ☐ Paper ☐ Electronic ☐ RON

Entry 3
- **DATE:** _____
- **TIME:** _____
- **NAME:** ☐ Signer ☐ Witness
- **IDENTITY VERIFIED:** ☐ D.L. ☐ Passport ☐ Credible Witness ☐ Other
- **WILLINGNESS & COMPETENCE:** ☐ Expressed willingness ☐ Mentally alert ☐ Indicated understanding
- **FORMAT:** ☐ Paper ☐ Electronic ☐ RON

Entry 4
- **DATE:** _____
- **TIME:** _____
- **NAME:** ☐ Signer ☐ Witness
- **IDENTITY VERIFIED:** ☐ D.L. ☐ Passport ☐ Credible Witness ☐ Other
- **WILLINGNESS & COMPETENCE:** ☐ Expressed willingness ☐ Mentally alert ☐ Indicated understanding
- **FORMAT:** ☐ Paper ☐ Electronic ☐ RON

DOCUMENT(S) SIGNED

Document	Type	SIGNER
☐ Borrower's Aff	Acknowledgment Jurat _____	1 2 3 4
☐ Compliance Agrmt	Acknowledgment Jurat _____	1 2 3 4
☐ Correction Agrmt	Acknowledgment Jurat _____	1 2 3 4
☐ Debts/Leins Aff	Acknowledgment Jurat _____	1 2 3 4
☐ Deed of Trust	Acknowledgment Jurat _____	1 2 3 4
☐ Distrib of Proceeds	Acknowledgment Jurat _____	1 2 3 4
☐ E&O Agrmt	Acknowledgment Jurat _____	1 2 3 4
☐ Grant Deed	Acknowledgment Jurat _____	1 2 3 4
☐ Marital Stat Aff	Acknowledgment Jurat _____	1 2 3 4
☐ Mortgage	Acknowledgment Jurat _____	1 2 3 4
☐ Occupancy/Fin Aff	Acknowledgment Jurat _____	1 2 3 4
☐ Owner's Aff	Acknowledgment Jurat _____	1 2 3 4
☐ Payoff Aff	Acknowledgment Jurat _____	1 2 3 4
☐ Quit-Claim Deed	Acknowledgment Jurat _____	1 2 3 4
☐ Sig/Name Aff	Acknowledgment Jurat _____	1 2 3 4
☐ Survey Aff	Acknowledgment Jurat _____	1 2 3 4
☐ Warranty Deed	Acknowledgment Jurat _____	1 2 3 4

Document	Type	SIGNER
☐ Minor Medical Consent	Acknowledgment Jurat _____	1 2 3 4
☐ Minor Passport Consent	Acknowledgment Jurat _____	1 2 3 4
☐ Minor Travel Consent	Acknowledgment Jurat _____	1 2 3 4
☐ Vehicle Duplicate Title	Acknowledgment Jurat _____	1 2 3 4
☐ Vehicle Lein Release	Acknowledgment Jurat _____	1 2 3 4
☐ Vehicle Odom/Vin Ver	Acknowledgment Jurat _____	1 2 3 4
☐ Vehicle Title Transfer	Acknowledgment Jurat _____	1 2 3 4
☐ Adv Health Care Dir	Acknowledgment Jurat _____	1 2 3 4
☐ Assign of Digital Assets	Acknowledgment Jurat _____	1 2 3 4
☐ Assign of Personal Prop	Acknowledgment Jurat _____	1 2 3 4
☐ HIPAA Release	Acknowledgment Jurat _____	1 2 3 4
☐ Living Trust	Acknowledgment Jurat _____	1 2 3 4
☐ Last Will & Testament	Acknowledgment Jurat _____	1 2 3 4
☐ POA	Acknowledgment Jurat _____	1 2 3 4
☐ Trust Certification	Acknowledgment Jurat Copy Oath SW	1 2 3 4

Document type options (right column): Acknowledgment · Jurat · Copy · Oath · SW

SIGNING ADDRESS	OTHERS IN ATTENDANCE	CLIENT / SIGNING SERVICE	FEE
		LENDER / LOAN NUMBER	

NOTES

#	ADDRESS	PHONE	EMAIL	SIGNATURE	INITIAL IF OATH/AFF TAKEN	RIGHT THUMB PRINT
1						
2						
3						
4						

Notary Journal Entries

Entry 1
DATE	
TIME	

NAME: ☐ Signer ☐ Witness

IDENTITY VERIFIED: ☐ D.L. ☐ Passport ☐ Credible Witness ☐ Other

WILLINGNESS & COMPETENCE: ☐ Expressed willingness ☐ Mentally alert ☐ Indicated understanding

FORMAT: ☐ Paper ☐ Electronic ☐ RON

Entry 2
DATE	
TIME	

NAME: ☐ Signer ☐ Witness

IDENTITY VERIFIED: ☐ D.L. ☐ Passport ☐ Credible Witness ☐ Other

WILLINGNESS & COMPETENCE: ☐ Expressed willingness ☐ Mentally alert ☐ Indicated understanding

FORMAT: ☐ Paper ☐ Electronic ☐ RON

Entry 3
DATE	
TIME	

NAME: ☐ Signer ☐ Witness

IDENTITY VERIFIED: ☐ D.L. ☐ Passport ☐ Credible Witness ☐ Other

WILLINGNESS & COMPETENCE: ☐ Expressed willingness ☐ Mentally alert ☐ Indicated understanding

FORMAT: ☐ Paper ☐ Electronic ☐ RON

Entry 4
DATE	
TIME	

NAME: ☐ Signer ☐ Witness

IDENTITY VERIFIED: ☐ D.L. ☐ Passport ☐ Credible Witness ☐ Other

WILLINGNESS & COMPETENCE: ☐ Expressed willingness ☐ Mentally alert ☐ Indicated understanding

FORMAT: ☐ Paper ☐ Electronic ☐ RON

DOCUMENT(S) SIGNED

Document	Type	SIGNER
☐ Borrower's Aff	Acknowledgment Jurat	1 2 3 4
☐ Compliance Agrmt	Acknowledgment Jurat	1 2 3 4
☐ Correction Agrmt	Acknowledgment Jurat	1 2 3 4
☐ Debts/Leins Aff	Acknowledgment Jurat	1 2 3 4
☐ Deed of Trust	Acknowledgment Jurat	1 2 3 4
☐ Distrib of Proceeds	Acknowledgment Jurat	1 2 3 4
☐ E&O Agrmt	Acknowledgment Jurat	1 2 3 4
☐ Grant Deed	Acknowledgment Jurat	1 2 3 4
☐ Marital Stat Aff	Acknowledgment Jurat	1 2 3 4
☐ Mortgage	Acknowledgment Jurat	1 2 3 4
☐ Occupancy/Fin Aff	Acknowledgment Jurat	1 2 3 4
☐ Owner's Aff	Acknowledgment Jurat	1 2 3 4
☐ Payoff Aff	Acknowledgment Jurat	1 2 3 4
☐ Quit-Claim Deed	Acknowledgment Jurat	1 2 3 4
☐ Sig/Name Aff	Acknowledgment Jurat	1 2 3 4
☐ Survey Aff	Acknowledgment Jurat	1 2 3 4
☐ Warranty Deed	Acknowledgment Jurat	1 2 3 4

Document	Type	SIGNER
☐ Minor Medical Consent	Acknowledgment Jurat Copy Oath SW	1 2 3 4
☐ Minor Passport Consent	Acknowledgment Jurat Copy Oath SW	1 2 3 4
☐ Minor Travel Consent	Acknowledgment Jurat Copy Oath SW	1 2 3 4
☐ Vehicle Duplicate Title	Acknowledgment Jurat Copy Oath SW	1 2 3 4
☐ Vehicle Lein Release	Acknowledgment Jurat Copy Oath SW	1 2 3 4
☐ Vehicle Odom/Vin Ver	Acknowledgment Jurat Copy Oath SW	1 2 3 4
☐ Vehicle Title Transfer	Acknowledgment Jurat Copy Oath SW	1 2 3 4
☐ Adv Health Care Dir	Acknowledgment Jurat Copy Oath SW	1 2 3 4
☐ Assign of Digital Assets	Acknowledgment Jurat Copy Oath SW	1 2 3 4
☐ Assign of Personal Prop	Acknowledgment Jurat Copy Oath SW	1 2 3 4
☐ HIPAA Release	Acknowledgment Jurat Copy Oath SW	1 2 3 4
☐ Living Trust	Acknowledgment Jurat Copy Oath SW	1 2 3 4
☐ Last Will & Testament	Acknowledgment Jurat Copy Oath SW	1 2 3 4
☐ POA	Acknowledgment Jurat Copy Oath SW	1 2 3 4
☐ Trust Certification	Acknowledgment Jurat Copy Oath SW	1 2 3 4

SIGNING ADDRESS	OTHERS IN ATTENDANCE	CLIENT / SIGNING SERVICE	FEE
		LENDER / LOAN NUMBER	

NOTES

_____

	ADDRESS	PHONE	SIGNATURE	INITIAL IF OATH/AFF TAKEN	RIGHT THUMB PRINT
1		EMAIL			
2	ADDRESS	PHONE	SIGNATURE	INITIAL IF OATH/AFF TAKEN	RIGHT THUMB PRINT
		EMAIL			
3	ADDRESS	PHONE	SIGNATURE	INITIAL IF OATH/AFF TAKEN	RIGHT THUMB PRINT
		EMAIL			
4	ADDRESS	PHONE	SIGNATURE	INITIAL IF OATH/AFF TAKEN	RIGHT THUMB PRINT
		EMAIL			

Notary Journal Entries

Entry 1
DATE		
TIME		

NAME	□ Signer □ Witness

IDENTITY VERIFIED: □ D.L. □ Passport □ Credible Witness □ Other

WILLINGNESS & COMPETENCE: □ Expressed willingness □ Mentally alert □ Indicated understanding

FORMAT: □ Paper □ Electronic □ RON

Entry 2
DATE		
TIME		

NAME	□ Signer □ Witness

IDENTITY VERIFIED: □ D.L. □ Passport □ Credible Witness □ Other

WILLINGNESS & COMPETENCE: □ Expressed willingness □ Mentally alert □ Indicated understanding

FORMAT: □ Paper □ Electronic □ RON

Entry 3
DATE		
TIME		

NAME	□ Signer □ Witness

IDENTITY VERIFIED: □ D.L. □ Passport □ Credible Witness □ Other

WILLINGNESS & COMPETENCE: □ Expressed willingness □ Mentally alert □ Indicated understanding

FORMAT: □ Paper □ Electronic □ RON

Entry 4
DATE		
TIME		

NAME	□ Signer □ Witness

IDENTITY VERIFIED: □ D.L. □ Passport □ Credible Witness □ Other

WILLINGNESS & COMPETENCE: □ Expressed willingness □ Mentally alert □ Indicated understanding

FORMAT: □ Paper □ Electronic □ RON

DOCUMENT(S) SIGNED

Document	Type			SIGNER			
□ Borrower's Aff	Acknowledgment	Jurat	____	1	2	3	4
□ Compliance Agrmt	Acknowledgment	Jurat	____	1	2	3	4
□ Correction Agrmt	Acknowledgment	Jurat	____	1	2	3	4
□ Debts/Leins Aff	Acknowledgment	Jurat	____	1	2	3	4
□ Deed of Trust	Acknowledgment	Jurat	____	1	2	3	4
□ Distrib of Proceeds	Acknowledgment	Jurat	____	1	2	3	4
□ E&O Agrmt	Acknowledgment	Jurat	____	1	2	3	4
□ Grant Deed	Acknowledgment	Jurat	____	1	2	3	4
□ Marital Stat Aff	Acknowledgment	Jurat	____	1	2	3	4
□ Mortgage	Acknowledgment	Jurat	____	1	2	3	4
□ Occupancy/Fin Aff	Acknowledgment	Jurat	____	1	2	3	4
□ Owner's Aff	Acknowledgment	Jurat	____	1	2	3	4
□ Payoff Aff	Acknowledgment	Jurat	____	1	2	3	4
□ Quit-Claim Deed	Acknowledgment	Jurat	____	1	2	3	4
□ Sig/Name Aff	Acknowledgment	Jurat	____	1	2	3	4
□ Survey Aff	Acknowledgment	Jurat	____	1	2	3	4
□ Warranty Deed	Acknowledgment	Jurat	____	1	2	3	4

Document	Type					SIGNER			
□ Minor Medical Consent	Acknowledgment	Jurat				1	2	3	4
□ Minor Passport Consent	Acknowledgment	Jurat				1	2	3	4
□ Minor Travel Consent	Acknowledgment	Jurat				1	2	3	4
□	Acknowledgment	Jurat	Copy	Oath	SW	1	2	3	4
□ Vehicle Duplicate Title	Acknowledgment	Jurat				1	2	3	4
□ Vehicle Lein Release	Acknowledgment	Jurat				1	2	3	4
□ Vehicle Odom/Vin Ver	Acknowledgment	Jurat				1	2	3	4
□	Acknowledgment	Jurat	Copy	Oath	SW	1	2	3	4
□ Vehicle Title Transfer	Acknowledgment	Jurat				1	2	3	4
□	Acknowledgment	Jurat	Copy	Oath	SW	1	2	3	4
□ Adv Health Care Dir	Acknowledgment	Jurat				1	2	3	4
□ Assign of Digital Assets	Acknowledgment	Jurat				1	2	3	4
□	Acknowledgment	Jurat	Copy	Oath	SW	1	2	3	4
□ Assign of Personal Prop	Acknowledgment	Jurat				1	2	3	4
□ HIPAA Release	Acknowledgment	Jurat				1	2	3	4
□	Acknowledgment	Jurat	Copy	Oath	SW	1	2	3	4
□ Living Trust ____	Acknowledgment	Jurat				1	2	3	4
□ Last Will & Testament	Acknowledgment	Jurat				1	2	3	4
□ POA ____	Acknowledgment	Jurat				1	2	3	4
□	Acknowledgment	Jurat	Copy	Oath	SW	1	2	3	4
□ Trust Certification	Acknowledgment	Jurat				1	2	3	4

SIGNING ADDRESS	OTHERS IN ATTENDANCE	CLIENT / SIGNING SERVICE	FEE
		LENDER / LOAN NUMBER	

NOTES

_____

#	ADDRESS	PHONE	EMAIL	SIGNATURE	INITIAL IF OATH/AFF TAKEN	RIGHT THUMB PRINT
1						
2						
3						
4						

Notary Journal Entry (Left Section)

#	DATE / TIME	NAME	IDENTITY VERIFIED	WILLINGNESS & COMPETENCE	FORMAT
1	DATE ___ TIME ___	☐ Signer ☐ Witness	☐ D.L. ☐ Passport ☐ Credible Witness ☐ Other	☐ Expressed willingness ☐ Mentally alert ☐ Indicated understanding	☐ Paper ☐ Electronic ☐ RON
2	DATE ___ TIME ___	☐ Signer ☐ Witness	☐ D.L. ☐ Passport ☐ Credible Witness ☐ Other	☐ Expressed willingness ☐ Mentally alert ☐ Indicated understanding	☐ Paper ☐ Electronic ☐ RON
3	DATE ___ TIME ___	☐ Signer ☐ Witness	☐ D.L. ☐ Passport ☐ Credible Witness ☐ Other	☐ Expressed willingness ☐ Mentally alert ☐ Indicated understanding	☐ Paper ☐ Electronic ☐ RON
4	DATE ___ TIME ___	☐ Signer ☐ Witness	☐ D.L. ☐ Passport ☐ Credible Witness ☐ Other	☐ Expressed willingness ☐ Mentally alert ☐ Indicated understanding	☐ Paper ☐ Electronic ☐ RON

DOCUMENT(S) SIGNED (Right Section — top)

Document	SIGNER 1 2 3 4	Notarial Act
☐ Minor Medical Consent	1 2 3 4	Acknowledgment Jurat Copy Oath SW
☐ Minor Passport Consent	1 2 3 4	Acknowledgment Jurat Copy Oath SW
☐ Minor Travel Consent	1 2 3 4	Acknowledgment Jurat Copy Oath SW
☐ Vehicle Duplicate Title	1 2 3 4	Acknowledgment Jurat Copy Oath SW
☐ Vehicle Lein Release	1 2 3 4	Acknowledgment Jurat Copy Oath SW
☐ Vehicle Odom/Vin Ver	1 2 3 4	Acknowledgment Jurat Copy Oath SW
☐ Vehicle Title Transfer	1 2 3 4	Acknowledgment Jurat Copy Oath SW
☐ Adv Health Care Dir	1 2 3 4	Acknowledgment Jurat Copy Oath SW
☐ Assign of Digital Assets	1 2 3 4	Acknowledgment Jurat Copy Oath SW
☐ Assign of Personal Prop	1 2 3 4	Acknowledgment Jurat Copy Oath SW
☐ HIPAA Release	1 2 3 4	Acknowledgment Jurat Copy Oath SW
☐ Living Trust ___	1 2 3 4	Acknowledgment Jurat Copy Oath SW
☐ Last Will & Testament	1 2 3 4	Acknowledgment Jurat Copy Oath SW
☐ POA ___	1 2 3 4	Acknowledgment Jurat Copy Oath SW
☐ Trust Certification	1 2 3 4	Acknowledgment Jurat Copy Oath SW

DOCUMENT(S) SIGNED (Right Section — bottom)

Document	SIGNER 1 2 3 4	Notarial Act
☐ Borrower's Aff	1 2 3 4	Acknowledgment Jurat
☐ Compliance Agrmt	1 2 3 4	Acknowledgment Jurat
☐ Correction Agrmt	1 2 3 4	Acknowledgment Jurat
☐ Debts/Leins Aff	1 2 3 4	Acknowledgment Jurat
☐ Deed of Trust	1 2 3 4	Acknowledgment Jurat
☐ Distrib of Proceeds	1 2 3 4	Acknowledgment Jurat
☐ E&O Agrmt	1 2 3 4	Acknowledgment Jurat
☐ Grant Deed	1 2 3 4	Acknowledgment Jurat
☐ Marital Stat Aff	1 2 3 4	Acknowledgment Jurat
☐ Mortgage	1 2 3 4	Acknowledgment Jurat
☐ Occupancy/Fin Aff	1 2 3 4	Acknowledgment Jurat
☐ Owner's Aff	1 2 3 4	Acknowledgment Jurat
☐ Payoff Aff	1 2 3 4	Acknowledgment Jurat
☐ Quit-Claim Deed	1 2 3 4	Acknowledgment Jurat
☐ Sig/Name Aff	1 2 3 4	Acknowledgment Jurat
☐ Survey Aff	1 2 3 4	Acknowledgment Jurat
☐ Warranty Deed	1 2 3 4	Acknowledgment Jurat

SIGNING ADDRESS	OTHERS IN ATTENDANCE	CLIENT / SIGNING SERVICE	FEE
		LENDER / LOAN NUMBER	

NOTES

	ADDRESS	PHONE	SIGNATURE	INITIAL IF OATH/AFF TAKEN	RIGHT THUMB PRINT
1		EMAIL			
2	ADDRESS	PHONE	SIGNATURE	INITIAL IF OATH/AFF TAKEN	RIGHT THUMB PRINT
		EMAIL			
3	ADDRESS	PHONE	SIGNATURE	INITIAL IF OATH/AFF TAKEN	RIGHT THUMB PRINT
		EMAIL			
4	ADDRESS	PHONE	SIGNATURE	INITIAL IF OATH/AFF TAKEN	RIGHT THUMB PRINT
		EMAIL			

Notary Journal Entries

Entry 1

DATE	
TIME	

NAME
☐ Signer ☐ Witness

IDENTITY VERIFIED
☐ D.L. ☐ Passport ☐ Credible Witness
☐ Other

WILLINGNESS & COMPETENCE
☐ Expressed willingness
☐ Mentally alert
☐ Indicated understanding

FORMAT
☐ Paper ☐ Electronic ☐ RON

Entry 2

DATE	
TIME	

NAME
☐ Signer ☐ Witness

IDENTITY VERIFIED
☐ D.L. ☐ Passport ☐ Credible Witness
☐ Other

WILLINGNESS & COMPETENCE
☐ Expressed willingness
☐ Mentally alert
☐ Indicated understanding

FORMAT
☐ Paper ☐ Electronic ☐ RON

Entry 3

DATE	
TIME	

NAME
☐ Signer ☐ Witness

IDENTITY VERIFIED
☐ D.L. ☐ Passport ☐ Credible Witness
☐ Other

WILLINGNESS & COMPETENCE
☐ Expressed willingness
☐ Mentally alert
☐ Indicated understanding

FORMAT
☐ Paper ☐ Electronic ☐ RON

Entry 4

DATE	
TIME	

NAME
☐ Signer ☐ Witness

IDENTITY VERIFIED
☐ D.L. ☐ Passport ☐ Credible Witness
☐ Other

WILLINGNESS & COMPETENCE
☐ Expressed willingness
☐ Mentally alert
☐ Indicated understanding

FORMAT
☐ Paper ☐ Electronic ☐ RON

DOCUMENT(S) SIGNED

Document	Type		SIGNER
☐ Borrower's Aff	Acknowledgment	Jurat	1 2 3 4
☐ Compliance Agrmt	Acknowledgment	Jurat	1 2 3 4
☐ Correction Agrmt	Acknowledgment	Jurat	1 2 3 4
☐ Debts/Leins Aff	Acknowledgment	Jurat	1 2 3 4
☐ Deed of Trust	Acknowledgment	Jurat	1 2 3 4
☐ Distrib of Proceeds	Acknowledgment	Jurat	1 2 3 4
☐ E&O Agrmt	Acknowledgment	Jurat	1 2 3 4
☐ Grant Deed	Acknowledgment	Jurat	1 2 3 4
☐ Marital Stat Aff	Acknowledgment	Jurat	1 2 3 4
☐ Mortgage	Acknowledgment	Jurat	1 2 3 4
☐ Occupancy/Fin Aff	Acknowledgment	Jurat	1 2 3 4
☐ Owner's Aff	Acknowledgment	Jurat	1 2 3 4
☐ Payoff Aff	Acknowledgment	Jurat	1 2 3 4
☐ Quit-Claim Deed	Acknowledgment	Jurat	1 2 3 4
☐ Sig/Name Aff	Acknowledgment	Jurat	1 2 3 4
☐ Survey Aff	Acknowledgment	Jurat	1 2 3 4
☐ Warranty Deed	Acknowledgment	Jurat	1 2 3 4

Document	Type			SIGNER
☐ Minor Medical Consent	Acknowledgment	Jurat		1 2 3 4
☐ Minor Passport Consent	Acknowledgment	Jurat		1 2 3 4
☐ Minor Travel Consent	Acknowledgment	Jurat		1 2 3 4
☐ Vehicle Duplicate Title	Acknowledgment	Jurat		1 2 3 4
☐ Vehicle Lein Release	Acknowledgment	Jurat		1 2 3 4
☐ Vehicle Odom/Vin Ver	Acknowledgment	Jurat		1 2 3 4
☐ Vehicle Title Transfer	Acknowledgment	Jurat		1 2 3 4
☐ Adv Health Care Dir	Acknowledgment	Jurat		1 2 3 4
☐ Assign of Digital Assets	Acknowledgment	Jurat		1 2 3 4
☐ Assign of Personal Prop	Acknowledgment	Jurat		1 2 3 4
☐ HIPAA Release	Acknowledgment	Jurat		1 2 3 4
☐ Living Trust	☐ Acknowledgment Jurat Copy Oath SW			1 2 3 4
☐ Last Will & Testament	Acknowledgment	Jurat	Copy Oath SW	1 2 3 4
☐ POA	☐ Acknowledgment Jurat Copy Oath SW			1 2 3 4
☐ Trust Certification	☐ Acknowledgment Jurat Copy Oath SW			1 2 3 4

SIGNING ADDRESS	OTHERS IN ATTENDANCE	CLIENT / SIGNING SERVICE	FEE
		LENDER / LOAN NUMBER	

NOTES

	ADDRESS	PHONE	EMAIL	SIGNATURE	INITIAL IF OATH/AFF TAKEN	RIGHT THUMB PRINT
1						
2						
3						
4						

Notary Journal Record

Signer Records

#	DATE / TIME	NAME	IDENTITY VERIFIED	WILLINGNESS & COMPETENCE	FORMAT
1	DATE _____ TIME _____	☐ Signer ☐ Witness	☐ D.L. ☐ Passport ☐ Credible Witness ☐ Other	☐ Expressed willingness ☐ Mentally alert ☐ Indicated understanding	☐ Paper ☐ Electronic ☐ RON
2	DATE _____ TIME _____	☐ Signer ☐ Witness	☐ D.L. ☐ Passport ☐ Credible Witness ☐ Other	☐ Expressed willingness ☐ Mentally alert ☐ Indicated understanding	☐ Paper ☐ Electronic ☐ RON
3	DATE _____ TIME _____	☐ Signer ☐ Witness	☐ D.L. ☐ Passport ☐ Credible Witness ☐ Other	☐ Expressed willingness ☐ Mentally alert ☐ Indicated understanding	☐ Paper ☐ Electronic ☐ RON
4	DATE _____ TIME _____	☐ Signer ☐ Witness	☐ D.L. ☐ Passport ☐ Credible Witness ☐ Other	☐ Expressed willingness ☐ Mentally alert ☐ Indicated understanding	☐ Paper ☐ Electronic ☐ RON

DOCUMENT(S) SIGNED

Document	Type	SIGNER 1	2	3	4
☐ Borrower's Aff	Acknowledgment Jurat	1	2	3	4
☐ Compliance Agrmt	Acknowledgment Jurat	1	2	3	4
☐ Correction Agrmt	Acknowledgment Jurat	1	2	3	4
☐ Debts/Leins Aff	Acknowledgment Jurat	1	2	3	4
☐ Deed of Trust	Acknowledgment Jurat	1	2	3	4
☐ Distrib of Proceeds	Acknowledgment Jurat	1	2	3	4
☐ E&O Agrmt	Acknowledgment Jurat	1	2	3	4
☐ Grant Deed	Acknowledgment Jurat	1	2	3	4
☐ Marital Stat Aff	Acknowledgment Jurat	1	2	3	4
☐ Mortgage	Acknowledgment Jurat	1	2	3	4
☐ Occupancy/Fin Aff	Acknowledgment Jurat	1	2	3	4
☐ Owner's Aff	Acknowledgment Jurat	1	2	3	4
☐ Payoff Aff	Acknowledgment Jurat	1	2	3	4
☐ Quit-Claim Deed	Acknowledgment Jurat	1	2	3	4
☐ Sig/Name Aff	Acknowledgment Jurat	1	2	3	4
☐ Survey Aff	Acknowledgment Jurat	1	2	3	4
☐ Warranty Deed	Acknowledgment Jurat	1	2	3	4

Document	Type	SIGNER 1	2	3	4
☐ Minor Medical Consent	Acknowledgment Jurat	1	2	3	4
☐ Minor Passport Consent	Acknowledgment Jurat Copy Oath SW	1	2	3	4
☐ Minor Travel Consent	Acknowledgment Jurat	1	2	3	4
☐ Vehicle Duplicate Title	Acknowledgment Jurat Copy Oath SW	1	2	3	4
☐ Vehicle Lein Release	Acknowledgment Jurat	1	2	3	4
☐ Vehicle Odom/Vin Ver	Acknowledgment Jurat	1	2	3	4
☐ Vehicle Title Transfer	Acknowledgment Jurat Copy Oath SW	1	2	3	4
☐ Adv Health Care Dir	Acknowledgment Jurat	1	2	3	4
☐ Assign of Digital Assets	Acknowledgment Jurat Copy Oath SW	1	2	3	4
☐ Assign of Personal Prop	Acknowledgment Jurat	1	2	3	4
☐ HIPAA Release	Acknowledgment Jurat	1	2	3	4
☐ Living Trust _____	Acknowledgment Jurat Copy Oath SW	1	2	3	4
☐ Last Will & Testament	Acknowledgment Jurat	1	2	3	4
☐ POA	Acknowledgment Jurat	1	2	3	4
☐ Trust Certification	Acknowledgment Jurat Copy Oath SW	1	2	3	4

SIGNING ADDRESS	OTHERS IN ATTENDANCE	CLIENT / SIGNING SERVICE	FEE
		LENDER / LOAN NUMBER	

NOTES

	ADDRESS	PHONE	SIGNATURE	INITIAL IF OATH/AFF TAKEN	RIGHT THUMB PRINT
1		EMAIL			
2		PHONE	SIGNATURE	INITIAL IF OATH/AFF TAKEN	RIGHT THUMB PRINT
		EMAIL			
3		PHONE	SIGNATURE	INITIAL IF OATH/AFF TAKEN	RIGHT THUMB PRINT
		EMAIL			
4		PHONE	SIGNATURE	INITIAL IF OATH/AFF TAKEN	RIGHT THUMB PRINT
		EMAIL			

Notary Entries (1–4)

#	DATE / TIME	NAME	IDENTITY VERIFIED	WILLINGNESS & COMPETENCE	FORMAT
1	DATE ___ TIME ___	☐ Signer ☐ Witness	☐ D.L. ☐ Passport ☐ Credible Witness ☐ Other	☐ Expressed willingness ☐ Mentally alert ☐ Indicated understanding	☐ Paper ☐ Electronic ☐ RON
2	DATE ___ TIME ___	☐ Signer ☐ Witness	☐ D.L. ☐ Passport ☐ Credible Witness ☐ Other	☐ Expressed willingness ☐ Mentally alert ☐ Indicated understanding	☐ Paper ☐ Electronic ☐ RON
3	DATE ___ TIME ___	☐ Signer ☐ Witness	☐ D.L. ☐ Passport ☐ Credible Witness ☐ Other	☐ Expressed willingness ☐ Mentally alert ☐ Indicated understanding	☐ Paper ☐ Electronic ☐ RON
4	DATE ___ TIME ___	☐ Signer ☐ Witness	☐ D.L. ☐ Passport ☐ Credible Witness ☐ Other	☐ Expressed willingness ☐ Mentally alert ☐ Indicated understanding	☐ Paper ☐ Electronic ☐ RON

DOCUMENT(S) SIGNED

Document	Type	SIGNER 1 2 3 4
☐ Borrower's Aff	Acknowledgment / Jurat	1 2 3 4
☐ Compliance Agrmt	Acknowledgment / Jurat	1 2 3 4
☐ Correction Agrmt	Acknowledgment / Jurat	1 2 3 4
☐ Debts/Leins Aff	Acknowledgment / Jurat	1 2 3 4
☐ Deed of Trust	Acknowledgment / Jurat	1 2 3 4
☐ Distrib of Proceeds	Acknowledgment / Jurat	1 2 3 4
☐ E&O Agrmt	Acknowledgment / Jurat	1 2 3 4
☐ Grant Deed	Acknowledgment / Jurat	1 2 3 4
☐ Marital Stat Aff	Acknowledgment / Jurat	1 2 3 4
☐ Mortgage	Acknowledgment / Jurat	1 2 3 4
☐ Occupancy/Fin Aff	Acknowledgment / Jurat	1 2 3 4
☐ Owner's Aff	Acknowledgment / Jurat	1 2 3 4
☐ Payoff Aff	Acknowledgment / Jurat	1 2 3 4
☐ Quit-Claim Deed	Acknowledgment / Jurat	1 2 3 4
☐ Sig/Name Aff	Acknowledgment / Jurat	1 2 3 4
☐ Survey Aff	Acknowledgment / Jurat	1 2 3 4
☐ Warranty Deed	Acknowledgment / Jurat	1 2 3 4

Document	Type	SIGNER 1 2 3 4
☐ Minor Medical Consent	Acknowledgment / Jurat / Copy / Oath / SW	1 2 3 4
☐ Minor Passport Consent	Acknowledgment / Jurat	1 2 3 4
☐ Minor Travel Consent	Acknowledgment / Jurat	1 2 3 4
☐ Vehicle Duplicate Title	Acknowledgment / Jurat / Copy / Oath / SW	1 2 3 4
☐ Vehicle Lein Release	Acknowledgment / Jurat	1 2 3 4
☐ Vehicle Odom/Vin Ver	Acknowledgment / Jurat	1 2 3 4
☐ Vehicle Title Transfer	Acknowledgment / Jurat / Copy / Oath / SW	1 2 3 4
☐ Adv Health Care Dir	Acknowledgment / Jurat	1 2 3 4
☐ Assign of Digital Assets	Acknowledgment / Jurat / Copy / Oath / SW	1 2 3 4
☐ Assign of Personal Prop	Acknowledgment / Jurat	1 2 3 4
☐ HIPAA Release	Acknowledgment / Jurat / Copy / Oath / SW	1 2 3 4
☐ Living Trust ___	Acknowledgment / Jurat	1 2 3 4
☐ Last Will & Testament	Acknowledgment / Jurat	1 2 3 4
☐ POA ___	Acknowledgment / Jurat	1 2 3 4
☐ Trust Certification	Acknowledgment / Jurat / Copy / Oath / SW	1 2 3 4

SIGNING ADDRESS	OTHERS IN ATTENDANCE	CLIENT / SIGNING SERVICE	FEE
		LENDER / LOAN NUMBER	

NOTES

#	ADDRESS / PHONE / EMAIL	SIGNATURE	INITIAL IF OATH/AFF TAKEN	RIGHT THUMB PRINT
1	ADDRESS / PHONE / EMAIL	SIGNATURE	INITIAL IF OATH/AFF TAKEN	RIGHT THUMB PRINT
2	ADDRESS / PHONE / EMAIL	SIGNATURE	INITIAL IF OATH/AFF TAKEN	RIGHT THUMB PRINT
3	ADDRESS / PHONE / EMAIL	SIGNATURE	INITIAL IF OATH/AFF TAKEN	RIGHT THUMB PRINT
4	ADDRESS / PHONE / EMAIL	SIGNATURE	INITIAL IF OATH/AFF TAKEN	RIGHT THUMB PRINT

Notary Journal Entries

Entry 1
DATE		
TIME		

NAME: ☐ Signer ☐ Witness

IDENTITY VERIFIED: ☐ D.L. ☐ Passport ☐ Credible Witness ☐ Other

WILLINGNESS & COMPETENCE: ☐ Expressed willingness ☐ Mentally alert ☐ Indicated understanding

FORMAT: ☐ Paper ☐ Electronic ☐ RON

Entry 2
DATE		
TIME		

NAME: ☐ Signer ☐ Witness

IDENTITY VERIFIED: ☐ D.L. ☐ Passport ☐ Credible Witness ☐ Other

WILLINGNESS & COMPETENCE: ☐ Expressed willingness ☐ Mentally alert ☐ Indicated understanding

FORMAT: ☐ Paper ☐ Electronic ☐ RON

Entry 3
DATE		
TIME		

NAME: ☐ Signer ☐ Witness

IDENTITY VERIFIED: ☐ D.L. ☐ Passport ☐ Credible Witness ☐ Other

WILLINGNESS & COMPETENCE: ☐ Expressed willingness ☐ Mentally alert ☐ Indicated understanding

FORMAT: ☐ Paper ☐ Electronic ☐ RON

Entry 4
DATE		
TIME		

NAME: ☐ Signer ☐ Witness

IDENTITY VERIFIED: ☐ D.L. ☐ Passport ☐ Credible Witness ☐ Other

WILLINGNESS & COMPETENCE: ☐ Expressed willingness ☐ Mentally alert ☐ Indicated understanding

FORMAT: ☐ Paper ☐ Electronic ☐ RON

DOCUMENT(S) SIGNED

Document	Act Type		SIGNER			
☐ Borrower's Aff	Acknowledgment	Jurat	1	2	3	4
☐ Compliance Agrmt	Acknowledgment	Jurat	1	2	3	4
☐ Correction Agrmt	Acknowledgment	Jurat	1	2	3	4
☐ Debts/Leins Aff	Acknowledgment	Jurat	1	2	3	4
☐ Deed of Trust	Acknowledgment	Jurat	1	2	3	4
☐ Distrib of Proceeds	Acknowledgment	Jurat	1	2	3	4
☐ E&O Agrmt	Acknowledgment	Jurat	1	2	3	4
☐ Grant Deed	Acknowledgment	Jurat	1	2	3	4
☐ Marital Stat Aff	Acknowledgment	Jurat	1	2	3	4
☐ Mortgage	Acknowledgment	Jurat	1	2	3	4
☐ Occupancy/Fin Aff	Acknowledgment	Jurat	1	2	3	4
☐ Owner's Aff	Acknowledgment	Jurat	1	2	3	4
☐ Payoff Aff	Acknowledgment	Jurat	1	2	3	4
☐ Quit-Claim Deed	Acknowledgment	Jurat	1	2	3	4
☐ Sig/Name Aff	Acknowledgment	Jurat	1	2	3	4
☐ Survey Aff	Acknowledgment	Jurat	1	2	3	4
☐ Warranty Deed	Acknowledgment	Jurat	1	2	3	4

Document	Act Type					SIGNER			
☐ Minor Medical Consent	Acknowledgment	Jurat				1	2	3	4
☐ Minor Passport Consent	Acknowledgment	Jurat				1	2	3	4
☐ Minor Travel Consent	Acknowledgment	Jurat				1	2	3	4
☐ Vehicle Duplicate Title	Acknowledgment	Jurat				1	2	3	4
☐ Vehicle Lein Release	Acknowledgment	Jurat				1	2	3	4
☐ Vehicle Odom/Vin Ver	Acknowledgment	Jurat				1	2	3	4
☐ Vehicle Title Transfer	Acknowledgment	Jurat				1	2	3	4
☐ Adv Health Care Dir	Acknowledgment	Jurat				1	2	3	4
☐ Assign of Digital Assets	Acknowledgment	Jurat				1	2	3	4
☐ Assign of Personal Prop	Acknowledgment	Jurat				1	2	3	4
☐ HIPAA Release	Acknowledgment	Jurat				1	2	3	4
☐ Living Trust	Acknowledgment	Jurat	Copy	Oath	SW	1	2	3	4
☐ Last Will & Testament	Acknowledgment	Jurat	Copy	Oath	SW	1	2	3	4
☐ POA	Acknowledgment	Jurat	Copy	Oath	SW	1	2	3	4
☐ Trust Certification	Acknowledgment	Jurat	Copy	Oath	SW	1	2	3	4

SIGNING ADDRESS	OTHERS IN ATTENDANCE	CLIENT / SIGNING SERVICE	FEE
		LENDER / LOAN NUMBER	

NOTES

_____

#	ADDRESS		SIGNATURE	PHONE		INITIAL IF OATH/AFF TAKEN	RIGHT THUMB PRINT
1	ADDRESS		SIGNATURE	PHONE / EMAIL		INITIAL IF OATH/AFF TAKEN	RIGHT THUMB PRINT
2	ADDRESS		SIGNATURE	PHONE / EMAIL		INITIAL IF OATH/AFF TAKEN	RIGHT THUMB PRINT
3	ADDRESS		SIGNATURE	PHONE / EMAIL		INITIAL IF OATH/AFF TAKEN	RIGHT THUMB PRINT
4	ADDRESS		SIGNATURE	PHONE / EMAIL		INITIAL IF OATH/AFF TAKEN	RIGHT THUMB PRINT

Notary Journal Entries

#	DATE / TIME	NAME	IDENTITY VERIFIED	WILLINGNESS & COMPETENCE	FORMAT
1	DATE ___ / TIME ___	☐ Signer ☐ Witness	☐ D.L. ☐ Passport ☐ Credible Witness ☐ Other	☐ Expressed willingness ☐ Mentally alert ☐ Indicated understanding	☐ Paper ☐ Electronic ☐ RON
2	DATE ___ / TIME ___	☐ Signer ☐ Witness	☐ D.L. ☐ Passport ☐ Credible Witness ☐ Other	☐ Expressed willingness ☐ Mentally alert ☐ Indicated understanding	☐ Paper ☐ Electronic ☐ RON
3	DATE ___ / TIME ___	☐ Signer ☐ Witness	☐ D.L. ☐ Passport ☐ Credible Witness ☐ Other	☐ Expressed willingness ☐ Mentally alert ☐ Indicated understanding	☐ Paper ☐ Electronic ☐ RON
4	DATE ___ / TIME ___	☐ Signer ☐ Witness	☐ D.L. ☐ Passport ☐ Credible Witness ☐ Other	☐ Expressed willingness ☐ Mentally alert ☐ Indicated understanding	☐ Paper ☐ Electronic ☐ RON

DOCUMENT(S) SIGNED

Document	Type	SIGNER
☐ Borrower's Aff	Acknowledgment Jurat ___	1 2 3 4
☐ Compliance Agrmt	Acknowledgment Jurat ___	1 2 3 4
☐ Correction Agrmt	Acknowledgment Jurat ___	1 2 3 4
☐ Debts/Leins Aff	Acknowledgment Jurat ___	1 2 3 4
☐ Deed of Trust	Acknowledgment Jurat ___	1 2 3 4
☐ Distrib of Proceeds	Acknowledgment Jurat ___	1 2 3 4
☐ E&O Agrmt	Acknowledgment Jurat ___	1 2 3 4
☐ Grant Deed	Acknowledgment Jurat ___	1 2 3 4
☐ Marital Stat Aff	Acknowledgment Jurat ___	1 2 3 4
☐ Mortgage	Acknowledgment Jurat ___	1 2 3 4
☐ Occupancy/Fin Aff	Acknowledgment Jurat ___	1 2 3 4
☐ Owner's Aff	Acknowledgment Jurat ___	1 2 3 4
☐ Payoff Aff	Acknowledgment Jurat ___	1 2 3 4
☐ Quit-Claim Deed	Acknowledgment Jurat ___	1 2 3 4
☐ Sig/Name Aff	Acknowledgment Jurat ___	1 2 3 4
☐ Survey Aff	Acknowledgment Jurat ___	1 2 3 4
☐ Warranty Deed	Acknowledgment Jurat ___	1 2 3 4

Document	Type	SIGNER
☐ Minor Medical Consent	Acknowledgment Jurat ___	1 2 3 4
☐ Minor Passport Consent	Acknowledgment Jurat ___	1 2 3 4
☐ Minor Travel Consent	Acknowledgment Jurat ___	1 2 3 4
☐ Vehicle Duplicate Title	Acknowledgment Jurat ___	1 2 3 4
☐ Vehicle Lein Release	Acknowledgment Jurat ___	1 2 3 4
☐ Vehicle Odom/Vin Ver	Acknowledgment Jurat ___	1 2 3 4
☐ Vehicle Title Transfer	Acknowledgment Jurat ___	1 2 3 4
☐ Adv Health Care Dir	Acknowledgment Jurat Copy Oath SW	1 2 3 4
☐ Assign of Digital Assets	Acknowledgment Jurat Copy Oath SW	1 2 3 4
☐ Assign of Personal Prop	Acknowledgment Jurat Copy Oath SW	1 2 3 4
☐ HIPAA Release	Acknowledgment Jurat Copy Oath SW	1 2 3 4
☐ Living Trust	Acknowledgment Jurat Copy Oath SW	1 2 3 4
☐ Last Will & Testament	Acknowledgment Jurat Copy Oath SW	1 2 3 4
☐ POA	Acknowledgment Jurat Copy Oath SW	1 2 3 4
☐ Trust Certification	Acknowledgment Jurat Copy Oath SW	1 2 3 4

SIGNING ADDRESS	OTHERS IN ATTENDANCE	CLIENT / SIGNING SERVICE	FEE
		LENDER / LOAN NUMBER	

NOTES

_____
_____
_____
_____
_____
_____
_____
_____
_____
_____
_____

#	ADDRESS	PHONE	EMAIL	SIGNATURE	INITIAL IF OATH/AFF TAKEN	RIGHT THUMB PRINT
1						
2						
3						
4						

Notary Journal Entry

#	DATE / TIME	NAME	IDENTITY VERIFIED	WILLINGNESS & COMPETENCE	FORMAT
1	DATE _____ / TIME _____	□ Signer □ Witness	□ D.L. □ Passport □ Credible Witness □ Other	□ Expressed willingness □ Mentally alert □ Indicated understanding	□ Paper □ Electronic □ RON
2	DATE _____ / TIME _____	□ Signer □ Witness	□ D.L. □ Passport □ Credible Witness □ Other	□ Expressed willingness □ Mentally alert □ Indicated understanding	□ Paper □ Electronic □ RON
3	DATE _____ / TIME _____	□ Signer □ Witness	□ D.L. □ Passport □ Credible Witness □ Other	□ Expressed willingness □ Mentally alert □ Indicated understanding	□ Paper □ Electronic □ RON
4	DATE _____ / TIME _____	□ Signer □ Witness	□ D.L. □ Passport □ Credible Witness □ Other	□ Expressed willingness □ Mentally alert □ Indicated understanding	□ Paper □ Electronic □ RON

DOCUMENT(S) SIGNED

	Document	Notarial Act	SIGNER
□	Borrower's Aff	Acknowledgment Jurat	1 2 3 4
□	Compliance Agrmt	Acknowledgment Jurat	1 2 3 4
□	Correction Agrmt	Acknowledgment Jurat	1 2 3 4
□	Debts/Leins Aff	Acknowledgment Jurat	1 2 3 4
□	Deed of Trust	Acknowledgment Jurat	1 2 3 4
□	Distrib of Proceeds	Acknowledgment Jurat	1 2 3 4
□	E&O Agrmt	Acknowledgment Jurat	1 2 3 4
□	Grant Deed	Acknowledgment Jurat	1 2 3 4
□	Marital Stat Aff	Acknowledgment Jurat	1 2 3 4
□	Mortgage	Acknowledgment Jurat	1 2 3 4
□	Occupancy/Fin Aff	Acknowledgment Jurat	1 2 3 4
□	Owner's Aff	Acknowledgment Jurat	1 2 3 4
□	Payoff Aff	Acknowledgment Jurat	1 2 3 4
□	Quit-Claim Deed	Acknowledgment Jurat	1 2 3 4
□	Sig/Name Aff	Acknowledgment Jurat	1 2 3 4
□	Survey Aff	Acknowledgment Jurat	1 2 3 4
□	Warranty Deed	Acknowledgment Jurat	1 2 3 4

	Document	Notarial Act	SIGNER
□	Minor Medical Consent	Acknowledgment Jurat	1 2 3 4
□	Minor Passport Consent	Acknowledgment Jurat	1 2 3 4
□	Minor Travel Consent	Acknowledgment Jurat	1 2 3 4
□	Vehicle Duplicate Title	Acknowledgment Jurat	1 2 3 4
□	Vehicle Lein Release	Acknowledgment Jurat	1 2 3 4
□	Vehicle Odom/Vin Ver	Acknowledgment Jurat	1 2 3 4
□	Vehicle Title Transfer	Acknowledgment Jurat	1 2 3 4
□	Adv Health Care Dir	Acknowledgment Jurat	1 2 3 4
□	Assign of Digital Assets	Acknowledgment Jurat	1 2 3 4
□	Assign of Personal Prop	Acknowledgment Jurat	1 2 3 4
□	HIPAA Release	Acknowledgment Jurat	1 2 3 4
□	Living Trust _____	Acknowledgment Jurat	1 2 3 4
□	Last Will & Testament	Acknowledgment Jurat	1 2 3 4
□	POA _____	Acknowledgment Jurat	1 2 3 4
□	Trust Certification	Acknowledgment Jurat	1 2 3 4

	Acknowledgment	Jurat	Copy	Oath	SW	SIGNER
□	Acknowledgment	Jurat	Copy	Oath	SW	1 2 3 4
□	Acknowledgment	Jurat	Copy	Oath	SW	1 2 3 4
□	Acknowledgment	Jurat	Copy	Oath	SW	1 2 3 4
□	Acknowledgment	Jurat	Copy	Oath	SW	1 2 3 4
□	Acknowledgment	Jurat	Copy	Oath	SW	1 2 3 4
□	Acknowledgment	Jurat	Copy	Oath	SW	1 2 3 4

Signing Address	Others in Attendance	Client / Signing Service Lender / Loan Number	Fee

Notes

1	Address	Phone Email	Signature	Initial if oath/aff taken	Right Thumb Print
2	Address	Phone Email	Signature	Initial if oath/aff taken	Right Thumb Print
3	Address	Phone Email	Signature	Initial if oath/aff taken	Right Thumb Print
4	Address	Phone Email	Signature	Initial if oath/aff taken	Right Thumb Print

Notary Entries

Entry 1
- **DATE:** _____ **TIME:** _____
- **NAME:** ☐ Signer ☐ Witness
- **IDENTITY VERIFIED:** ☐ D.L. ☐ Passport ☐ Credible Witness ☐ Other
- **WILLINGNESS & COMPETENCE:** ☐ Expressed willingness ☐ Mentally alert ☐ Indicated understanding
- **FORMAT:** ☐ Paper ☐ Electronic ☐ RON

Entry 2
- **DATE:** _____ **TIME:** _____
- **NAME:** ☐ Signer ☐ Witness
- **IDENTITY VERIFIED:** ☐ D.L. ☐ Passport ☐ Credible Witness ☐ Other
- **WILLINGNESS & COMPETENCE:** ☐ Expressed willingness ☐ Mentally alert ☐ Indicated understanding
- **FORMAT:** ☐ Paper ☐ Electronic ☐ RON

Entry 3
- **DATE:** _____ **TIME:** _____
- **NAME:** ☐ Signer ☐ Witness
- **IDENTITY VERIFIED:** ☐ D.L. ☐ Passport ☐ Credible Witness ☐ Other
- **WILLINGNESS & COMPETENCE:** ☐ Expressed willingness ☐ Mentally alert ☐ Indicated understanding
- **FORMAT:** ☐ Paper ☐ Electronic ☐ RON

Entry 4
- **DATE:** _____ **TIME:** _____
- **NAME:** ☐ Signer ☐ Witness
- **IDENTITY VERIFIED:** ☐ D.L. ☐ Passport ☐ Credible Witness ☐ Other
- **WILLINGNESS & COMPETENCE:** ☐ Expressed willingness ☐ Mentally alert ☐ Indicated understanding
- **FORMAT:** ☐ Paper ☐ Electronic ☐ RON

DOCUMENT(S) SIGNED

Document	Notarial Act	Signer
☐ Borrower's Aff	Acknowledgment Jurat _____	1 2 3 4
☐ Compliance Agrmt	Acknowledgment Jurat _____	1 2 3 4
☐ Correction Agrmt	Acknowledgment Jurat _____	1 2 3 4
☐ Debs/Leins Aff	Acknowledgment Jurat _____	1 2 3 4
☐ Deed of Trust	Acknowledgment Jurat _____	1 2 3 4
☐ Distrib of Proceeds	Acknowledgment Jurat _____	1 2 3 4
☐ E&O Agrmt	Acknowledgment Jurat _____	1 2 3 4
☐ Grant Deed	Acknowledgment Jurat _____	1 2 3 4
☐ Marital Stat Aff	Acknowledgment Jurat _____	1 2 3 4
☐ Mortgage	Acknowledgment Jurat _____	1 2 3 4
☐ Occupancy/Fin Aff	Acknowledgment Jurat _____	1 2 3 4
☐ Owner's Aff	Acknowledgment Jurat _____	1 2 3 4
☐ Payoff Aff	Acknowledgment Jurat _____	1 2 3 4
☐ Qui-Claim Deed	Acknowledgment Jurat _____	1 2 3 4
☐ Sig/Name Aff	Acknowledgment Jurat _____	1 2 3 4
☐ Survey Aff	Acknowledgment Jurat _____	1 2 3 4
☐ Warranty Deed	Acknowledgment Jurat _____	1 2 3 4

Document	Notarial Act	Signer
☐ Minor Medical Consent	Acknowledgment Jurat _____	1 2 3 4
☐ Minor Passport Consent	Acknowledgment Jurat _____	1 2 3 4
☐ Minor Travel Consent	Acknowledgment Jurat _____	1 2 3 4
☐ Vehicle Duplicate Title	Acknowledgment Jurat _____	1 2 3 4
☐ Vehicle Lein Release	Acknowledgment Jurat _____	1 2 3 4
☐ Vehicle Odom/Vin Ver	Acknowledgment Jurat _____	1 2 3 4
☐ Vehicle Title Transfer	Acknowledgment Jurat _____	1 2 3 4
☐ Adv Health Care Dir	Acknowledgment Jurat _____	1 2 3 4
☐ Assign of Digital Assets	Acknowledgment Jurat _____	1 2 3 4
☐ Assign of Personal Prop	Acknowledgment Jurat _____	1 2 3 4
☐ HIPAA Release	Acknowledgment Jurat _____	1 2 3 4
☐ Living Trust	Acknowledgment Jurat _____	1 2 3 4
☐ Last Will & Testament	Acknowledgment Jurat _____	1 2 3 4
☐ POA	Acknowledgment Jurat _____	1 2 3 4
☐ Trust Certification	Acknowledgment Jurat _____	1 2 3 4

Additional act columns: Acknowledgment Jurat Copy Oath SW — 1 2 3 4

SIGNING ADDRESS	OTHERS IN ATTENDANCE	CLIENT / SIGNING SERVICE	FEE
		LENDER / LOAN NUMBER	

NOTES

	ADDRESS	SIGNATURE	PHONE	INITIAL IF OATH/AFF TAKEN	RIGHT THUMB PRINT
1			PHONE / EMAIL		
2			PHONE / EMAIL		
3			PHONE / EMAIL		
4			PHONE / EMAIL		

1

DATE	NAME ☐ Signer ☐ Witness	IDENTITY VERIFIED ☐ D.L. ☐ Passport ☐ Credible Witness ☐ Other	WILLINGNESS & COMPETENCE ☐ Expressed willingness ☐ Mentally alert ☐ Indicated understanding	FORMAT ☐ Paper ☐ Electronic ☐ RON
TIME				

2

DATE	NAME ☐ Signer ☐ Witness	IDENTITY VERIFIED ☐ D.L. ☐ Passport ☐ Credible Witness ☐ Other	WILLINGNESS & COMPETENCE ☐ Expressed willingness ☐ Mentally alert ☐ Indicated understanding	FORMAT ☐ Paper ☐ Electronic ☐ RON
TIME				

3

DATE	NAME ☐ Signer ☐ Witness	IDENTITY VERIFIED ☐ D.L. ☐ Passport ☐ Credible Witness ☐ Other	WILLINGNESS & COMPETENCE ☐ Expressed willingness ☐ Mentally alert ☐ Indicated understanding	FORMAT ☐ Paper ☐ Electronic ☐ RON
TIME				

4

DATE	NAME ☐ Signer ☐ Witness	IDENTITY VERIFIED ☐ D.L. ☐ Passport ☐ Credible Witness ☐ Other	WILLINGNESS & COMPETENCE ☐ Expressed willingness ☐ Mentally alert ☐ Indicated understanding	FORMAT ☐ Paper ☐ Electronic ☐ RON
TIME				

DOCUMENT(S) SIGNED

Document	Type	SIGNER 1	2	3	4
☐ Borrower's Aff	Acknowledgment Jurat	1	2	3	4
☐ Compliance Agrmt	Acknowledgment Jurat	1	2	3	4
☐ Correction Agrmt	Acknowledgment Jurat	1	2	3	4
☐ Debs/Leins Aff	Acknowledgment Jurat	1	2	3	4
☐ Deed of Trust	Acknowledgment Jurat	1	2	3	4
☐ Distrib of Proceeds	Acknowledgment Jurat	1	2	3	4
☐ E&O Agrmt	Acknowledgment Jurat	1	2	3	4
☐ Grant Deed	Acknowledgment Jurat	1	2	3	4
☐ Marital Stat Aff	Acknowledgment Jurat	1	2	3	4
☐ Mortgage	Acknowledgment Jurat	1	2	3	4
☐ Occupancy/Fin Aff	Acknowledgment Jurat	1	2	3	4
☐ Owner's Aff	Acknowledgment Jurat	1	2	3	4
☐ Payoff Aff	Acknowledgment Jurat	1	2	3	4
☐ Quit-Claim Deed	Acknowledgment Jurat	1	2	3	4
☐ Sig/Name Aff	Acknowledgment Jurat	1	2	3	4
☐ Survey Aff	Acknowledgment Jurat	1	2	3	4
☐ Warranty Deed	Acknowledgment Jurat	1	2	3	4

Document	Type	SIGNER 1	2	3	4
☐ Minor Medical Consent	Acknowledgment Jurat	1	2	3	4
☐ Minor Passport Consent	Acknowledgment Jurat	1	2	3	4
☐ Minor Travel Consent	Acknowledgment Jurat	1	2	3	4
☐ Vehicle Duplicate Title	Acknowledgment Jurat	1	2	3	4
☐ Vehicle Lein Release	Acknowledgment Jurat	1	2	3	4
☐ Vehicle Odom/Vin Ver	Acknowledgment Jurat	1	2	3	4
☐ Vehicle Title Transfer	Acknowledgment Jurat	1	2	3	4
☐ Adv Health Care Dir	Acknowledgment Jurat	1	2	3	4
☐ Assign of Digital Assets	Acknowledgment Jurat	1	2	3	4
☐ Assign of Personal Prop	Acknowledgment Jurat	1	2	3	4
☐ HIPAA Release	Acknowledgment Jurat	1	2	3	4
☐ Living Trust	Acknowledgment Jurat	1	2	3	4
☐ Last Will & Testament	Acknowledgment Jurat	1	2	3	4
☐ POA	Acknowledgment Jurat	1	2	3	4
☐ Trust Certification	Acknowledgment Jurat	1	2	3	4

The right portion additional columns per signer row: Acknowledgment Jurat Copy Oath SW — 1 2 3 4

Signing Address	Others in Attendance	Client / Signing Service Lender / Loan Number	Fee

Notes

1	Address	Phone Email	Signature	Initial if oath/aff taken	Right Thumb Print
2	Address	Phone Email	Signature	Initial if oath/aff taken	Right Thumb Print
3	Address	Phone Email	Signature	Initial if oath/aff taken	Right Thumb Print
4	Address	Phone Email	Signature	Initial if oath/aff taken	Right Thumb Print

Notary Journal Entries

#	DATE / TIME	NAME	IDENTITY VERIFIED	WILLINGNESS & COMPETENCE	FORMAT
1	DATE ___ TIME ___	☐ Signer ☐ Witness	☐ D.L. ☐ Passport ☐ Credible Witness ☐ Other	☐ Expressed willingness ☐ Mentally alert ☐ Indicated understanding	☐ Paper ☐ Electronic ☐ RON
2	DATE ___ TIME ___	☐ Signer ☐ Witness	☐ D.L. ☐ Passport ☐ Credible Witness ☐ Other	☐ Expressed willingness ☐ Mentally alert ☐ Indicated understanding	☐ Paper ☐ Electronic ☐ RON
3	DATE ___ TIME ___	☐ Signer ☐ Witness	☐ D.L. ☐ Passport ☐ Credible Witness ☐ Other	☐ Expressed willingness ☐ Mentally alert ☐ Indicated understanding	☐ Paper ☐ Electronic ☐ RON
4	DATE ___ TIME ___	☐ Signer ☐ Witness	☐ D.L. ☐ Passport ☐ Credible Witness ☐ Other	☐ Expressed willingness ☐ Mentally alert ☐ Indicated understanding	☐ Paper ☐ Electronic ☐ RON

DOCUMENT(S) SIGNED

Document	Type	SIGNER 1	2	3	4
☐ Borrower's Aff	Acknowledgment Jurat	1	2	3	4
☐ Compliance Agrmt	Acknowledgment Jurat	1	2	3	4
☐ Correction Agrmt	Acknowledgment Jurat	1	2	3	4
☐ Debts/Leins Aff	Acknowledgment Jurat	1	2	3	4
☐ Deed of Trust	Acknowledgment Jurat	1	2	3	4
☐ Distrib of Proceeds	Acknowledgment Jurat	1	2	3	4
☐ E&O Agrmt	Acknowledgment Jurat	1	2	3	4
☐ Grant Deed	Acknowledgment Jurat	1	2	3	4
☐ Marital Stat Aff	Acknowledgment Jurat	1	2	3	4
☐ Mortgage	Acknowledgment Jurat	1	2	3	4
☐ Occupancy/Fin Aff	Acknowledgment Jurat	1	2	3	4
☐ Owner's Aff	Acknowledgment Jurat	1	2	3	4
☐ Payoff Aff	Acknowledgment Jurat	1	2	3	4
☐ Quit-Claim Deed	Acknowledgment Jurat	1	2	3	4
☐ Sig/Name Aff	Acknowledgment Jurat	1	2	3	4
☐ Survey Aff	Acknowledgment Jurat	1	2	3	4
☐ Warranty Deed	Acknowledgment Jurat	1	2	3	4

Document	Type	SIGNER 1	2	3	4
☐ Minor Medical Consent	Acknowledgment Jurat	1	2	3	4
☐ Minor Passport Consent	Acknowledgment Jurat	1	2	3	4
☐ Minor Travel Consent	Acknowledgment Jurat	1	2	3	4
☐	Acknowledgment Jurat Copy Oath SW	1	2	3	4
☐ Vehicle Duplicate Title	Acknowledgment Jurat	1	2	3	4
☐ Vehicle Lein Release	Acknowledgment Jurat	1	2	3	4
☐ Vehicle Odom/Vin Ver	Acknowledgment Jurat	1	2	3	4
☐ Vehicle Title Transfer	Acknowledgment Jurat	1	2	3	4
☐	Acknowledgment Jurat Copy Oath SW	1	2	3	4
☐ Adv Health Care Dir	Acknowledgment Jurat	1	2	3	4
☐ Assign of Digital Assets	Acknowledgment Jurat	1	2	3	4
☐ Assign of Personal Prop	Acknowledgment Jurat	1	2	3	4
☐ HIPAA Release	Acknowledgment Jurat	1	2	3	4
☐ Living Trust _____	Acknowledgment Jurat	1	2	3	4
☐ Last Will & Testament	Acknowledgment Jurat	1	2	3	4
☐ POA _____	Acknowledgment Jurat	1	2	3	4
☐ Trust Certification	Acknowledgment Jurat Copy Oath SW	1	2	3	4

SIGNING ADDRESS	OTHERS IN ATTENDANCE	CLIENT / SIGNING SERVICE	FEE
		LENDER / LOAN NUMBER	

NOTES

_____
_____
_____
_____
_____
_____
_____
_____
_____
_____
_____
_____

		PHONE	SIGNATURE	INITIAL IF OATH/AFF TAKEN	RIGHT THUMB PRINT
1	ADDRESS	EMAIL			
2	ADDRESS	PHONE / EMAIL	SIGNATURE	INITIAL IF OATH/AFF TAKEN	RIGHT THUMB PRINT
3	ADDRESS	PHONE / EMAIL	SIGNATURE	INITIAL IF OATH/AFF TAKEN	RIGHT THUMB PRINT
4	ADDRESS	PHONE / EMAIL	SIGNATURE	INITIAL IF OATH/AFF TAKEN	RIGHT THUMB PRINT

Notary Journal Entries

Entries 1–4

#	DATE / TIME	NAME	IDENTITY VERIFIED	WILLINGNESS & COMPETENCE	FORMAT
1	DATE: ___ / TIME: ___	☐ Signer ☐ Witness	☐ D.L. ☐ Passport ☐ Credible Witness ☐ Other	☐ Expressed willingness ☐ Mentally alert ☐ Indicated understanding	☐ Paper ☐ Electronic ☐ RON
2	DATE: ___ / TIME: ___	☐ Signer ☐ Witness	☐ D.L. ☐ Passport ☐ Credible Witness ☐ Other	☐ Expressed willingness ☐ Mentally alert ☐ Indicated understanding	☐ Paper ☐ Electronic ☐ RON
3	DATE: ___ / TIME: ___	☐ Signer ☐ Witness	☐ D.L. ☐ Passport ☐ Credible Witness ☐ Other	☐ Expressed willingness ☐ Mentally alert ☐ Indicated understanding	☐ Paper ☐ Electronic ☐ RON
4	DATE: ___ / TIME: ___	☐ Signer ☐ Witness	☐ D.L. ☐ Passport ☐ Credible Witness ☐ Other	☐ Expressed willingness ☐ Mentally alert ☐ Indicated understanding	☐ Paper ☐ Electronic ☐ RON

DOCUMENT(S) SIGNED

Document	Type	SIGNER
☐ Borrower's Aff	Acknowledgment / Jurat	1 2 3 4
☐ Compliance Agrmt	Acknowledgment / Jurat	1 2 3 4
☐ Correction Agrmt	Acknowledgment / Jurat	1 2 3 4
☐ Debts/Leins Aff	Acknowledgment / Jurat	1 2 3 4
☐ Deed of Trust	Acknowledgment / Jurat	1 2 3 4
☐ Distrib of Proceeds	Acknowledgment / Jurat	1 2 3 4
☐ E&O Agrmt	Acknowledgment / Jurat	1 2 3 4
☐ Grant Deed	Acknowledgment / Jurat	1 2 3 4
☐ Marital Stat Aff	Acknowledgment / Jurat	1 2 3 4
☐ Mortgage	Acknowledgment / Jurat	1 2 3 4
☐ Occupancy/Fin Aff	Acknowledgment / Jurat	1 2 3 4
☐ Owner's Aff	Acknowledgment / Jurat	1 2 3 4
☐ Payoff Aff	Acknowledgment / Jurat	1 2 3 4
☐ Quit-Claim Deed	Acknowledgment / Jurat	1 2 3 4
☐ Sig/Name Aff	Acknowledgment / Jurat	1 2 3 4
☐ Survey Aff	Acknowledgment / Jurat	1 2 3 4
☐ Warranty Deed	Acknowledgment / Jurat	1 2 3 4
☐ Minor Medical Consent	Acknowledgment / Jurat	1 2 3 4
☐ Minor Passport Consent	Acknowledgment / Jurat	1 2 3 4
☐ Minor Travel Consent	Acknowledgment / Jurat	1 2 3 4
☐ Vehicle Duplicate Title	Acknowledgment / Jurat	1 2 3 4
☐ Vehicle Lein Release	Acknowledgment / Jurat	1 2 3 4
☐ Vehicle Odom/Vin Ver	Acknowledgment / Jurat	1 2 3 4
☐ Vehicle Title Transfer	Acknowledgment / Jurat	1 2 3 4
☐ Adv Health Care Dir	Acknowledgment / Jurat	1 2 3 4
☐ Assign of Digital Assets	Acknowledgment / Jurat	1 2 3 4
☐ Assign of Personal Prop	Acknowledgment / Jurat	1 2 3 4
☐ HIPAA Release	Acknowledgment / Jurat	1 2 3 4
☐ Living Trust ____	Acknowledgment / Jurat	1 2 3 4
☐ Last Will & Testament	Acknowledgment / Jurat	1 2 3 4
☐ POA ____	Acknowledgment / Jurat	1 2 3 4
☐ Trust Certification	Acknowledgment / Jurat	1 2 3 4

Additional notarial acts (right-side secondary columns): Jurat, Copy, Oath, SW — 1 2 3 4

SIGNING ADDRESS	OTHERS IN ATTENDANCE	CLIENT / SIGNING SERVICE	FEE
		LENDER / LOAN NUMBER	

NOTES

		PHONE	SIGNATURE	INITIAL IF OATH/AFF TAKEN	RIGHT THUMB PRINT
1	ADDRESS	EMAIL			
2	ADDRESS	PHONE	SIGNATURE	INITIAL IF OATH/AFF TAKEN	RIGHT THUMB PRINT
		EMAIL			
3	ADDRESS	PHONE	SIGNATURE	INITIAL IF OATH/AFF TAKEN	RIGHT THUMB PRINT
		EMAIL			
4	ADDRESS	PHONE	SIGNATURE	INITIAL IF OATH/AFF TAKEN	RIGHT THUMB PRINT
		EMAIL			

Notary Journal Entries

Entry 1
DATE		
TIME		

- NAME: ☐ Signer ☐ Witness
- IDENTITY VERIFIED: ☐ D.L. ☐ Passport ☐ Credible Witness ☐ Other
- WILLINGNESS & COMPETENCE: ☐ Expressed willingness ☐ Mentally alert ☐ Indicated understanding
- FORMAT: ☐ Paper ☐ Electronic ☐ RON

Entry 2
DATE		
TIME		

- NAME: ☐ Signer ☐ Witness
- IDENTITY VERIFIED: ☐ D.L. ☐ Passport ☐ Credible Witness ☐ Other
- WILLINGNESS & COMPETENCE: ☐ Expressed willingness ☐ Mentally alert ☐ Indicated understanding
- FORMAT: ☐ Paper ☐ Electronic ☐ RON

Entry 3
DATE		
TIME		

- NAME: ☐ Signer ☐ Witness
- IDENTITY VERIFIED: ☐ D.L. ☐ Passport ☐ Credible Witness ☐ Other
- WILLINGNESS & COMPETENCE: ☐ Expressed willingness ☐ Mentally alert ☐ Indicated understanding
- FORMAT: ☐ Paper ☐ Electronic ☐ RON

Entry 4
DATE		
TIME		

- NAME: ☐ Signer ☐ Witness
- IDENTITY VERIFIED: ☐ D.L. ☐ Passport ☐ Credible Witness ☐ Other
- WILLINGNESS & COMPETENCE: ☐ Expressed willingness ☐ Mentally alert ☐ Indicated understanding
- FORMAT: ☐ Paper ☐ Electronic ☐ RON

DOCUMENT(S) SIGNED

Document	Notarial Act	SIGNER
☐ Borrower's Aff	Acknowledgment Jurat	1 2 3 4
☐ Compliance Agrmt	Acknowledgment Jurat	1 2 3 4
☐ Correction Agrmt	Acknowledgment Jurat	1 2 3 4
☐ Debts/Leins Aff	Acknowledgment Jurat	1 2 3 4
☐ Deed of Trust	Acknowledgment Jurat	1 2 3 4
☐ Distrib of Proceeds	Acknowledgment Jurat	1 2 3 4
☐ E&O Agrmt	Acknowledgment Jurat	1 2 3 4
☐ Grant Deed	Acknowledgment Jurat	1 2 3 4
☐ Marital Stat Aff	Acknowledgment Jurat	1 2 3 4
☐ Mortgage	Acknowledgment Jurat	1 2 3 4
☐ Occupancy/Fin Aff	Acknowledgment Jurat	1 2 3 4
☐ Owner's Aff	Acknowledgment Jurat	1 2 3 4
☐ Payoff Aff	Acknowledgment Jurat	1 2 3 4
☐ Quit-Claim Deed	Acknowledgment Jurat	1 2 3 4
☐ Sig/Name Aff	Acknowledgment Jurat	1 2 3 4
☐ Survey Aff	Acknowledgment Jurat	1 2 3 4
☐ Warranty Deed	Acknowledgment Jurat	1 2 3 4

Document	Notarial Act	SIGNER
☐ Minor Medical Consent	Acknowledgment Jurat	1 2 3 4
☐ Minor Passport Consent	Acknowledgment Jurat	1 2 3 4
☐ Minor Travel Consent	Acknowledgment Jurat	1 2 3 4
☐ Vehicle Duplicate Title	Acknowledgment Jurat	1 2 3 4
☐ Vehicle Lein Release	Acknowledgment Jurat	1 2 3 4
☐ Vehicle Odom/Vin Ver	Acknowledgment Jurat	1 2 3 4
☐ Vehicle Title Transfer	Acknowledgment Jurat	1 2 3 4
☐ Adv Health Care Dir	Acknowledgment Jurat	1 2 3 4
☐ Assign of Digital Assets	Acknowledgment Jurat	1 2 3 4
☐ Assign of Personal Prop	Acknowledgment Jurat	1 2 3 4
☐ HIPAA Release	Acknowledgment Jurat	1 2 3 4
☐ Living Trust	Acknowledgment Jurat	1 2 3 4
☐ Last Will & Testament	Acknowledgment Jurat	1 2 3 4
☐ POA	Acknowledgment Jurat	1 2 3 4
☐ Trust Certification	Acknowledgment Jurat	1 2 3 4

☐ Acknowledgment Jurat Copy Oath SW   1 2 3 4

SIGNING ADDRESS	OTHERS IN ATTENDANCE	CLIENT / SIGNING SERVICE	FEE
		LENDER / LOAN NUMBER	

NOTES

	ADDRESS	PHONE	SIGNATURE	INITIAL IF OATH/AFF TAKEN	RIGHT THUMB PRINT
1		EMAIL			
2	ADDRESS	PHONE	SIGNATURE	INITIAL IF OATH/AFF TAKEN	RIGHT THUMB PRINT
		EMAIL			
3	ADDRESS	PHONE	SIGNATURE	INITIAL IF OATH/AFF TAKEN	RIGHT THUMB PRINT
		EMAIL			
4	ADDRESS	PHONE	SIGNATURE	INITIAL IF OATH/AFF TAKEN	RIGHT THUMB PRINT
		EMAIL			

1	DATE TIME	NAME ☐ Signer ☐ Witness	IDENTITY VERIFIED ☐ D.L. ☐ Passport ☐ Credible Witness ☐ Other	WILLINGNESS & COMPETENCE ☐ Expressed willingness ☐ Mentally alert ☐ Indicated understanding	FORMAT ☐ Paper ☐ Electronic ☐ RON
2	DATE TIME	NAME ☐ Signer ☐ Witness	IDENTITY VERIFIED ☐ D.L. ☐ Passport ☐ Credible Witness ☐ Other	WILLINGNESS & COMPETENCE ☐ Expressed willingness ☐ Mentally alert ☐ Indicated understanding	FORMAT ☐ Paper ☐ Electronic ☐ RON
3	DATE TIME	NAME ☐ Signer ☐ Witness	IDENTITY VERIFIED ☐ D.L. ☐ Passport ☐ Credible Witness ☐ Other	WILLINGNESS & COMPETENCE ☐ Expressed willingness ☐ Mentally alert ☐ Indicated understanding	FORMAT ☐ Paper ☐ Electronic ☐ RON
4	DATE TIME	NAME ☐ Signer ☐ Witness	IDENTITY VERIFIED ☐ D.L. ☐ Passport ☐ Credible Witness ☐ Other	WILLINGNESS & COMPETENCE ☐ Expressed willingness ☐ Mentally alert ☐ Indicated understanding	FORMAT ☐ Paper ☐ Electronic ☐ RON

DOCUMENT(S) SIGNED

Document				Signer			
☐ Borrower's Aff	Acknowledgment	Jurat	______	1	2	3	4
☐ Compliance Agrmt	Acknowledgment	Jurat	______	1	2	3	4
☐ Correction Agrmt	Acknowledgment	Jurat	______	1	2	3	4
☐ Debts/Leins Aff	Acknowledgment	Jurat	______	1	2	3	4
☐ Deed of Trust	Acknowledgment	Jurat	______	1	2	3	4
☐ Distrib of Proceeds	Acknowledgment	Jurat	______	1	2	3	4
☐ E&O Agrmt	Acknowledgment	Jurat	______	1	2	3	4
☐ Grant Deed	Acknowledgment	Jurat	______	1	2	3	4
☐ Marital Stat Aff	Acknowledgment	Jurat	______	1	2	3	4
☐ Mortgage	Acknowledgment	Jurat	______	1	2	3	4
☐ Occupancy/Fin Aff	Acknowledgment	Jurat	______	1	2	3	4
☐ Owner's Aff	Acknowledgment	Jurat	______	1	2	3	4
☐ Payoff Aff	Acknowledgment	Jurat	______	1	2	3	4
☐ Quit-Claim Deed	Acknowledgment	Jurat	______	1	2	3	4
☐ Sig/Name Aff	Acknowledgment	Jurat	______	1	2	3	4
☐ Survey Aff	Acknowledgment	Jurat	______	1	2	3	4
☐ Warranty Deed	Acknowledgment	Jurat	______	1	2	3	4

Document				Signer			
☐ Minor Medical Consent	Acknowledgment	Jurat	______	1	2	3	4
☐ Minor Passport Consent	Acknowledgment	Jurat	______	1	2	3	4
☐ Minor Travel Consent	Acknowledgment	Jurat	______	1	2	3	4
☐ Vehicle Duplicate Title	Acknowledgment	Jurat	______	1	2	3	4
☐ Vehicle Lein Release	Acknowledgment	Jurat	______	1	2	3	4
☐ Vehicle Odom/Vin Ver	Acknowledgment	Jurat	______	1	2	3	4
☐ Vehicle Title Transfer	Acknowledgment	Jurat	______	1	2	3	4
☐ Adv Health Care Dir	Acknowledgment	Jurat	______	1	2	3	4
☐ Assign of Digital Assets	Acknowledgment	Jurat	______	1	2	3	4
☐ Assign of Personal Prop	Acknowledgment	Jurat	______	1	2	3	4
☐ HIPAA Release	Acknowledgment	Jurat	______	1	2	3	4
☐ Living Trust ______	Acknowledgment	Jurat	______	1	2	3	4
☐ Last Will & Testament	Acknowledgment	Jurat	______	1	2	3	4
☐ POA ______	Acknowledgment	Jurat	______	1	2	3	4
☐ Trust Certification	Acknowledgment	Jurat	______	1	2	3	4

☐ ______									
	Acknowledgment	Jurat	Copy	Oath	SW	1	2	3	4
☐ ______									
	Acknowledgment	Jurat	Copy	Oath	SW	1	2	3	4
☐ ______									
	Acknowledgment	Jurat	Copy	Oath	SW	1	2	3	4
☐ ______									
	Acknowledgment	Jurat	Copy	Oath	SW	1	2	3	4
☐ ______									
	Acknowledgment	Jurat	Copy	Oath	SW	1	2	3	4
☐ ______									
	Acknowledgment	Jurat	Copy	Oath	SW	1	2	3	4

SIGNING ADDRESS	OTHERS IN ATTENDANCE	CLIENT / SIGNING SERVICE	FEE
		LENDER / LOAN NUMBER	

NOTES

#	ADDRESS	PHONE	EMAIL	SIGNATURE	INITIAL IF OATH/AFF TAKEN	RIGHT THUMB PRINT
1						
2						
3						
4						

Notary Journal Entries

#	DATE / TIME	NAME	IDENTITY VERIFIED	WILLINGNESS & COMPETENCE	FORMAT
1	DATE ____ TIME ____	☐ Signer ☐ Witness	☐ D.L. ☐ Passport ☐ Credible Witness ☐ Other	☐ Expressed willingness ☐ Mentally alert ☐ Indicated understanding	☐ Paper ☐ Electronic ☐ RON
2	DATE ____ TIME ____	☐ Signer ☐ Witness	☐ D.L. ☐ Passport ☐ Credible Witness ☐ Other	☐ Expressed willingness ☐ Mentally alert ☐ Indicated understanding	☐ Paper ☐ Electronic ☐ RON
3	DATE ____ TIME ____	☐ Signer ☐ Witness	☐ D.L. ☐ Passport ☐ Credible Witness ☐ Other	☐ Expressed willingness ☐ Mentally alert ☐ Indicated understanding	☐ Paper ☐ Electronic ☐ RON
4	DATE ____ TIME ____	☐ Signer ☐ Witness	☐ D.L. ☐ Passport ☐ Credible Witness ☐ Other	☐ Expressed willingness ☐ Mentally alert ☐ Indicated understanding	☐ Paper ☐ Electronic ☐ RON

DOCUMENT(S) SIGNED

Document	Type	SIGNER 1	2	3	4
☐ Borrower's Aff	Acknowledgment Jurat	1	2	3	4
☐ Compliance Agrmt	Acknowledgment Jurat	1	2	3	4
☐ Correction Agrmt	Acknowledgment Jurat	1	2	3	4
☐ Debts/Leins Aff	Acknowledgment Jurat	1	2	3	4
☐ Deed of Trust	Acknowledgment Jurat	1	2	3	4
☐ Distrib of Proceeds	Acknowledgment Jurat	1	2	3	4
☐ E&O Agrmt	Acknowledgment Jurat	1	2	3	4
☐ Grant Deed	Acknowledgment Jurat	1	2	3	4
☐ Marital Stat Aff	Acknowledgment Jurat	1	2	3	4
☐ Mortgage	Acknowledgment Jurat	1	2	3	4
☐ Occupancy/Fin Aff	Acknowledgment Jurat	1	2	3	4
☐ Owner's Aff	Acknowledgment Jurat	1	2	3	4
☐ Payoff Aff	Acknowledgment Jurat	1	2	3	4
☐ Quit-Claim Deed	Acknowledgment Jurat	1	2	3	4
☐ Sig/Name Aff	Acknowledgment Jurat	1	2	3	4
☐ Survey Aff	Acknowledgment Jurat	1	2	3	4
☐ Warranty Deed	Acknowledgment Jurat	1	2	3	4

Document	Type	SIGNER 1	2	3	4
☐ Minor Medical Consent	Acknowledgment Jurat	1	2	3	4
☐ Minor Passport Consent	Acknowledgment Jurat	1	2	3	4
☐ Minor Travel Consent	Acknowledgment Jurat	1	2	3	4
☐ Vehicle Duplicate Title	Acknowledgment Jurat Copy Oath SW	1	2	3	4
☐ Vehicle Lein Release	Acknowledgment Jurat	1	2	3	4
☐ Vehicle Odom/Vin Ver	Acknowledgment Jurat Copy Oath SW	1	2	3	4
☐ Vehicle Title Transfer	Acknowledgment Jurat	1	2	3	4
☐ Adv Health Care Dir	Acknowledgment Jurat Copy Oath SW	1	2	3	4
☐ Assign of Digital Assets	Acknowledgment Jurat Copy Oath SW	1	2	3	4
☐ Assign of Personal Prop	Acknowledgment Jurat	1	2	3	4
☐ HIPAA Release	Acknowledgment Jurat	1	2	3	4
☐ Living Trust ____	Acknowledgment Jurat Copy Oath SW	1	2	3	4
☐ Last Will & Testament	Acknowledgment Jurat	1	2	3	4
☐ POA ____	Acknowledgment Jurat Copy Oath SW	1	2	3	4
☐ Trust Certification	Acknowledgment Jurat Copy Oath SW	1	2	3	4

SIGNING ADDRESS	OTHERS IN ATTENDANCE	CLIENT / SIGNING SERVICE	FEE
		LENDER / LOAN NUMBER	

NOTES

	ADDRESS	SIGNATURE	PHONE	EMAIL	INITIAL IF OATH/AFF TAKEN	RIGHT THUMB PRINT
1						
2						
3						
4						

		NAME	IDENTITY VERIFIED	WILLINGNESS & COMPETENCE	FORMAT
1	DATE / TIME	☐ Signer ☐ Witness	☐ D.L. ☐ Passport ☐ Credible Witness ☐ Other	☐ Expressed willingness ☐ Mentally alert ☐ Indicated understanding	☐ Paper ☐ Electronic ☐ RON
2	DATE / TIME	☐ Signer ☐ Witness	☐ D.L. ☐ Passport ☐ Credible Witness ☐ Other	☐ Expressed willingness ☐ Mentally alert ☐ Indicated understanding	☐ Paper ☐ Electronic ☐ RON
3	DATE / TIME	☐ Signer ☐ Witness	☐ D.L. ☐ Passport ☐ Credible Witness ☐ Other	☐ Expressed willingness ☐ Mentally alert ☐ Indicated understanding	☐ Paper ☐ Electronic ☐ RON
4	DATE / TIME	☐ Signer ☐ Witness	☐ D.L. ☐ Passport ☐ Credible Witness ☐ Other	☐ Expressed willingness ☐ Mentally alert ☐ Indicated understanding	☐ Paper ☐ Electronic ☐ RON

DOCUMENT(S) SIGNED

Document			SIGNER
			1 2 3 4
☐ Borrower's Aff	Acknowledgment	Jurat	1 2 3 4
☐ Compliance Agrmt	Acknowledgment	Jurat	1 2 3 4
☐ Correction Agrmt	Acknowledgment	Jurat	1 2 3 4
☐ Debts/Leins Aff	Acknowledgment	Jurat	1 2 3 4
☐ Deed of Trust	Acknowledgment	Jurat	1 2 3 4
☐ Distrib of Proceeds	Acknowledgment	Jurat	1 2 3 4
☐ E&O Agrmt	Acknowledgment	Jurat	1 2 3 4
☐ Grant Deed	Acknowledgment	Jurat	1 2 3 4
☐ Marital Stat Aff	Acknowledgment	Jurat	1 2 3 4
☐ Mortgage	Acknowledgment	Jurat	1 2 3 4
☐ Occupancy/Fin Aff	Acknowledgment	Jurat	1 2 3 4
☐ Owner's Aff	Acknowledgment	Jurat	1 2 3 4
☐ Payoff Aff	Acknowledgment	Jurat	1 2 3 4
☐ Quit-Claim Deed	Acknowledgment	Jurat	1 2 3 4
☐ Sig/Name Aff	Acknowledgment	Jurat	1 2 3 4
☐ Survey Aff	Acknowledgment	Jurat	1 2 3 4
☐ Warranty Deed	Acknowledgment	Jurat	1 2 3 4

Document			SIGNER
			1 2 3 4
☐ Minor Medical Consent	Acknowledgment	Jurat	1 2 3 4
☐ Minor Passport Consent	Acknowledgment	Jurat	1 2 3 4
☐ Minor Travel Consent	Acknowledgment	Jurat	1 2 3 4
☐ Vehicle Duplicate Title	Acknowledgment	Jurat	1 2 3 4
☐ Vehicle Lein Release	Acknowledgment	Jurat	1 2 3 4
☐ Vehicle Odom/Vin Ver	Acknowledgment	Jurat	1 2 3 4
☐ Vehicle Title Transfer	Acknowledgment	Jurat	1 2 3 4
☐ Adv Health Care Dir	Acknowledgment	Jurat	1 2 3 4
☐ Assign of Digital Assets	Acknowledgment	Jurat	1 2 3 4
☐ Assign of Personal Prop	Acknowledgment	Jurat	1 2 3 4
☐ HIPAA Release	Acknowledgment	Jurat	1 2 3 4
☐ Living Trust	Acknowledgment	Jurat	1 2 3 4
☐ Last Will & Testament	Acknowledgment	Jurat	1 2 3 4
☐ POA	Acknowledgment	Jurat	1 2 3 4
☐ Trust Certification	Acknowledgment	Jurat	1 2 3 4

The document(s) signed section also includes notarial act checkboxes: Acknowledgment, Jurat, Copy, Oath, SW with SIGNER columns 1 2 3 4.

SIGNING ADDRESS	OTHERS IN ATTENDANCE	CLIENT / SIGNING SERVICE	FEE
		LENDER / LOAN NUMBER	

NOTES

_____
_____
_____
_____
_____
_____
_____
_____
_____
_____
_____

	ADDRESS	PHONE	SIGNATURE	INITIAL IF OATH/AFF TAKEN	RIGHT THUMB PRINT
1		EMAIL			
2	ADDRESS	PHONE	SIGNATURE	INITIAL IF OATH/AFF TAKEN	RIGHT THUMB PRINT
		EMAIL			
3	ADDRESS	PHONE	SIGNATURE	INITIAL IF OATH/AFF TAKEN	RIGHT THUMB PRINT
		EMAIL			
4	ADDRESS	PHONE	SIGNATURE	INITIAL IF OATH/AFF TAKEN	RIGHT THUMB PRINT
		EMAIL			

Notary Journal Entries

Entry 1
- **DATE:**
- **TIME:**
- **NAME:** ☐ Signer ☐ Witness
- **IDENTITY VERIFIED:** ☐ D.L. ☐ Passport ☐ Credible Witness ☐ Other
- **WILLINGNESS & COMPETENCE:** ☐ Expressed willingness ☐ Mentally alert ☐ Indicated understanding
- **FORMAT:** ☐ Paper ☐ Electronic ☐ RON

Entry 2
- **DATE:**
- **TIME:**
- **NAME:** ☐ Signer ☐ Witness
- **IDENTITY VERIFIED:** ☐ D.L. ☐ Passport ☐ Credible Witness ☐ Other
- **WILLINGNESS & COMPETENCE:** ☐ Expressed willingness ☐ Mentally alert ☐ Indicated understanding
- **FORMAT:** ☐ Paper ☐ Electronic ☐ RON

Entry 3
- **DATE:**
- **TIME:**
- **NAME:** ☐ Signer ☐ Witness
- **IDENTITY VERIFIED:** ☐ D.L. ☐ Passport ☐ Credible Witness ☐ Other
- **WILLINGNESS & COMPETENCE:** ☐ Expressed willingness ☐ Mentally alert ☐ Indicated understanding
- **FORMAT:** ☐ Paper ☐ Electronic ☐ RON

Entry 4
- **DATE:**
- **TIME:**
- **NAME:** ☐ Signer ☐ Witness
- **IDENTITY VERIFIED:** ☐ D.L. ☐ Passport ☐ Credible Witness ☐ Other
- **WILLINGNESS & COMPETENCE:** ☐ Expressed willingness ☐ Mentally alert ☐ Indicated understanding
- **FORMAT:** ☐ Paper ☐ Electronic ☐ RON

DOCUMENT(S) SIGNED

Document	Notarial Act	Signer
☐ Borrower's Aff	Acknowledgment / Jurat	1 2 3 4
☐ Compliance Agrmt	Acknowledgment / Jurat	1 2 3 4
☐ Correction Agrmt	Acknowledgment / Jurat	1 2 3 4
☐ Debts/Leins Aff	Acknowledgment / Jurat	1 2 3 4
☐ Deed of Trust	Acknowledgment / Jurat	1 2 3 4
☐ Distrib of Proceeds	Acknowledgment / Jurat	1 2 3 4
☐ E&O Agrmt	Acknowledgment / Jurat	1 2 3 4
☐ Grant Deed	Acknowledgment / Jurat	1 2 3 4
☐ Marital Stat Aff	Acknowledgment / Jurat	1 2 3 4
☐ Mortgage	Acknowledgment / Jurat	1 2 3 4
☐ Occupancy/Fin Aff	Acknowledgment / Jurat	1 2 3 4
☐ Owner's Aff	Acknowledgment / Jurat	1 2 3 4
☐ Payoff Aff	Acknowledgment / Jurat	1 2 3 4
☐ Quit-Claim Deed	Acknowledgment / Jurat	1 2 3 4
☐ Sig/Name Aff	Acknowledgment / Jurat	1 2 3 4
☐ Survey Aff	Acknowledgment / Jurat	1 2 3 4
☐ Warranty Deed	Acknowledgment / Jurat	1 2 3 4

Document	Notarial Act	Signer
☐ Minor Medical Consent	Acknowledgment / Jurat	1 2 3 4
☐ Minor Passport Consent	Acknowledgment / Jurat	1 2 3 4
☐ Minor Travel Consent	Acknowledgment / Jurat	1 2 3 4
☐ Vehicle Duplicate Title	Acknowledgment / Jurat	1 2 3 4
☐ Vehicle Lein Release	Acknowledgment / Jurat	1 2 3 4
☐ Vehicle Odom/Vin Ver	Acknowledgment / Jurat	1 2 3 4
☐ Vehicle Title Transfer	Acknowledgment / Jurat	1 2 3 4
☐ Adv. Health Care Dir	Acknowledgment / Jurat	1 2 3 4
☐ Assign of Digital Assets	Acknowledgment / Jurat	1 2 3 4
☐ Assign of Personal Prop	Acknowledgment / Jurat	1 2 3 4
☐ HIPAA Release	Acknowledgment / Jurat	1 2 3 4
☐ Living Trust	Acknowledgment / Jurat	1 2 3 4
☐ Last Will & Testament	Acknowledgment / Jurat	1 2 3 4
☐ POA	Acknowledgment / Jurat	1 2 3 4
☐ Trust Certification	Acknowledgment / Jurat	1 2 3 4

(Additional notarial act options: Acknowledgment, Jurat, Copy, Oath, SW — 1 2 3 4)

SIGNING ADDRESS	OTHERS IN ATTENDANCE	CLIENT / SIGNING SERVICE	FEE
		LENDER / LOAN NUMBER	

NOTES

	ADDRESS	SIGNATURE	PHONE	INITIAL IF OATH/AFF TAKEN	RIGHT THUMB PRINT
1			EMAIL		
2	ADDRESS	SIGNATURE	PHONE / EMAIL	INITIAL IF OATH/AFF TAKEN	RIGHT THUMB PRINT
3	ADDRESS	SIGNATURE	PHONE / EMAIL	INITIAL IF OATH/AFF TAKEN	RIGHT THUMB PRINT
4	ADDRESS	SIGNATURE	PHONE / EMAIL	INITIAL IF OATH/AFF TAKEN	RIGHT THUMB PRINT

Entry 1

DATE: _____   **TIME:** _____

NAME: ☐ Signer ☐ Witness

IDENTITY VERIFIED: ☐ D.L. ☐ Passport ☐ Credible Witness ☐ Other

WILLINGNESS & COMPETENCE: ☐ Expressed willingness ☐ Mentally alert ☐ Indicated understanding

FORMAT: ☐ Paper ☐ Electronic ☐ RON

Entry 2

DATE: _____   **TIME:** _____

NAME: ☐ Signer ☐ Witness

IDENTITY VERIFIED: ☐ D.L. ☐ Passport ☐ Credible Witness ☐ Other

WILLINGNESS & COMPETENCE: ☐ Expressed willingness ☐ Mentally alert ☐ Indicated understanding

FORMAT: ☐ Paper ☐ Electronic ☐ RON

Entry 3

DATE: _____   **TIME:** _____

NAME: ☐ Signer ☐ Witness

IDENTITY VERIFIED: ☐ D.L. ☐ Passport ☐ Credible Witness ☐ Other

WILLINGNESS & COMPETENCE: ☐ Expressed willingness ☐ Mentally alert ☐ Indicated understanding

FORMAT: ☐ Paper ☐ Electronic ☐ RON

Entry 4

DATE: _____   **TIME:** _____

NAME: ☐ Signer ☐ Witness

IDENTITY VERIFIED: ☐ D.L. ☐ Passport ☐ Credible Witness ☐ Other

WILLINGNESS & COMPETENCE: ☐ Expressed willingness ☐ Mentally alert ☐ Indicated understanding

FORMAT: ☐ Paper ☐ Electronic ☐ RON

DOCUMENT(S) SIGNED

Document	Type	SIGNER 1	2	3	4
☐ Borrower's Aff	Acknowledgment Jurat	1	2	3	4
☐ Compliance Agrmt	Acknowledgment Jurat	1	2	3	4
☐ Correction Agrmt	Acknowledgment Jurat	1	2	3	4
☐ Debs/Leins Aff	Acknowledgment Jurat	1	2	3	4
☐ Deed of Trust	Acknowledgment Jurat	1	2	3	4
☐ Distrib of Proceeds	Acknowledgment Jurat	1	2	3	4
☐ E&O Agrmt	Acknowledgment Jurat	1	2	3	4
☐ Grant Deed	Acknowledgment Jurat	1	2	3	4
☐ Marital Stat Aff	Acknowledgment Jurat	1	2	3	4
☐ Mortgage	Acknowledgment Jurat	1	2	3	4
☐ Occupancy/Fin Aff	Acknowledgment Jurat	1	2	3	4
☐ Owner's Aff	Acknowledgment Jurat	1	2	3	4
☐ Payoff Aff	Acknowledgment Jurat	1	2	3	4
☐ Quit-Claim Deed	Acknowledgment Jurat	1	2	3	4
☐ Sig/Name Aff	Acknowledgment Jurat	1	2	3	4
☐ Survey Aff	Acknowledgment Jurat	1	2	3	4
☐ Warranty Deed	Acknowledgment Jurat	1	2	3	4

Document	Type	SIGNER 1	2	3	4
☐ Minor Medical Consent	Acknowledgment Jurat	1	2	3	4
☐ Minor Passport Consent	Acknowledgment Jurat	1	2	3	4
☐ Minor Travel Consent	Acknowledgment Jurat	1	2	3	4
☐ Vehicle Duplicate Title	Acknowledgment Jurat	1	2	3	4
☐ Vehicle Lein Release	Acknowledgment Jurat	1	2	3	4
☐ Vehicle Odom/Vin Ver	Acknowledgment Jurat	1	2	3	4
☐ Vehicle Title Transfer	Acknowledgment Jurat	1	2	3	4
☐ Adv Health Care Dir	Acknowledgment Jurat	1	2	3	4
☐ Assign of Digital Assets	Acknowledgment Jurat	1	2	3	4
☐ Assign of Personal Prop	Acknowledgment Jurat	1	2	3	4
☐ HIPAA Release	Acknowledgment Jurat	1	2	3	4
☐ Living Trust	Acknowledgment Jurat	1	2	3	4
☐ Last Will & Testament	Acknowledgment Jurat	1	2	3	4
☐ POA	Acknowledgment Jurat	1	2	3	4
☐ Trust Certification	Acknowledgment Jurat	1	2	3	4

For the second column, additional codes appear: ☐ ____ Acknowledgment Jurat Copy Oath SW 1 2 3 4

SIGNING ADDRESS	OTHERS IN ATTENDANCE	CLIENT / SIGNING SERVICE	FEE
		LENDER / LOAN NUMBER	

NOTES

_____

1	ADDRESS	PHONE	SIGNATURE	INITIAL IF OATH/AFF TAKEN	RIGHT THUMB PRINT
		EMAIL		
2	ADDRESS	PHONE	SIGNATURE	INITIAL IF OATH/AFF TAKEN	RIGHT THUMB PRINT
		EMAIL		
3	ADDRESS	PHONE	SIGNATURE	INITIAL IF OATH/AFF TAKEN	RIGHT THUMB PRINT
		EMAIL		
4	ADDRESS	PHONE	SIGNATURE	INITIAL IF OATH/AFF TAKEN	RIGHT THUMB PRINT
		EMAIL		

Journal Entries

#	FORMAT	WILLINGNESS & COMPETENCE	IDENTITY VERIFIED	NAME	DATE / TIME
1	☐ Paper ☐ Electronic ☐ RON	☐ Expressed willingness ☐ Mentally alert ☐ Indicated understanding	☐ D.L. ☐ Passport ☐ Credible Witness ☐ Other	☐ Signer ☐ Witness	DATE ___ TIME ___
2	☐ Paper ☐ Electronic ☐ RON	☐ Expressed willingness ☐ Mentally alert ☐ Indicated understanding	☐ D.L. ☐ Passport ☐ Credible Witness ☐ Other	☐ Signer ☐ Witness	DATE ___ TIME ___
3	☐ Paper ☐ Electronic ☐ RON	☐ Expressed willingness ☐ Mentally alert ☐ Indicated understanding	☐ D.L. ☐ Passport ☐ Credible Witness ☐ Other	☐ Signer ☐ Witness	DATE ___ TIME ___
4	☐ Paper ☐ Electronic ☐ RON	☐ Expressed willingness ☐ Mentally alert ☐ Indicated understanding	☐ D.L. ☐ Passport ☐ Credible Witness ☐ Other	☐ Signer ☐ Witness	DATE ___ TIME ___

DOCUMENT(S) SIGNED

Document	Type	SIGNER
☐ Borrower's Aff	Acknowledgment Jurat	1 2 3 4
☐ Compliance Agrmt	Acknowledgment Jurat	1 2 3 4
☐ Correction Agrmt	Acknowledgment Jurat	1 2 3 4
☐ Debts/Leins Aff	Acknowledgment Jurat	1 2 3 4
☐ Deed of Trust	Acknowledgment Jurat	1 2 3 4
☐ Distrib of Proceeds	Acknowledgment Jurat	1 2 3 4
☐ E&O Agrmt	Acknowledgment Jurat	1 2 3 4
☐ Grant Deed	Acknowledgment Jurat	1 2 3 4
☐ Marital Stat Aff	Acknowledgment Jurat	1 2 3 4
☐ Mortgage	Acknowledgment Jurat	1 2 3 4
☐ Occupancy/Fin Aff	Acknowledgment Jurat	1 2 3 4
☐ Owner's Aff	Acknowledgment Jurat	1 2 3 4
☐ Payoff Aff	Acknowledgment Jurat	1 2 3 4
☐ Quit-Claim Deed	Acknowledgment Jurat	1 2 3 4
☐ Sig/Name Aff	Acknowledgment Jurat	1 2 3 4
☐ Survey Aff	Acknowledgment Jurat	1 2 3 4
☐ Warranty Deed	Acknowledgment Jurat	1 2 3 4

Document	Type	SIGNER
☐ Minor Medical Consent	Acknowledgment Jurat	1 2 3 4
☐ Minor Passport Consent	Acknowledgment Jurat	1 2 3 4
☐ Minor Travel Consent	Acknowledgment Jurat	1 2 3 4
☐	Acknowledgment Jurat Copy Oath SW	1 2 3 4
☐ Vehicle Duplicate Title	Acknowledgment Jurat	1 2 3 4
☐ Vehicle Lein Release	Acknowledgment Jurat	1 2 3 4
☐ Vehicle Odom/Vin Ver	Acknowledgment Jurat	1 2 3 4
☐ Vehicle Title Transfer	Acknowledgment Jurat	1 2 3 4
☐	Acknowledgment Jurat Copy Oath SW	1 2 3 4
☐ Adv Health Care Dir	Acknowledgment Jurat	1 2 3 4
☐ Assign of Digital Assets	Acknowledgment Jurat	1 2 3 4
☐ Assign of Personal Prop	Acknowledgment Jurat	1 2 3 4
☐ HIPAA Release	Acknowledgment Jurat	1 2 3 4
☐	Acknowledgment Jurat Copy Oath SW	1 2 3 4
☐ Living Trust	Acknowledgment Jurat	1 2 3 4
☐ Last Will & Testament	Acknowledgment Jurat	1 2 3 4
☐ POA	Acknowledgment Jurat	1 2 3 4
☐	Acknowledgment Jurat Copy Oath SW	1 2 3 4
☐ Trust Certification	Acknowledgment Jurat	1 2 3 4

SIGNING ADDRESS	OTHERS IN ATTENDANCE	CLIENT / SIGNING SERVICE	FEE
		LENDER / LOAN NUMBER	

NOTES

	ADDRESS	PHONE	SIGNATURE	INITIAL IF OATH/AFF TAKEN	RIGHT THUMB PRINT
1		EMAIL			
2	ADDRESS	PHONE	SIGNATURE	INITIAL IF OATH/AFF TAKEN	RIGHT THUMB PRINT
		EMAIL			
3	ADDRESS	PHONE	SIGNATURE	INITIAL IF OATH/AFF TAKEN	RIGHT THUMB PRINT
		EMAIL			
4	ADDRESS	PHONE	SIGNATURE	INITIAL IF OATH/AFF TAKEN	RIGHT THUMB PRINT
		EMAIL			

Notary Journal Entries

Entry 1
- **DATE:**
- **TIME:**
- **NAME:** ☐ Signer ☐ Witness
- **IDENTITY VERIFIED:** ☐ D.L. ☐ Passport ☐ Credible Witness ☐ Other
- **WILLINGNESS & COMPETENCE:** ☐ Expressed willingness ☐ Mentally alert ☐ Indicated understanding
- **FORMAT:** ☐ Paper ☐ Electronic ☐ RON

Entry 2
- **DATE:**
- **TIME:**
- **NAME:** ☐ Signer ☐ Witness
- **IDENTITY VERIFIED:** ☐ D.L. ☐ Passport ☐ Credible Witness ☐ Other
- **WILLINGNESS & COMPETENCE:** ☐ Expressed willingness ☐ Mentally alert ☐ Indicated understanding
- **FORMAT:** ☐ Paper ☐ Electronic ☐ RON

Entry 3
- **DATE:**
- **TIME:**
- **NAME:** ☐ Signer ☐ Witness
- **IDENTITY VERIFIED:** ☐ D.L. ☐ Passport ☐ Credible Witness ☐ Other
- **WILLINGNESS & COMPETENCE:** ☐ Expressed willingness ☐ Mentally alert ☐ Indicated understanding
- **FORMAT:** ☐ Paper ☐ Electronic ☐ RON

Entry 4
- **DATE:**
- **TIME:**
- **NAME:** ☐ Signer ☐ Witness
- **IDENTITY VERIFIED:** ☐ D.L. ☐ Passport ☐ Credible Witness ☐ Other
- **WILLINGNESS & COMPETENCE:** ☐ Expressed willingness ☐ Mentally alert ☐ Indicated understanding
- **FORMAT:** ☐ Paper ☐ Electronic ☐ RON

DOCUMENT(S) SIGNED

Document	Type	SIGNER
☐ Borrower's Aff	Acknowledgment Jurat	1 2 3 4
☐ Compliance Agrmt	Acknowledgment Jurat	1 2 3 4
☐ Correction Agrmt	Acknowledgment Jurat	1 2 3 4
☐ Debts/Leins Aff	Acknowledgment Jurat	1 2 3 4
☐ Deed of Trust	Acknowledgment Jurat	1 2 3 4
☐ Distrib of Proceeds	Acknowledgment Jurat	1 2 3 4
☐ E&O Agrmt	Acknowledgment Jurat	1 2 3 4
☐ Grant Deed	Acknowledgment Jurat	1 2 3 4
☐ Marital Stat Aff	Acknowledgment Jurat	1 2 3 4
☐ Mortgage	Acknowledgment Jurat	1 2 3 4
☐ Occupancy/Fin Aff	Acknowledgment Jurat	1 2 3 4
☐ Owner's Aff	Acknowledgment Jurat	1 2 3 4
☐ Payoff Aff	Acknowledgment Jurat	1 2 3 4
☐ Quit-Claim Deed	Acknowledgment Jurat	1 2 3 4
☐ Sig/Name Aff	Acknowledgment Jurat	1 2 3 4
☐ Survey Aff	Acknowledgment Jurat	1 2 3 4
☐ Warranty Deed	Acknowledgment Jurat	1 2 3 4
☐ Minor Medical Consent	Acknowledgment Jurat	1 2 3 4
☐ Minor Passport Consent	Acknowledgment Jurat	1 2 3 4
☐ Minor Travel Consent	Acknowledgment Jurat	1 2 3 4
☐ Vehicle Duplicate Title	Acknowledgment Jurat	1 2 3 4
☐ Vehicle Lein Release	Acknowledgment Jurat	1 2 3 4
☐ Vehicle Odom/Vin Ver	Acknowledgment Jurat	1 2 3 4
☐ Vehicle Title Transfer	Acknowledgment Jurat	1 2 3 4
☐ Adv Health Care Dir	Acknowledgment Jurat	1 2 3 4
☐ Assign of Digital Assets	Acknowledgment Jurat	1 2 3 4
☐ Assign of Personal Prop	Acknowledgment Jurat	1 2 3 4
☐ HIPAA Release	Acknowledgment Jurat	1 2 3 4
☐ Living Trust	Acknowledgment Jurat	1 2 3 4
☐ Last Will & Testament	Acknowledgment Jurat	1 2 3 4
☐ POA	Acknowledgment Jurat	1 2 3 4
☐ Trust Certification	Acknowledgment Jurat	1 2 3 4

Additional certification options (right column): Acknowledgment Jurat Copy Oath SW 1 2 3 4

SIGNING ADDRESS	OTHERS IN ATTENDANCE	CLIENT / SIGNING SERVICE	FEE
		LENDER / LOAN NUMBER	

NOTES

	ADDRESS	PHONE	EMAIL	SIGNATURE	INITIAL IF OATH/AFF TAKEN	RIGHT THUMB PRINT
1						
2						
3						
4						

Notary Journal Entries

Entry 1
Field	Details
DATE	
TIME	
NAME	☐ Signer ☐ Witness
IDENTITY VERIFIED	☐ D.L. ☐ Passport ☐ Credible Witness ☐ Other
WILLINGNESS & COMPETENCE	☐ Expressed willingness ☐ Mentally alert ☐ Indicated understanding
FORMAT	☐ Paper ☐ Electronic ☐ RON

Entry 2
Field	Details
DATE	
TIME	
NAME	☐ Signer ☐ Witness
IDENTITY VERIFIED	☐ D.L. ☐ Passport ☐ Credible Witness ☐ Other
WILLINGNESS & COMPETENCE	☐ Expressed willingness ☐ Mentally alert ☐ Indicated understanding
FORMAT	☐ Paper ☐ Electronic ☐ RON

Entry 3
Field	Details
DATE	
TIME	
NAME	☐ Signer ☐ Witness
IDENTITY VERIFIED	☐ D.L. ☐ Passport ☐ Credible Witness ☐ Other
WILLINGNESS & COMPETENCE	☐ Expressed willingness ☐ Mentally alert ☐ Indicated understanding
FORMAT	☐ Paper ☐ Electronic ☐ RON

Entry 4
Field	Details
DATE	
TIME	
NAME	☐ Signer ☐ Witness
IDENTITY VERIFIED	☐ D.L. ☐ Passport ☐ Credible Witness ☐ Other
WILLINGNESS & COMPETENCE	☐ Expressed willingness ☐ Mentally alert ☐ Indicated understanding
FORMAT	☐ Paper ☐ Electronic ☐ RON

DOCUMENT(S) SIGNED

Document	Type		SIGNER
☐ Borrower's Aff	Acknowledgment	Jurat	1 2 3 4
☐ Compliance Agrmt	Acknowledgment	Jurat	1 2 3 4
☐ Correction Agrmt	Acknowledgment	Jurat	1 2 3 4
☐ Debts/Leins Aff	Acknowledgment	Jurat	1 2 3 4
☐ Deed of Trust	Acknowledgment	Jurat	1 2 3 4
☐ Distrib of Proceeds	Acknowledgment	Jurat	1 2 3 4
☐ E&O Agrmt	Acknowledgment	Jurat	1 2 3 4
☐ Grant Deed	Acknowledgment	Jurat	1 2 3 4
☐ Marital Stat Aff	Acknowledgment	Jurat	1 2 3 4
☐ Mortgage	Acknowledgment	Jurat	1 2 3 4
☐ Occupancy/Fin Aff	Acknowledgment	Jurat	1 2 3 4
☐ Owner's Aff	Acknowledgment	Jurat	1 2 3 4
☐ Payoff Aff	Acknowledgment	Jurat	1 2 3 4
☐ Quit-Claim Deed	Acknowledgment	Jurat	1 2 3 4
☐ Sig/Name Aff	Acknowledgment	Jurat	1 2 3 4
☐ Survey Aff	Acknowledgment	Jurat	1 2 3 4
☐ Warranty Deed	Acknowledgment	Jurat	1 2 3 4

Document	Type		SIGNER	Options
☐ Minor Medical Consent	Acknowledgment	Jurat	1 2 3 4	
☐ Minor Passport Consent	Acknowledgment	Jurat	1 2 3 4	☐ Acknowledgment Jurat Copy Oath SW 1 2 3 4
☐ Minor Travel Consent	Acknowledgment	Jurat	1 2 3 4	
☐ Vehicle Duplicate Title	Acknowledgment	Jurat	1 2 3 4	☐ Acknowledgment Jurat Copy Oath SW 1 2 3 4
☐ Vehicle Lein Release	Acknowledgment	Jurat	1 2 3 4	
☐ Vehicle Odom/Vin Ver	Acknowledgment	Jurat	1 2 3 4	☐ Acknowledgment Jurat Copy Oath SW 1 2 3 4
☐ Vehicle Title Transfer	Acknowledgment	Jurat	1 2 3 4	
☐ Adv Health Care Dir	Acknowledgment	Jurat	1 2 3 4	☐ Acknowledgment Jurat Copy Oath SW 1 2 3 4
☐ Assign of Digital Assets	Acknowledgment	Jurat	1 2 3 4	☐ Acknowledgment Jurat Copy Oath SW 1 2 3 4
☐ Assign of Personal Prop	Acknowledgment	Jurat	1 2 3 4	☐ Acknowledgment Jurat Copy Oath SW 1 2 3 4
☐ HIPAA Release	Acknowledgment	Jurat	1 2 3 4	
☐ Living Trust	Acknowledgment	Jurat	1 2 3 4	☐ Acknowledgment Jurat Copy Oath SW 1 2 3 4
☐ Last Will & Testament	Acknowledgment	Jurat	1 2 3 4	
☐ POA	Acknowledgment	Jurat	1 2 3 4	☐ Acknowledgment Jurat Copy Oath SW 1 2 3 4
☐ Trust Certification	Acknowledgment	Jurat	1 2 3 4	

SIGNING ADDRESS	OTHERS IN ATTENDANCE	CLIENT / SIGNING SERVICE	FEE
		LENDER / LOAN NUMBER	

NOTES

_____
_____
_____
_____
_____
_____
_____
_____
_____
_____
_____
_____

	ADDRESS	SIGNATURE	INITIAL IF OATH/AFF TAKEN	RIGHT THUMB PRINT
1	PHONE / EMAIL			
2	ADDRESS / PHONE / EMAIL	SIGNATURE	INITIAL IF OATH/AFF TAKEN	RIGHT THUMB PRINT
3	ADDRESS / PHONE / EMAIL	SIGNATURE	INITIAL IF OATH/AFF TAKEN	RIGHT THUMB PRINT
4	ADDRESS / PHONE / EMAIL	SIGNATURE	INITIAL IF OATH/AFF TAKEN	RIGHT THUMB PRINT

Notary Journal Entries (1–4)

#			
1	DATE / TIME	NAME ☐ Signer ☐ Witness	IDENTITY VERIFIED ☐ D.L. ☐ Passport ☐ Credible Witness ☐ Other	WILLINGNESS & COMPETENCE ☐ Expressed willingness ☐ Mentally alert ☐ Indicated understanding	FORMAT ☐ Paper ☐ Electronic ☐ RON
2	DATE / TIME	NAME ☐ Signer ☐ Witness	IDENTITY VERIFIED ☐ D.L. ☐ Passport ☐ Credible Witness ☐ Other	WILLINGNESS & COMPETENCE ☐ Expressed willingness ☐ Mentally alert ☐ Indicated understanding	FORMAT ☐ Paper ☐ Electronic ☐ RON
3	DATE / TIME	NAME ☐ Signer ☐ Witness	IDENTITY VERIFIED ☐ D.L. ☐ Passport ☐ Credible Witness ☐ Other	WILLINGNESS & COMPETENCE ☐ Expressed willingness ☐ Mentally alert ☐ Indicated understanding	FORMAT ☐ Paper ☐ Electronic ☐ RON
4	DATE / TIME	NAME ☐ Signer ☐ Witness	IDENTITY VERIFIED ☐ D.L. ☐ Passport ☐ Credible Witness ☐ Other	WILLINGNESS & COMPETENCE ☐ Expressed willingness ☐ Mentally alert ☐ Indicated understanding	FORMAT ☐ Paper ☐ Electronic ☐ RON

DOCUMENT(S) SIGNED

Document	Type	SIGNER 1 2 3 4
☐ Borrower's Aff	Acknowledgment / Jurat	1 2 3 4
☐ Compliance Agrmt	Acknowledgment / Jurat	1 2 3 4
☐ Correction Agrmt	Acknowledgment / Jurat	1 2 3 4
☐ Debts/Leins Aff	Acknowledgment / Jurat	1 2 3 4
☐ Deed of Trust	Acknowledgment / Jurat	1 2 3 4
☐ Distrib of Proceeds	Acknowledgment / Jurat	1 2 3 4
☐ E&O Agrmt	Acknowledgment / Jurat	1 2 3 4
☐ Grant Deed	Acknowledgment / Jurat	1 2 3 4
☐ Marital Stat Aff	Acknowledgment / Jurat	1 2 3 4
☐ Mortgage	Acknowledgment / Jurat	1 2 3 4
☐ Occupancy/Fin Aff	Acknowledgment / Jurat	1 2 3 4
☐ Owner's Aff	Acknowledgment / Jurat	1 2 3 4
☐ Payoff Aff	Acknowledgment / Jurat	1 2 3 4
☐ Quit-Claim Deed	Acknowledgment / Jurat	1 2 3 4
☐ Sig/Name Aff	Acknowledgment / Jurat	1 2 3 4
☐ Survey Aff	Acknowledgment / Jurat	1 2 3 4
☐ Warranty Deed	Acknowledgment / Jurat	1 2 3 4
☐ Minor Medical Consent	Acknowledgment / Jurat	1 2 3 4
☐ Minor Passport Consent	Acknowledgment / Jurat	1 2 3 4
☐ Minor Travel Consent	Acknowledgment / Jurat	1 2 3 4
☐ Vehicle Duplicate Title	Acknowledgment / Jurat	1 2 3 4
☐ Vehicle Lein Release	Acknowledgment / Jurat	1 2 3 4
☐ Vehicle Odom/Vin Ver	Acknowledgment / Jurat	1 2 3 4
☐ Vehicle Title Transfer	Acknowledgment / Jurat	1 2 3 4
☐ Adv Health Care Dir	Acknowledgment / Jurat	1 2 3 4
☐ Assign of Digital Assets	Acknowledgment / Jurat	1 2 3 4
☐ Assign of Personal Prop	Acknowledgment / Jurat	1 2 3 4
☐ HIPAA Release	Acknowledgment / Jurat	1 2 3 4
☐ Living Trust	Acknowledgment / Jurat	1 2 3 4
☐ Last Will & Testament	Acknowledgment / Jurat	1 2 3 4
☐ POA	Acknowledgment / Jurat	1 2 3 4
☐ Trust Certification	Acknowledgment / Jurat	1 2 3 4

Additional columns (for right-side document list): ☐ Copy ☐ Oath ☐ SW

SIGNING ADDRESS	OTHERS IN ATTENDANCE	CLIENT / SIGNING SERVICE	FEE
		LENDER / LOAN NUMBER	

NOTES

_____
_____
_____
_____
_____
_____
_____
_____
_____
_____
_____
_____

#		SIGNATURE	INITIAL IF OATH/AFF TAKEN	RIGHT THUMB PRINT
1	ADDRESS / PHONE / EMAIL			
2	ADDRESS / PHONE / EMAIL			
3	ADDRESS / PHONE / EMAIL			
4	ADDRESS / PHONE / EMAIL			

Notary Journal Entries

Entry 1
DATE	TIME	NAME	IDENTITY VERIFIED	WILLINGNESS & COMPETENCE	FORMAT
		☐ Signer ☐ Witness	☐ D.L. ☐ Passport ☐ Credible Witness ☐ Other	☐ Expressed willingness ☐ Mentally alert ☐ Indicated understanding	☐ Paper ☐ Electronic ☐ RON

Entry 2
DATE	TIME	NAME	IDENTITY VERIFIED	WILLINGNESS & COMPETENCE	FORMAT
		☐ Signer ☐ Witness	☐ D.L. ☐ Passport ☐ Credible Witness ☐ Other	☐ Expressed willingness ☐ Mentally alert ☐ Indicated understanding	☐ Paper ☐ Electronic ☐ RON

Entry 3
DATE	TIME	NAME	IDENTITY VERIFIED	WILLINGNESS & COMPETENCE	FORMAT
		☐ Signer ☐ Witness	☐ D.L. ☐ Passport ☐ Credible Witness ☐ Other	☐ Expressed willingness ☐ Mentally alert ☐ Indicated understanding	☐ Paper ☐ Electronic ☐ RON

Entry 4
DATE	TIME	NAME	IDENTITY VERIFIED	WILLINGNESS & COMPETENCE	FORMAT
		☐ Signer ☐ Witness	☐ D.L. ☐ Passport ☐ Credible Witness ☐ Other	☐ Expressed willingness ☐ Mentally alert ☐ Indicated understanding	☐ Paper ☐ Electronic ☐ RON

DOCUMENT(S) SIGNED

Document	Notarial Act	SIGNER 1 2 3 4
☐ Borrower's Aff	Acknowledgment Jurat	1 2 3 4
☐ Compliance Agrmt	Acknowledgment Jurat	1 2 3 4
☐ Correction Agrmt	Acknowledgment Jurat	1 2 3 4
☐ Debts/Leins Aff	Acknowledgment Jurat	1 2 3 4
☐ Deed of Trust	Acknowledgment Jurat	1 2 3 4
☐ Distrib of Proceeds	Acknowledgment Jurat	1 2 3 4
☐ E&O Agrmt	Acknowledgment Jurat	1 2 3 4
☐ Grant Deed	Acknowledgment Jurat	1 2 3 4
☐ Marital Stat Aff	Acknowledgment Jurat	1 2 3 4
☐ Mortgage	Acknowledgment Jurat	1 2 3 4
☐ Occupancy/Fin Aff	Acknowledgment Jurat	1 2 3 4
☐ Owner's Aff	Acknowledgment Jurat	1 2 3 4
☐ Payoff Aff	Acknowledgment Jurat	1 2 3 4
☐ Quit-Claim Deed	Acknowledgment Jurat	1 2 3 4
☐ Sig/Name Aff	Acknowledgment Jurat	1 2 3 4
☐ Survey Aff	Acknowledgment Jurat	1 2 3 4
☐ Warranty Deed	Acknowledgment Jurat	1 2 3 4

Document	Notarial Act	SIGNER 1 2 3 4
☐ Minor Medical Consent	Acknowledgment Jurat Copy Oath SW	1 2 3 4
☐ Minor Passport Consent	Acknowledgment Jurat	1 2 3 4
☐ Minor Travel Consent	Acknowledgment Jurat	1 2 3 4
☐ Vehicle Duplicate Title	Acknowledgment Jurat Copy Oath SW	1 2 3 4
☐ Vehicle Lein Release	Acknowledgment Jurat	1 2 3 4
☐ Vehicle Odom/Vin Ver	Acknowledgment Jurat	1 2 3 4
☐ Vehicle Title Transfer	Acknowledgment Jurat Copy Oath SW	1 2 3 4
☐ Adv Health Care Dir	Acknowledgment Jurat	1 2 3 4
☐ Assign of Digital Assets	Acknowledgment Jurat Copy Oath SW	1 2 3 4
☐ Assign of Personal Prop	Acknowledgment Jurat	1 2 3 4
☐ HIPAA Release	Acknowledgment Jurat	1 2 3 4
☐ Living Trust _____	Acknowledgment Jurat Copy Oath SW	1 2 3 4
☐ Last Will & Testament	Acknowledgment Jurat	1 2 3 4
☐ POA _____	Acknowledgment Jurat	1 2 3 4
☐ Trust Certification	Acknowledgment Jurat Copy Oath SW	1 2 3 4

SIGNING ADDRESS	OTHERS IN ATTENDANCE	CLIENT / SIGNING SERVICE	FEE
		LENDER / LOAN NUMBER	

NOTES

	ADDRESS	PHONE	EMAIL	SIGNATURE	INITIAL IF OATH/AFF TAKEN	RIGHT THUMB PRINT
1						
2						
3						
4						

Signer Entries

#	DATE / TIME	NAME	IDENTITY VERIFIED	WILLINGNESS & COMPETENCE	FORMAT
1	DATE ___ / TIME ___	☐ Signer ☐ Witness	☐ D.L. ☐ Passport ☐ Credible Witness ☐ Other	☐ Expressed willingness ☐ Mentally alert ☐ Indicated understanding	☐ Paper ☐ Electronic ☐ RON
2	DATE ___ / TIME ___	☐ Signer ☐ Witness	☐ D.L. ☐ Passport ☐ Credible Witness ☐ Other	☐ Expressed willingness ☐ Mentally alert ☐ Indicated understanding	☐ Paper ☐ Electronic ☐ RON
3	DATE ___ / TIME ___	☐ Signer ☐ Witness	☐ D.L. ☐ Passport ☐ Credible Witness ☐ Other	☐ Expressed willingness ☐ Mentally alert ☐ Indicated understanding	☐ Paper ☐ Electronic ☐ RON
4	DATE ___ / TIME ___	☐ Signer ☐ Witness	☐ D.L. ☐ Passport ☐ Credible Witness ☐ Other	☐ Expressed willingness ☐ Mentally alert ☐ Indicated understanding	☐ Paper ☐ Electronic ☐ RON

Document(s) Signed

Document	Type	Signer
☐ Borrower's Aff	Acknowledgment Jurat	1 2 3 4
☐ Compliance Agrmt	Acknowledgment Jurat	1 2 3 4
☐ Correction Agrmt	Acknowledgment Jurat	1 2 3 4
☐ Debts/Leins Aff	Acknowledgment Jurat	1 2 3 4
☐ Deed of Trust	Acknowledgment Jurat	1 2 3 4
☐ Distrib of Proceeds	Acknowledgment Jurat	1 2 3 4
☐ E&O Agrmt	Acknowledgment Jurat	1 2 3 4
☐ Grant Deed	Acknowledgment Jurat	1 2 3 4
☐ Marital Stat Aff	Acknowledgment Jurat	1 2 3 4
☐ Mortgage	Acknowledgment Jurat	1 2 3 4
☐ Occupancy/Fin Aff	Acknowledgment Jurat	1 2 3 4
☐ Owner's Aff	Acknowledgment Jurat	1 2 3 4
☐ Payoff Aff	Acknowledgment Jurat	1 2 3 4
☐ Quit-Claim Deed	Acknowledgment Jurat	1 2 3 4
☐ Sig/Name Aff	Acknowledgment Jurat	1 2 3 4
☐ Survey Aff	Acknowledgment Jurat	1 2 3 4
☐ Warranty Deed	Acknowledgment Jurat	1 2 3 4
☐ Minor Medical Consent	Acknowledgment Jurat Copy Oath SW	1 2 3 4
☐ Minor Passport Consent	Acknowledgment Jurat Copy Oath SW	1 2 3 4
☐ Minor Travel Consent	Acknowledgment Jurat Copy Oath SW	1 2 3 4
☐ Vehicle Duplicate Title	Acknowledgment Jurat Copy Oath SW	1 2 3 4
☐ Vehicle Lein Release	Acknowledgment Jurat Copy Oath SW	1 2 3 4
☐ Vehicle Odom/Vin Ver	Acknowledgment Jurat Copy Oath SW	1 2 3 4
☐ Vehicle Title Transfer	Acknowledgment Jurat Copy Oath SW	1 2 3 4
☐ Adv Health Care Dir	Acknowledgment Jurat Copy Oath SW	1 2 3 4
☐ Assign of Digital Assets	Acknowledgment Jurat Copy Oath SW	1 2 3 4
☐ Assign of Personal Prop	Acknowledgment Jurat Copy Oath SW	1 2 3 4
☐ HIPAA Release	Acknowledgment Jurat Copy Oath SW	1 2 3 4
☐ Living Trust ___	Acknowledgment Jurat Copy Oath SW	1 2 3 4
☐ Last Will & Testament	Acknowledgment Jurat Copy Oath SW	1 2 3 4
☐ POA ___	Acknowledgment Jurat Copy Oath SW	1 2 3 4
☐ Trust Certification	Acknowledgment Jurat Copy Oath SW	1 2 3 4

SIGNING ADDRESS	OTHERS IN ATTENDANCE	CLIENT / SIGNING SERVICE	FEE
		LENDER / LOAN NUMBER	

NOTES

_____

	ADDRESS	PHONE	SIGNATURE	INITIAL IF OATH/AFF TAKEN	RIGHT THUMB PRINT
1		PHONE / EMAIL	SIGNATURE	INITIAL IF OATH/AFF TAKEN	RIGHT THUMB PRINT
2	ADDRESS	PHONE / EMAIL	SIGNATURE	INITIAL IF OATH/AFF TAKEN	RIGHT THUMB PRINT
3	ADDRESS	PHONE / EMAIL	SIGNATURE	INITIAL IF OATH/AFF TAKEN	RIGHT THUMB PRINT
4	ADDRESS	PHONE / EMAIL	SIGNATURE	INITIAL IF OATH/AFF TAKEN	RIGHT THUMB PRINT

Notary Journal Entries

#	DATE / TIME	NAME	IDENTITY VERIFIED	WILLINGNESS & COMPETENCE	FORMAT
1	DATE _____ / TIME _____	☐ Signer ☐ Witness	☐ D.L. ☐ Passport ☐ Credible Witness ☐ Other	☐ Expressed willingness ☐ Mentally alert ☐ Indicated understanding	☐ Paper ☐ Electronic ☐ RON
2	DATE _____ / TIME _____	☐ Signer ☐ Witness	☐ D.L. ☐ Passport ☐ Credible Witness ☐ Other	☐ Expressed willingness ☐ Mentally alert ☐ Indicated understanding	☐ Paper ☐ Electronic ☐ RON
3	DATE _____ / TIME _____	☐ Signer ☐ Witness	☐ D.L. ☐ Passport ☐ Credible Witness ☐ Other	☐ Expressed willingness ☐ Mentally alert ☐ Indicated understanding	☐ Paper ☐ Electronic ☐ RON
4	DATE _____ / TIME _____	☐ Signer ☐ Witness	☐ D.L. ☐ Passport ☐ Credible Witness ☐ Other	☐ Expressed willingness ☐ Mentally alert ☐ Indicated understanding	☐ Paper ☐ Electronic ☐ RON

DOCUMENT(S) SIGNED

Document	Type	SIGNER
☐ Borrower's Aff	Acknowledgment Jurat	1 2 3 4
☐ Compliance Agrmt	Acknowledgment Jurat	1 2 3 4
☐ Correction Agrmt	Acknowledgment Jurat	1 2 3 4
☐ Debts/Leins Aff	Acknowledgment Jurat	1 2 3 4
☐ Deed of Trust	Acknowledgment Jurat	1 2 3 4
☐ Distrib of Proceeds	Acknowledgment Jurat	1 2 3 4
☐ E&O Agrmt	Acknowledgment Jurat	1 2 3 4
☐ Grant Deed	Acknowledgment Jurat	1 2 3 4
☐ Marital Stat Aff	Acknowledgment Jurat	1 2 3 4
☐ Mortgage	Acknowledgment Jurat	1 2 3 4
☐ Occupancy/Fin Aff	Acknowledgment Jurat	1 2 3 4
☐ Owner's Aff	Acknowledgment Jurat	1 2 3 4
☐ Payoff Aff	Acknowledgment Jurat	1 2 3 4
☐ Quit-Claim Deed	Acknowledgment Jurat	1 2 3 4
☐ Sig/Name Aff	Acknowledgment Jurat	1 2 3 4
☐ Survey Aff	Acknowledgment Jurat	1 2 3 4
☐ Warranty Deed	Acknowledgment Jurat	1 2 3 4

Document	Type	SIGNER
☐ Minor Medical Consent	Acknowledgment Jurat	1 2 3 4
☐ Minor Passport Consent	Acknowledgment Jurat	1 2 3 4
☐ Minor Travel Consent	Acknowledgment Jurat	1 2 3 4
☐ Vehicle Duplicate Title	Acknowledgment Jurat	1 2 3 4
☐ Vehicle Lein Release	Acknowledgment Jurat	1 2 3 4
☐ Vehicle Odom/Vin Ver	Acknowledgment Jurat	1 2 3 4
☐ Vehicle Title Transfer	Acknowledgment Jurat	1 2 3 4
☐ Adv Health Care Dir	Acknowledgment Jurat	1 2 3 4
☐ Assign of Digital Assets	Acknowledgment Jurat	1 2 3 4
☐ Assign of Personal Prop	Acknowledgment Jurat	1 2 3 4
☐ HIPAA Release	Acknowledgment Jurat	1 2 3 4
☐ Living Trust	Acknowledgment Jurat	1 2 3 4
☐ Last Will & Testament	Acknowledgment Jurat	1 2 3 4
☐ POA	Acknowledgment Jurat	1 2 3 4
☐ Trust Certification	Acknowledgment Jurat	1 2 3 4

Additional notarial act columns (Acknowledgment, Jurat, Copy, Oath, SW) with SIGNER 1 2 3 4:

☐ Acknowledgment Jurat Copy Oath SW — 1 2 3 4 (for grouped document sections)

SIGNING ADDRESS	OTHERS IN ATTENDANCE	CLIENT / SIGNING SERVICE	FEE
		LENDER / LOAN NUMBER	

NOTES

	ADDRESS	PHONE	SIGNATURE	INITIAL IF OATH/AFF TAKEN	RIGHT THUMB PRINT
1		EMAIL			
2	ADDRESS	PHONE	SIGNATURE	INITIAL IF OATH/AFF TAKEN	RIGHT THUMB PRINT
		EMAIL			
3	ADDRESS	PHONE	SIGNATURE	INITIAL IF OATH/AFF TAKEN	RIGHT THUMB PRINT
		EMAIL			
4	ADDRESS	PHONE	SIGNATURE	INITIAL IF OATH/AFF TAKEN	RIGHT THUMB PRINT
		EMAIL			

Entries

Entry 1
- DATE:
- TIME:
- NAME: ☐ Signer ☐ Witness
- IDENTITY VERIFIED: ☐ D.L. ☐ Passport ☐ Credible Witness ☐ Other
- WILLINGNESS & COMPETENCE: ☐ Expressed willingness ☐ Mentally alert ☐ Indicated understanding
- FORMAT: ☐ Paper ☐ Electronic ☐ RON

Entry 2
- DATE:
- TIME:
- NAME: ☐ Signer ☐ Witness
- IDENTITY VERIFIED: ☐ D.L. ☐ Passport ☐ Credible Witness ☐ Other
- WILLINGNESS & COMPETENCE: ☐ Expressed willingness ☐ Mentally alert ☐ Indicated understanding
- FORMAT: ☐ Paper ☐ Electronic ☐ RON

Entry 3
- DATE:
- TIME:
- NAME: ☐ Signer ☐ Witness
- IDENTITY VERIFIED: ☐ D.L. ☐ Passport ☐ Credible Witness ☐ Other
- WILLINGNESS & COMPETENCE: ☐ Expressed willingness ☐ Mentally alert ☐ Indicated understanding
- FORMAT: ☐ Paper ☐ Electronic ☐ RON

Entry 4
- DATE:
- TIME:
- NAME: ☐ Signer ☐ Witness
- IDENTITY VERIFIED: ☐ D.L. ☐ Passport ☐ Credible Witness ☐ Other
- WILLINGNESS & COMPETENCE: ☐ Expressed willingness ☐ Mentally alert ☐ Indicated understanding
- FORMAT: ☐ Paper ☐ Electronic ☐ RON

DOCUMENT(S) SIGNED

Document	Notarial Act	SIGNER
☐ Borrower's Aff	Acknowledgment Jurat	1 2 3 4
☐ Compliance Agrmt	Acknowledgment Jurat	1 2 3 4
☐ Correction Agrmt	Acknowledgment Jurat	1 2 3 4
☐ Debts/Leins Aff	Acknowledgment Jurat	1 2 3 4
☐ Deed of Trust	Acknowledgment Jurat	1 2 3 4
☐ Distrib of Proceeds	Acknowledgment Jurat	1 2 3 4
☐ E&O Agrmt	Acknowledgment Jurat	1 2 3 4
☐ Grant Deed	Acknowledgment Jurat	1 2 3 4
☐ Marital Stat Aff	Acknowledgment Jurat	1 2 3 4
☐ Mortgage	Acknowledgment Jurat	1 2 3 4
☐ Occupancy/Fin Aff	Acknowledgment Jurat	1 2 3 4
☐ Owner's Aff	Acknowledgment Jurat	1 2 3 4
☐ Payoff Aff	Acknowledgment Jurat	1 2 3 4
☐ Quit-Claim Deed	Acknowledgment Jurat	1 2 3 4
☐ Sig/Name Aff	Acknowledgment Jurat	1 2 3 4
☐ Survey Aff	Acknowledgment Jurat	1 2 3 4
☐ Warranty Deed	Acknowledgment Jurat	1 2 3 4

Document	Notarial Act	SIGNER
☐ Minor Medical Consent	Acknowledgment Jurat	1 2 3 4
☐ Minor Passport Consent	Acknowledgment Jurat	1 2 3 4
☐ Minor Travel Consent	Acknowledgment Jurat	1 2 3 4
☐ Vehicle Duplicate Title	Acknowledgment Jurat	1 2 3 4
☐ Vehicle Lein Release	Acknowledgment Jurat	1 2 3 4
☐ Vehicle Odom/Vin Ver	Acknowledgment Jurat	1 2 3 4
☐ Vehicle Title Transfer	Acknowledgment Jurat	1 2 3 4
☐ Adv Health Care Dir	Acknowledgment Jurat	1 2 3 4
☐ Assign of Digital Assets	Acknowledgment Jurat	1 2 3 4
☐ Assign of Personal Prop	Acknowledgment Jurat	1 2 3 4
☐ HIPAA Release	Acknowledgment Jurat	1 2 3 4
☐ Living Trust	Acknowledgment Jurat	1 2 3 4
☐ Last Will & Testament	Acknowledgment Jurat	1 2 3 4
☐ POA	Acknowledgment Jurat	1 2 3 4
☐ Trust Certification	Acknowledgment Jurat	1 2 3 4

Additional items (checkbox columns): Copy Oath SW — 1 2 3 4

SIGNING ADDRESS	OTHERS IN ATTENDANCE	CLIENT / SIGNING SERVICE	FEE
		LENDER / LOAN NUMBER	

NOTES

#	ADDRESS	PHONE	EMAIL	SIGNATURE	INITIAL IF OATH/AFF TAKEN	RIGHT THUMB PRINT
1						
2						
3						
4						

Notary Record Entries

Entries 1–4

#	NAME	IDENTITY VERIFIED	WILLINGNESS & COMPETENCE	FORMAT
1	DATE ___ TIME ___ ☐ Signer ☐ Witness	☐ D.L. ☐ Passport ☐ Credible Witness ☐ Other	☐ Expressed willingness ☐ Mentally alert ☐ Indicated understanding	☐ Paper ☐ Electronic ☐ RON
2	DATE ___ TIME ___ ☐ Signer ☐ Witness	☐ D.L. ☐ Passport ☐ Credible Witness ☐ Other	☐ Expressed willingness ☐ Mentally alert ☐ Indicated understanding	☐ Paper ☐ Electronic ☐ RON
3	DATE ___ TIME ___ ☐ Signer ☐ Witness	☐ D.L. ☐ Passport ☐ Credible Witness ☐ Other	☐ Expressed willingness ☐ Mentally alert ☐ Indicated understanding	☐ Paper ☐ Electronic ☐ RON
4	DATE ___ TIME ___ ☐ Signer ☐ Witness	☐ D.L. ☐ Passport ☐ Credible Witness ☐ Other	☐ Expressed willingness ☐ Mentally alert ☐ Indicated understanding	☐ Paper ☐ Electronic ☐ RON

DOCUMENT(S) SIGNED

Document	Notarial Act	SIGNER
☐ Borrower's Aff	Acknowledgment Jurat	1 2 3 4
☐ Compliance Agrmt	Acknowledgment Jurat	1 2 3 4
☐ Correction Agrmt	Acknowledgment Jurat	1 2 3 4
☐ Debts/Leins Aff	Acknowledgment Jurat	1 2 3 4
☐ Deed of Trust	Acknowledgment Jurat	1 2 3 4
☐ Distrib of Proceeds	Acknowledgment Jurat	1 2 3 4
☐ E&O Agrmt	Acknowledgment Jurat	1 2 3 4
☐ Grant Deed	Acknowledgment Jurat	1 2 3 4
☐ Marital Stat Aff	Acknowledgment Jurat	1 2 3 4
☐ Mortgage	Acknowledgment Jurat	1 2 3 4
☐ Occupancy/Fin Aff	Acknowledgment Jurat	1 2 3 4
☐ Owner's Aff	Acknowledgment Jurat	1 2 3 4
☐ Payoff Aff	Acknowledgment Jurat	1 2 3 4
☐ Quit-Claim Deed	Acknowledgment Jurat	1 2 3 4
☐ Sig/Name Aff	Acknowledgment Jurat	1 2 3 4
☐ Survey Aff	Acknowledgment Jurat	1 2 3 4
☐ Warranty Deed	Acknowledgment Jurat	1 2 3 4

Document	Notarial Act	SIGNER
☐ Minor Medical Consent	Acknowledgment Jurat	1 2 3 4
☐ Minor Passport Consent	Acknowledgment Jurat	1 2 3 4
☐ Minor Travel Consent	Acknowledgment Jurat	1 2 3 4
☐ Vehicle Duplicate Title	Acknowledgment Jurat	1 2 3 4
☐ Vehicle Lein Release	Acknowledgment Jurat	1 2 3 4
☐ Vehicle Odom/Vin Ver	Acknowledgment Jurat	1 2 3 4
☐ Vehicle Title Transfer	Acknowledgment Jurat	1 2 3 4
☐ Adv Health Care Dir	Acknowledgment Jurat	1 2 3 4
☐ Assign of Digital Assets	Acknowledgment Jurat	1 2 3 4
☐ Assign of Personal Prop	Acknowledgment Jurat	1 2 3 4
☐ HIPAA Release	Acknowledgment Jurat	1 2 3 4
☐ Living Trust	Acknowledgment Jurat	1 2 3 4
☐ Last Will & Testament	Acknowledgment Jurat	1 2 3 4
☐ POA _____	Acknowledgment Jurat	1 2 3 4
☐ Trust Certification	Acknowledgment Jurat	1 2 3 4

Additional notarial acts (right section): Acknowledgment Jurat Copy Oath SW — 1 2 3 4

SIGNING ADDRESS	OTHERS IN ATTENDANCE	CLIENT / SIGNING SERVICE	FEE
		LENDER / LOAN NUMBER	

NOTES

	SIGNATURE		PHONE	ADDRESS
		INITIAL IF OATH/AFF TAKEN	EMAIL	
		RIGHT THUMB PRINT		

#					
1	ADDRESS	PHONE / EMAIL	SIGNATURE	INITIAL IF OATH/AFF TAKEN	RIGHT THUMB PRINT
2	ADDRESS	PHONE / EMAIL	SIGNATURE	INITIAL IF OATH/AFF TAKEN	RIGHT THUMB PRINT
3	ADDRESS	PHONE / EMAIL	SIGNATURE	INITIAL IF OATH/AFF TAKEN	RIGHT THUMB PRINT
4	ADDRESS	PHONE / EMAIL	SIGNATURE	INITIAL IF OATH/AFF TAKEN	RIGHT THUMB PRINT

Notary Journal Entries

Entry 1
DATE		
TIME		

NAME: □ Signer □ Witness

IDENTITY VERIFIED: □ D.L. □ Passport □ Credible Witness □ Other

WILLINGNESS & COMPETENCE: □ Expressed willingness □ Mentally alert □ Indicated understanding

FORMAT: □ Paper □ Electronic □ RON

Entry 2
DATE		
TIME		

NAME: □ Signer □ Witness

IDENTITY VERIFIED: □ D.L. □ Passport □ Credible Witness □ Other

WILLINGNESS & COMPETENCE: □ Expressed willingness □ Mentally alert □ Indicated understanding

FORMAT: □ Paper □ Electronic □ RON

Entry 3
DATE		
TIME		

NAME: □ Signer □ Witness

IDENTITY VERIFIED: □ D.L. □ Passport □ Credible Witness □ Other

WILLINGNESS & COMPETENCE: □ Expressed willingness □ Mentally alert □ Indicated understanding

FORMAT: □ Paper □ Electronic □ RON

Entry 4
DATE		
TIME		

NAME: □ Signer □ Witness

IDENTITY VERIFIED: □ D.L. □ Passport □ Credible Witness □ Other

WILLINGNESS & COMPETENCE: □ Expressed willingness □ Mentally alert □ Indicated understanding

FORMAT: □ Paper □ Electronic □ RON

DOCUMENT(S) SIGNED

Document	Type	SIGNER 1	2	3	4
□ Borrower's Aff	Acknowledgment Jurat	1	2	3	4
□ Compliance Agrmt	Acknowledgment Jurat	1	2	3	4
□ Correction Agrmt	Acknowledgment Jurat	1	2	3	4
□ Debts/Leins Aff	Acknowledgment Jurat	1	2	3	4
□ Deed of Trust	Acknowledgment Jurat	1	2	3	4
□ Distrib of Proceeds	Acknowledgment Jurat	1	2	3	4
□ E&O Agrmt	Acknowledgment Jurat	1	2	3	4
□ Grant Deed	Acknowledgment Jurat	1	2	3	4
□ Marital Stat Aff	Acknowledgment Jurat	1	2	3	4
□ Mortgage	Acknowledgment Jurat	1	2	3	4
□ Occupancy/Fin Aff	Acknowledgment Jurat	1	2	3	4
□ Owner's Aff	Acknowledgment Jurat	1	2	3	4
□ Payoff Aff	Acknowledgment Jurat	1	2	3	4
□ Quit-Claim Deed	Acknowledgment Jurat	1	2	3	4
□ Sig/Name Aff	Acknowledgment Jurat	1	2	3	4
□ Survey Aff	Acknowledgment Jurat	1	2	3	4
□ Warranty Deed	Acknowledgment Jurat	1	2	3	4

Document	Type	SIGNER 1	2	3	4
□ Minor Medical Consent	Acknowledgment Jurat	1	2	3	4
□ Minor Passport Consent	Acknowledgment Jurat	1	2	3	4
□ Minor Travel Consent	Acknowledgment Jurat	1	2	3	4
□ Vehicle Duplicate Title	Acknowledgment Jurat	1	2	3	4
□ Vehicle Lein Release	Acknowledgment Jurat	1	2	3	4
□ Vehicle Odom/Vin Ver	Acknowledgment Jurat	1	2	3	4
□ Vehicle Title Transfer	Acknowledgment Jurat	1	2	3	4
□ Adv Health Care Dir	Acknowledgment Jurat	1	2	3	4
□ Assign of Digital Assets	Acknowledgment Jurat	1	2	3	4
□ Assign of Personal Prop	Acknowledgment Jurat	1	2	3	4
□ HIPAA Release	Acknowledgment Jurat	1	2	3	4
□ Living Trust	Acknowledgment Jurat	1	2	3	4
□ Last Will & Testament	Acknowledgment Jurat	1	2	3	4
□ POA	Acknowledgment Jurat	1	2	3	4
□ Trust Certification	Acknowledgment Jurat	1	2	3	4

Right-side document list also includes columns: Acknowledgment Jurat Copy Oath SW

SIGNING ADDRESS	OTHERS IN ATTENDANCE	CLIENT / SIGNING SERVICE	FEE
		LENDER / LOAN NUMBER	

NOTES

_____

	ADDRESS	PHONE	SIGNATURE	INITIAL IF OATH/AFF TAKEN	RIGHT THUMB PRINT
1		EMAIL			
2	ADDRESS	PHONE	SIGNATURE	INITIAL IF OATH/AFF TAKEN	RIGHT THUMB PRINT
		EMAIL			
3	ADDRESS	PHONE	SIGNATURE	INITIAL IF OATH/AFF TAKEN	RIGHT THUMB PRINT
		EMAIL			
4	ADDRESS	PHONE	SIGNATURE	INITIAL IF OATH/AFF TAKEN	RIGHT THUMB PRINT
		EMAIL			

Notary Journal Entries

Entry 1
Field	Details
DATE	
TIME	
NAME	☐ Signer ☐ Witness
IDENTITY VERIFIED	☐ D.L. ☐ Passport ☐ Credible Witness ☐ Other
WILLINGNESS & COMPETENCE	☐ Expressed willingness ☐ Mentally alert ☐ Indicated understanding
FORMAT	☐ Paper ☐ Electronic ☐ RON

Entry 2
Field	Details
DATE	
TIME	
NAME	☐ Signer ☐ Witness
IDENTITY VERIFIED	☐ D.L. ☐ Passport ☐ Credible Witness ☐ Other
WILLINGNESS & COMPETENCE	☐ Expressed willingness ☐ Mentally alert ☐ Indicated understanding
FORMAT	☐ Paper ☐ Electronic ☐ RON

Entry 3
Field	Details
DATE	
TIME	
NAME	☐ Signer ☐ Witness
IDENTITY VERIFIED	☐ D.L. ☐ Passport ☐ Credible Witness ☐ Other
WILLINGNESS & COMPETENCE	☐ Expressed willingness ☐ Mentally alert ☐ Indicated understanding
FORMAT	☐ Paper ☐ Electronic ☐ RON

Entry 4
Field	Details
DATE	
TIME	
NAME	☐ Signer ☐ Witness
IDENTITY VERIFIED	☐ D.L. ☐ Passport ☐ Credible Witness ☐ Other
WILLINGNESS & COMPETENCE	☐ Expressed willingness ☐ Mentally alert ☐ Indicated understanding
FORMAT	☐ Paper ☐ Electronic ☐ RON

DOCUMENT(S) SIGNED

Document	Type		SIGNER
☐ Borrower's Aff	Acknowledgment	Jurat ___	1 2 3 4
☐ Compliance Agrmt	Acknowledgment	Jurat ___	1 2 3 4
☐ Correction Agrmt	Acknowledgment	Jurat ___	1 2 3 4
☐ Debts/Leins Aff	Acknowledgment	Jurat ___	1 2 3 4
☐ Deed of Trust	Acknowledgment	Jurat ___	1 2 3 4
☐ Distrib of Proceeds	Acknowledgment	Jurat ___	1 2 3 4
☐ E&O Agrmt	Acknowledgment	Jurat ___	1 2 3 4
☐ Grant Deed	Acknowledgment	Jurat ___	1 2 3 4
☐ Marital Stat Aff	Acknowledgment	Jurat ___	1 2 3 4
☐ Mortgage	Acknowledgment	Jurat ___	1 2 3 4
☐ Occupancy/Fin Aff	Acknowledgment	Jurat ___	1 2 3 4
☐ Owner's Aff	Acknowledgment	Jurat ___	1 2 3 4
☐ Payoff Aff	Acknowledgment	Jurat ___	1 2 3 4
☐ Quit-Claim Deed	Acknowledgment	Jurat ___	1 2 3 4
☐ Sig/Name Aff	Acknowledgment	Jurat ___	1 2 3 4
☐ Survey Aff	Acknowledgment	Jurat ___	1 2 3 4
☐ Warranty Deed	Acknowledgment	Jurat ___	1 2 3 4

Document	Type		SIGNER
☐ Minor Medical Consent	Acknowledgment	Jurat ___	1 2 3 4
☐ Minor Passport Consent	Acknowledgment	Jurat Copy Oath SW ___	1 2 3 4
☐ Minor Travel Consent	Acknowledgment	Jurat ___	1 2 3 4
☐ Vehicle Duplicate Title	Acknowledgment	Jurat Copy Oath SW ___	1 2 3 4
☐ Vehicle Lein Release	Acknowledgment	Jurat ___	1 2 3 4
☐ Vehicle Odom/Vin Ver	Acknowledgment	Jurat Copy Oath SW ___	1 2 3 4
☐ Vehicle Title Transfer	Acknowledgment	Jurat ___	1 2 3 4
☐ Adv Health Care Dir	Acknowledgment	Jurat Copy Oath SW ___	1 2 3 4
☐ Assign of Digital Assets	Acknowledgment	Jurat ___	1 2 3 4
☐ Assign of Personal Prop	Acknowledgment	Jurat ___	1 2 3 4
☐ HIPAA Release	Acknowledgment	Jurat ___	1 2 3 4
☐ Living Trust	Acknowledgment	Jurat Copy Oath SW ___	1 2 3 4
☐ Last Will & Testament	Acknowledgment	Jurat ___	1 2 3 4
☐ POA	Acknowledgment	Jurat Copy Oath SW ___	1 2 3 4
☐ Trust Certification	Acknowledgment	Jurat Copy Oath SW ___	1 2 3 4

SIGNING ADDRESS	OTHERS IN ATTENDANCE	CLIENT / SIGNING SERVICE	FEE
		LENDER / LOAN NUMBER	

NOTES

	ADDRESS	SIGNATURE	PHONE	INITIAL IF OATH/AFF TAKEN	RIGHT THUMB PRINT
1			PHONE / EMAIL		
2	ADDRESS	SIGNATURE	PHONE / EMAIL	INITIAL IF OATH/AFF TAKEN	RIGHT THUMB PRINT
3	ADDRESS	SIGNATURE	PHONE / EMAIL	INITIAL IF OATH/AFF TAKEN	RIGHT THUMB PRINT
4	ADDRESS	SIGNATURE	PHONE / EMAIL	INITIAL IF OATH/AFF TAKEN	RIGHT THUMB PRINT

Notary Journal Entry Form

Signer Records

#		Name	Identity Verified	Willingness & Competence	Format
1	DATE: ___ / TIME: ___	☐ Signer ☐ Witness	☐ D.L. ☐ Passport ☐ Credible Witness ☐ Other	☐ Expressed willingness ☐ Mentally alert ☐ Indicated understanding	☐ Paper ☐ Electronic ☐ RON
2	DATE: ___ / TIME: ___	☐ Signer ☐ Witness	☐ D.L. ☐ Passport ☐ Credible Witness ☐ Other	☐ Expressed willingness ☐ Mentally alert ☐ Indicated understanding	☐ Paper ☐ Electronic ☐ RON
3	DATE: ___ / TIME: ___	☐ Signer ☐ Witness	☐ D.L. ☐ Passport ☐ Credible Witness ☐ Other	☐ Expressed willingness ☐ Mentally alert ☐ Indicated understanding	☐ Paper ☐ Electronic ☐ RON
4	DATE: ___ / TIME: ___	☐ Signer ☐ Witness	☐ D.L. ☐ Passport ☐ Credible Witness ☐ Other	☐ Expressed willingness ☐ Mentally alert ☐ Indicated understanding	☐ Paper ☐ Electronic ☐ RON

Document(s) Signed

Document	Act		Signer 1	2	3	4
☐ Borrower's Aff	Acknowledgment	Jurat	1	2	3	4
☐ Compliance Agrmt	Acknowledgment	Jurat	1	2	3	4
☐ Correction Agrmt	Acknowledgment	Jurat	1	2	3	4
☐ Debts/Leins Aff	Acknowledgment	Jurat	1	2	3	4
☐ Deed of Trust	Acknowledgment	Jurat	1	2	3	4
☐ Distrib of Proceeds	Acknowledgment	Jurat	1	2	3	4
☐ E&O Agrmt	Acknowledgment	Jurat	1	2	3	4
☐ Grant Deed	Acknowledgment	Jurat	1	2	3	4
☐ Marital Stat Aff	Acknowledgment	Jurat	1	2	3	4
☐ Mortgage	Acknowledgment	Jurat	1	2	3	4
☐ Occupancy/Fin Aff	Acknowledgment	Jurat	1	2	3	4
☐ Owner's Aff	Acknowledgment	Jurat	1	2	3	4
☐ Payoff Aff	Acknowledgment	Jurat	1	2	3	4
☐ Quit-Claim Deed	Acknowledgment	Jurat	1	2	3	4
☐ Sig/Name Aff	Acknowledgment	Jurat	1	2	3	4
☐ Survey Aff	Acknowledgment	Jurat	1	2	3	4
☐ Warranty Deed	Acknowledgment	Jurat	1	2	3	4

Document	Act					Signer 1	2	3	4
☐ Minor Medical Consent	Acknowledgment	Jurat				1	2	3	4
☐ Minor Passport Consent	Acknowledgment	Jurat	Copy	Oath	SW	1	2	3	4
☐ Minor Travel Consent	Acknowledgment	Jurat	Copy	Oath	SW	1	2	3	4
☐ Vehicle Duplicate Title	Acknowledgment	Jurat				1	2	3	4
☐ Vehicle Lein Release	Acknowledgment	Jurat	Copy	Oath	SW	1	2	3	4
☐ Vehicle Odom/Vin Ver	Acknowledgment	Jurat				1	2	3	4
☐ Vehicle Title Transfer	Acknowledgment	Jurat	Copy	Oath	SW	1	2	3	4
☐ Adv Health Care Dir	Acknowledgment	Jurat				1	2	3	4
☐ Assign of Digital Assets	Acknowledgment	Jurat	Copy	Oath	SW	1	2	3	4
☐ Assign of Personal Prop	Acknowledgment	Jurat				1	2	3	4
☐ HIPAA Release	Acknowledgment	Jurat				1	2	3	4
☐ Living Trust ___	Acknowledgment	Jurat	Copy	Oath	SW	1	2	3	4
☐ Last Will & Testament	Acknowledgment	Jurat				1	2	3	4
☐ POA ___	Acknowledgment	Jurat	Copy	Oath	SW	1	2	3	4
☐ Trust Certification	Acknowledgment	Jurat	Copy	Oath	SW	1	2	3	4

SIGNING ADDRESS	OTHERS IN ATTENDANCE	CLIENT / SIGNING SERVICE	FEE
		LENDER / LOAN NUMBER	

NOTES

	ADDRESS	PHONE	EMAIL	SIGNATURE	INITIAL IF OATH/AFF TAKEN	RIGHT THUMB PRINT
1						
2						
3						
4						

Notary Journal Entry Log

Entry 1

DATE	
TIME	

NAME: ☐ Signer ☐ Witness

IDENTITY VERIFIED: ☐ D.L. ☐ Passport ☐ Credible Witness ☐ Other

WILLINGNESS & COMPETENCE: ☐ Expressed willingness ☐ Mentally alert ☐ Indicated understanding

FORMAT: ☐ Paper ☐ Electronic ☐ RON

Entry 2

DATE	
TIME	

NAME: ☐ Signer ☐ Witness

IDENTITY VERIFIED: ☐ D.L. ☐ Passport ☐ Credible Witness ☐ Other

WILLINGNESS & COMPETENCE: ☐ Expressed willingness ☐ Mentally alert ☐ Indicated understanding

FORMAT: ☐ Paper ☐ Electronic ☐ RON

Entry 3

DATE	
TIME	

NAME: ☐ Signer ☐ Witness

IDENTITY VERIFIED: ☐ D.L. ☐ Passport ☐ Credible Witness ☐ Other

WILLINGNESS & COMPETENCE: ☐ Expressed willingness ☐ Mentally alert ☐ Indicated understanding

FORMAT: ☐ Paper ☐ Electronic ☐ RON

Entry 4

DATE	
TIME	

NAME: ☐ Signer ☐ Witness

IDENTITY VERIFIED: ☐ D.L. ☐ Passport ☐ Credible Witness ☐ Other

WILLINGNESS & COMPETENCE: ☐ Expressed willingness ☐ Mentally alert ☐ Indicated understanding

FORMAT: ☐ Paper ☐ Electronic ☐ RON

DOCUMENT(S) SIGNED

Document	Type		SIGNER			
☐ Borrower's Aff	Acknowledgment	Jurat ___	1	2	3	4
☐ Compliance Agrmt	Acknowledgment	Jurat ___	1	2	3	4
☐ Correction Agrmt	Acknowledgment	Jurat ___	1	2	3	4
☐ Debts/Leins Aff	Acknowledgment	Jurat ___	1	2	3	4
☐ Deed of Trust	Acknowledgment	Jurat ___	1	2	3	4
☐ Distrib of Proceeds	Acknowledgment	Jurat ___	1	2	3	4
☐ E&O Agrmt	Acknowledgment	Jurat ___	1	2	3	4
☐ Grant Deed	Acknowledgment	Jurat ___	1	2	3	4
☐ Marital Stat Aff	Acknowledgment	Jurat ___	1	2	3	4
☐ Mortgage	Acknowledgment	Jurat ___	1	2	3	4
☐ Occupancy/Fin Aff	Acknowledgment	Jurat ___	1	2	3	4
☐ Owner's Aff	Acknowledgment	Jurat ___	1	2	3	4
☐ Payoff Aff	Acknowledgment	Jurat ___	1	2	3	4
☐ Qui-Claim Deed	Acknowledgment	Jurat ___	1	2	3	4
☐ Sig/Name Aff	Acknowledgment	Jurat ___	1	2	3	4
☐ Survey Aff	Acknowledgment	Jurat ___	1	2	3	4
☐ Warranty Deed	Acknowledgment	Jurat ___	1	2	3	4

Document	Type		SIGNER			
☐ Minor Medical Consent	Acknowledgment	Jurat ___	1	2	3	4
☐ Minor Passport Consent	Acknowledgment	Jurat ___	1	2	3	4
☐ Minor Travel Consent	Acknowledgment	Jurat ___	1	2	3	4
☐ Vehicle Duplicate Title	Acknowledgment	Jurat ___	1	2	3	4
☐ Vehicle Lein Release	Acknowledgment	Jurat ___	1	2	3	4
☐ Vehicle Odom/Vin Ver	Acknowledgment	Jurat ___	1	2	3	4
☐ Vehicle Title Transfer	Acknowledgment	Jurat ___	1	2	3	4
☐ Adv Health Care Dir	Acknowledgment	Jurat ___	1	2	3	4
☐ Assign of Digital Assets	Acknowledgment	Jurat ___	1	2	3	4
☐ Assign of Personal Prop	Acknowledgment	Jurat ___	1	2	3	4
☐ HIPAA Release	Acknowledgment	Jurat ___	1	2	3	4
☐ Living Trust	Acknowledgment	Jurat ___	1	2	3	4
☐ Last Will & Testament	Acknowledgment	Jurat ___	1	2	3	4
☐ POA	Acknowledgment	Jurat ___	1	2	3	4
☐ Trust Certification	Acknowledgment	Jurat ___	1	2	3	4

Additional notarial act columns (right section): Acknowledgment — Jurat — Copy — Oath — SW — 1 2 3 4

SIGNING ADDRESS	OTHERS IN ATTENDANCE	CLIENT / SIGNING SERVICE	FEE
		LENDER / LOAN NUMBER	

NOTES

	ADDRESS	SIGNATURE	PHONE	INITIAL IF OATH/AFF TAKEN	RIGHT THUMB PRINT
1			EMAIL		
2	ADDRESS	SIGNATURE	PHONE / EMAIL	INITIAL IF OATH/AFF TAKEN	RIGHT THUMB PRINT
3	ADDRESS	SIGNATURE	PHONE / EMAIL	INITIAL IF OATH/AFF TAKEN	RIGHT THUMB PRINT
4	ADDRESS	SIGNATURE	PHONE / EMAIL	INITIAL IF OATH/AFF TAKEN	RIGHT THUMB PRINT

Notary Journal Entry (Entries 1–4)

Each entry block contains:

#	DATE / TIME	NAME	IDENTITY VERIFIED	WILLINGNESS & COMPETENCE	FORMAT
1	DATE ___ / TIME ___	☐ Signer ☐ Witness	☐ D.L. ☐ Passport ☐ Credible Witness ☐ Other	☐ Expressed willingness ☐ Mentally alert ☐ Indicated understanding	☐ Paper ☐ Electronic ☐ RON
2	DATE ___ / TIME ___	☐ Signer ☐ Witness	☐ D.L. ☐ Passport ☐ Credible Witness ☐ Other	☐ Expressed willingness ☐ Mentally alert ☐ Indicated understanding	☐ Paper ☐ Electronic ☐ RON
3	DATE ___ / TIME ___	☐ Signer ☐ Witness	☐ D.L. ☐ Passport ☐ Credible Witness ☐ Other	☐ Expressed willingness ☐ Mentally alert ☐ Indicated understanding	☐ Paper ☐ Electronic ☐ RON
4	DATE ___ / TIME ___	☐ Signer ☐ Witness	☐ D.L. ☐ Passport ☐ Credible Witness ☐ Other	☐ Expressed willingness ☐ Mentally alert ☐ Indicated understanding	☐ Paper ☐ Electronic ☐ RON

DOCUMENT(S) SIGNED

Document	Type	SIGNER 1 2 3 4
☐ Borrower's Aff	Acknowledgment Jurat	____ 1 2 3 4
☐ Compliance Agrmt	Acknowledgment Jurat	____ 1 2 3 4
☐ Correction Agrmt	Acknowledgment Jurat	____ 1 2 3 4
☐ Debts/Leins Aff	Acknowledgment Jurat	____ 1 2 3 4
☐ Deed of Trust	Acknowledgment Jurat	____ 1 2 3 4
☐ Distrib of Proceeds	Acknowledgment Jurat	____ 1 2 3 4
☐ E&O Agrmt	Acknowledgment Jurat	____ 1 2 3 4
☐ Grant Deed	Acknowledgment Jurat	____ 1 2 3 4
☐ Marital Stat Aff	Acknowledgment Jurat	____ 1 2 3 4
☐ Mortgage	Acknowledgment Jurat	____ 1 2 3 4
☐ Occupancy/Fin Aff	Acknowledgment Jurat	____ 1 2 3 4
☐ Owner's Aff	Acknowledgment Jurat	____ 1 2 3 4
☐ Payoff Aff	Acknowledgment Jurat	____ 1 2 3 4
☐ Quit-Claim Deed	Acknowledgment Jurat	____ 1 2 3 4
☐ Sig/Name Aff	Acknowledgment Jurat	____ 1 2 3 4
☐ Survey Aff	Acknowledgment Jurat	____ 1 2 3 4
☐ Warranty Deed	Acknowledgment Jurat	____ 1 2 3 4
☐ Minor Medical Consent	Acknowledgment Jurat	____ 1 2 3 4
☐ Minor Passport Consent	Acknowledgment Jurat	____ 1 2 3 4
☐ Minor Travel Consent	Acknowledgment Jurat	____ 1 2 3 4
☐ Vehicle Duplicate Title	Acknowledgment Jurat	____ 1 2 3 4
☐ Vehicle Lein Release	Acknowledgment Jurat	____ 1 2 3 4
☐ Vehicle Odom/Vin Ver	Acknowledgment Jurat	____ 1 2 3 4
☐ Vehicle Title Transfer	Acknowledgment Jurat	____ 1 2 3 4
☐ Adv Health Care Dir	Acknowledgment Jurat	____ 1 2 3 4
☐ Assign of Digital Assets	Acknowledgment Jurat	____ 1 2 3 4
☐ Assign of Personal Prop	Acknowledgment Jurat	____ 1 2 3 4
☐ HIPAA Release	Acknowledgment Jurat	____ 1 2 3 4
☐ Living Trust ____	Acknowledgment Jurat	____ 1 2 3 4
☐ Last Will & Testament	Acknowledgment Jurat	____ 1 2 3 4
☐ POA ____	Acknowledgment Jurat	____ 1 2 3 4
☐ Trust Certification	Acknowledgment Jurat	____ 1 2 3 4

The right-hand document column also includes notarial act options: Acknowledgment, Jurat, Copy, Oath, SW with Signer columns 1 2 3 4.

SIGNING ADDRESS	OTHERS IN ATTENDANCE	CLIENT / SIGNING SERVICE	FEE
		LENDER / LOAN NUMBER	

NOTES

	ADDRESS	PHONE	SIGNATURE	INITIAL IF OATH/AFF TAKEN	RIGHT THUMB PRINT
1		EMAIL			
2	ADDRESS	PHONE	SIGNATURE	INITIAL IF OATH/AFF TAKEN	RIGHT THUMB PRINT
		EMAIL			
3	ADDRESS	PHONE	SIGNATURE	INITIAL IF OATH/AFF TAKEN	RIGHT THUMB PRINT
		EMAIL			
4	ADDRESS	PHONE	SIGNATURE	INITIAL IF OATH/AFF TAKEN	RIGHT THUMB PRINT
		EMAIL			

Entry 1

DATE		IDENTITY VERIFIED	WILLINGNESS & COMPETENCE	FORMAT
TIME	NAME ☐ Signer ☐ Witness	☐ D.L. ☐ Passport ☐ Credible Witness ☐ Other	☐ Expressed willingness ☐ Mentally alert ☐ Indicated understanding	☐ Paper ☐ Electronic ☐ RON

Entry 2

DATE		IDENTITY VERIFIED	WILLINGNESS & COMPETENCE	FORMAT
TIME	NAME ☐ Signer ☐ Witness	☐ D.L. ☐ Passport ☐ Credible Witness ☐ Other	☐ Expressed willingness ☐ Mentally alert ☐ Indicated understanding	☐ Paper ☐ Electronic ☐ RON

Entry 3

DATE		IDENTITY VERIFIED	WILLINGNESS & COMPETENCE	FORMAT
TIME	NAME ☐ Signer ☐ Witness	☐ D.L. ☐ Passport ☐ Credible Witness ☐ Other	☐ Expressed willingness ☐ Mentally alert ☐ Indicated understanding	☐ Paper ☐ Electronic ☐ RON

Entry 4

DATE		IDENTITY VERIFIED	WILLINGNESS & COMPETENCE	FORMAT
TIME	NAME ☐ Signer ☐ Witness	☐ D.L. ☐ Passport ☐ Credible Witness ☐ Other	☐ Expressed willingness ☐ Mentally alert ☐ Indicated understanding	☐ Paper ☐ Electronic ☐ RON

DOCUMENT(S) SIGNED — SIGNER 1 2 3 4

Document	Type	Signer
☐ Borrower's Aff	Acknowledgment Jurat	1 2 3 4
☐ Compliance Agrmt	Acknowledgment Jurat	1 2 3 4
☐ Correction Agrmt	Acknowledgment Jurat	1 2 3 4
☐ Debts/Leins Aff	Acknowledgment Jurat	1 2 3 4
☐ Deed of Trust	Acknowledgment Jurat	1 2 3 4
☐ Distrib of Proceeds	Acknowledgment Jurat	1 2 3 4
☐ E&O Agrmt	Acknowledgment Jurat	1 2 3 4
☐ Grant Deed	Acknowledgment Jurat	1 2 3 4
☐ Marital Stat Aff	Acknowledgment Jurat	1 2 3 4
☐ Mortgage	Acknowledgment Jurat	1 2 3 4
☐ Occupancy/Fin Aff	Acknowledgment Jurat	1 2 3 4
☐ Owner's Aff	Acknowledgment Jurat	1 2 3 4
☐ Payoff Aff	Acknowledgment Jurat	1 2 3 4
☐ Quit-Claim Deed	Acknowledgment Jurat	1 2 3 4
☐ Sig/Name Aff	Acknowledgment Jurat	1 2 3 4
☐ Survey Aff	Acknowledgment Jurat	1 2 3 4
☐ Warranty Deed	Acknowledgment Jurat	1 2 3 4

DOCUMENT(S) SIGNED (continued) — SIGNER 1 2 3 4

Document	Type	Signer
☐ Minor Medical Consent	Acknowledgment Jurat	1 2 3 4
☐ Minor Passport Consent	Acknowledgment Jurat	1 2 3 4
☐ Minor Travel Consent	Acknowledgment Jurat	1 2 3 4
☐ Vehicle Duplicate Title	Acknowledgment Jurat	1 2 3 4
☐ Vehicle Lein Release	Acknowledgment Jurat	1 2 3 4
☐ Vehicle Odom/Vin Ver	Acknowledgment Jurat	1 2 3 4
☐ Vehicle Title Transfer	Acknowledgment Jurat	1 2 3 4
☐ Adv Health Care Dir	Acknowledgment Jurat	1 2 3 4
☐ Assign of Digital Assets	Acknowledgment Jurat	1 2 3 4
☐ Assign of Personal Prop	Acknowledgment Jurat	1 2 3 4
☐ HIPAA Release	Acknowledgment Jurat	1 2 3 4
☐ Living Trust	Acknowledgment Jurat	1 2 3 4
☐ Last Will & Testament	Acknowledgment Jurat	1 2 3 4
☐ POA	Acknowledgment Jurat	1 2 3 4
☐ Trust Certification	Acknowledgment Jurat Copy Oath SW	1 2 3 4

SIGNING ADDRESS	OTHERS IN ATTENDANCE	CLIENT / SIGNING SERVICE	FEE
		LENDER / LOAN NUMBER	

NOTES

_____

#	ADDRESS	SIGNATURE	PHONE	EMAIL	INITIAL IF OATH/AFF TAKEN	RIGHT THUMB PRINT
1						
2						
3						
4						

Notary Journal Entries

Entries 1–4

#	DATE / TIME	NAME	IDENTITY VERIFIED	WILLINGNESS & COMPETENCE	FORMAT
1	DATE ____ / TIME ____	☐ Signer ☐ Witness	☐ D.L. ☐ Passport ☐ Credible Witness ☐ Other	☐ Expressed willingness ☐ Mentally alert ☐ Indicated understanding	☐ Paper ☐ Electronic ☐ RON
2	DATE ____ / TIME ____	☐ Signer ☐ Witness	☐ D.L. ☐ Passport ☐ Credible Witness ☐ Other	☐ Expressed willingness ☐ Mentally alert ☐ Indicated understanding	☐ Paper ☐ Electronic ☐ RON
3	DATE ____ / TIME ____	☐ Signer ☐ Witness	☐ D.L. ☐ Passport ☐ Credible Witness ☐ Other	☐ Expressed willingness ☐ Mentally alert ☐ Indicated understanding	☐ Paper ☐ Electronic ☐ RON
4	DATE ____ / TIME ____	☐ Signer ☐ Witness	☐ D.L. ☐ Passport ☐ Credible Witness ☐ Other	☐ Expressed willingness ☐ Mentally alert ☐ Indicated understanding	☐ Paper ☐ Electronic ☐ RON

DOCUMENT(S) SIGNED

Document	Notarial Act			SIGNER 1	2	3	4
☐ Borrower's Aff	Acknowledgment	Jurat	____	1	2	3	4
☐ Compliance Agrmt	Acknowledgment	Jurat	____	1	2	3	4
☐ Correction Agrmt	Acknowledgment	Jurat	____	1	2	3	4
☐ Debts/Leins Aff	Acknowledgment	Jurat	____	1	2	3	4
☐ Deed of Trust	Acknowledgment	Jurat	____	1	2	3	4
☐ Distrib of Proceeds	Acknowledgment	Jurat	____	1	2	3	4
☐ E&O Agrmt	Acknowledgment	Jurat	____	1	2	3	4
☐ Grant Deed	Acknowledgment	Jurat	____	1	2	3	4
☐ Marital Stat Aff	Acknowledgment	Jurat	____	1	2	3	4
☐ Mortgage	Acknowledgment	Jurat	____	1	2	3	4
☐ Occupancy/Fin Aff	Acknowledgment	Jurat	____	1	2	3	4
☐ Owner's Aff	Acknowledgment	Jurat	____	1	2	3	4
☐ Payoff Aff	Acknowledgment	Jurat	____	1	2	3	4
☐ Quit-Claim Deed	Acknowledgment	Jurat	____	1	2	3	4
☐ Sig/Name Aff	Acknowledgment	Jurat	____	1	2	3	4
☐ Survey Aff	Acknowledgment	Jurat	____	1	2	3	4
☐ Warranty Deed	Acknowledgment	Jurat	____	1	2	3	4

Document	Notarial Act					SIGNER 1	2	3	4
☐ Minor Medical Consent	Acknowledgment	Jurat				1	2	3	4
☐ Minor Passport Consent	Acknowledgment	Jurat	Copy	Oath	SW	1	2	3	4
☐ Minor Travel Consent	Acknowledgment	Jurat				1	2	3	4
☐ Vehicle Duplicate Title	Acknowledgment	Jurat				1	2	3	4
☐ Vehicle Lein Release	Acknowledgment	Jurat	Copy	Oath	SW	1	2	3	4
☐ Vehicle Odom/Vin Ver	Acknowledgment	Jurat				1	2	3	4
☐ Vehicle Title Transfer	Acknowledgment	Jurat	Copy	Oath	SW	1	2	3	4
☐ Adv Health Care Dir	Acknowledgment	Jurat				1	2	3	4
☐ Assign of Digital Assets	Acknowledgment	Jurat	Copy	Oath	SW	1	2	3	4
☐ Assign of Personal Prop	Acknowledgment	Jurat				1	2	3	4
☐ HIPAA Release	Acknowledgment	Jurat				1	2	3	4
☐ Living Trust	Acknowledgment	Jurat	Copy	Oath	SW	1	2	3	4
☐ Last Will & Testament	Acknowledgment	Jurat				1	2	3	4
☐ POA	Acknowledgment	Jurat				1	2	3	4
☐ Trust Certification	Acknowledgment	Jurat	Copy	Oath	SW	1	2	3	4

SIGNING ADDRESS	OTHERS IN ATTENDANCE	CLIENT / SIGNING SERVICE	FEE
		LENDER / LOAN NUMBER	

NOTES

#	ADDRESS	PHONE / EMAIL	SIGNATURE	INITIAL IF OATH/AFF TAKEN	RIGHT THUMB PRINT
1		PHONE / EMAIL			
2		PHONE / EMAIL			
3		PHONE / EMAIL			
4		PHONE / EMAIL			

Notary Journal Entry (Entries 1–4)

Each entry (1, 2, 3, 4) contains the following fields:

1
- DATE:
- TIME:
- NAME: ☐ Signer ☐ Witness
- IDENTITY VERIFIED: ☐ D.L. ☐ Passport ☐ Credible Witness ☐ Other
- WILLINGNESS & COMPETENCE: ☐ Expressed willingness ☐ Mentally alert ☐ Indicated understanding
- FORMAT: ☐ Paper ☐ Electronic ☐ RON

2
- DATE:
- TIME:
- NAME: ☐ Signer ☐ Witness
- IDENTITY VERIFIED: ☐ D.L. ☐ Passport ☐ Credible Witness ☐ Other
- WILLINGNESS & COMPETENCE: ☐ Expressed willingness ☐ Mentally alert ☐ Indicated understanding
- FORMAT: ☐ Paper ☐ Electronic ☐ RON

3
- DATE:
- TIME:
- NAME: ☐ Signer ☐ Witness
- IDENTITY VERIFIED: ☐ D.L. ☐ Passport ☐ Credible Witness ☐ Other
- WILLINGNESS & COMPETENCE: ☐ Expressed willingness ☐ Mentally alert ☐ Indicated understanding
- FORMAT: ☐ Paper ☐ Electronic ☐ RON

4
- DATE:
- TIME:
- NAME: ☐ Signer ☐ Witness
- IDENTITY VERIFIED: ☐ D.L. ☐ Passport ☐ Credible Witness ☐ Other
- WILLINGNESS & COMPETENCE: ☐ Expressed willingness ☐ Mentally alert ☐ Indicated understanding
- FORMAT: ☐ Paper ☐ Electronic ☐ RON

DOCUMENT(S) SIGNED

Document	Acts					SIGNER 1	2	3	4
☐ Borrower's Aff	Acknowledgment	Jurat				1	2	3	4
☐ Compliance Agrmt	Acknowledgment	Jurat				1	2	3	4
☐ Correction Agrmt	Acknowledgment	Jurat				1	2	3	4
☐ Debts/Leins Aff	Acknowledgment	Jurat				1	2	3	4
☐ Deed of Trust	Acknowledgment	Jurat				1	2	3	4
☐ Distrib of Proceeds	Acknowledgment	Jurat				1	2	3	4
☐ E&O Agrmt	Acknowledgment	Jurat				1	2	3	4
☐ Grant Deed	Acknowledgment	Jurat				1	2	3	4
☐ Marital Stat Aff	Acknowledgment	Jurat				1	2	3	4
☐ Mortgage	Acknowledgment	Jurat				1	2	3	4
☐ Occupancy/Fin Aff	Acknowledgment	Jurat				1	2	3	4
☐ Owner's Aff	Acknowledgment	Jurat				1	2	3	4
☐ Payoff Aff	Acknowledgment	Jurat				1	2	3	4
☐ Quit-Claim Deed	Acknowledgment	Jurat				1	2	3	4
☐ Sig/Name Aff	Acknowledgment	Jurat				1	2	3	4
☐ Survey Aff	Acknowledgment	Jurat				1	2	3	4
☐ Warranty Deed	Acknowledgment	Jurat				1	2	3	4

Document	Acts					SIGNER 1	2	3	4
☐ Minor Medical Consent	Acknowledgment	Jurat	Copy	Oath	SW	1	2	3	4
☐ Minor Passport Consent	Acknowledgment	Jurat				1	2	3	4
☐ Minor Travel Consent	Acknowledgment	Jurat				1	2	3	4
☐ Vehicle Duplicate Title	Acknowledgment	Jurat	Copy	Oath	SW	1	2	3	4
☐ Vehicle Lein Release	Acknowledgment	Jurat				1	2	3	4
☐ Vehicle Odom/Vin Ver	Acknowledgment	Jurat	Copy	Oath	SW	1	2	3	4
☐ Vehicle Title Transfer	Acknowledgment	Jurat				1	2	3	4
☐ Adv Health Care Dir	Acknowledgment	Jurat	Copy	Oath	SW	1	2	3	4
☐ Assign of Digital Assets	Acknowledgment	Jurat				1	2	3	4
☐ Assign of Personal Prop	Acknowledgment	Jurat				1	2	3	4
☐ HIPAA Release	Acknowledgment	Jurat				1	2	3	4
☐ Living Trust	Acknowledgment	Jurat	Copy	Oath	SW	1	2	3	4
☐ Last Will & Testament	Acknowledgment	Jurat				1	2	3	4
☐ POA	Acknowledgment	Jurat				1	2	3	4
☐ Trust Certification	Acknowledgment	Jurat	Copy	Oath	SW	1	2	3	4

SIGNING ADDRESS	OTHERS IN ATTENDANCE	CLIENT / SIGNING SERVICE	FEE
		LENDER / LOAN NUMBER	

NOTES

	ADDRESS	PHONE	SIGNATURE	INITIAL IF OATH/AFF TAKEN	RIGHT THUMB PRINT
1		EMAIL			
2	ADDRESS	PHONE	SIGNATURE	INITIAL IF OATH/AFF TAKEN	RIGHT THUMB PRINT
		EMAIL			
3	ADDRESS	PHONE	SIGNATURE	INITIAL IF OATH/AFF TAKEN	RIGHT THUMB PRINT
		EMAIL			
4	ADDRESS	PHONE	SIGNATURE	INITIAL IF OATH/AFF TAKEN	RIGHT THUMB PRINT
		EMAIL			

Notary Journal Entries

Entry 1
- **DATE:**
- **TIME:**
- **NAME:** ☐ Signer ☐ Witness
- **IDENTITY VERIFIED:** ☐ D.L. ☐ Passport ☐ Credible Witness ☐ Other
- **WILLINGNESS & COMPETENCE:** ☐ Expressed willingness ☐ Mentally alert ☐ Indicated understanding
- **FORMAT:** ☐ Paper ☐ Electronic ☐ RON

Entry 2
- **DATE:**
- **TIME:**
- **NAME:** ☐ Signer ☐ Witness
- **IDENTITY VERIFIED:** ☐ D.L. ☐ Passport ☐ Credible Witness ☐ Other
- **WILLINGNESS & COMPETENCE:** ☐ Expressed willingness ☐ Mentally alert ☐ Indicated understanding
- **FORMAT:** ☐ Paper ☐ Electronic ☐ RON

Entry 3
- **DATE:**
- **TIME:**
- **NAME:** ☐ Signer ☐ Witness
- **IDENTITY VERIFIED:** ☐ D.L. ☐ Passport ☐ Credible Witness ☐ Other
- **WILLINGNESS & COMPETENCE:** ☐ Expressed willingness ☐ Mentally alert ☐ Indicated understanding
- **FORMAT:** ☐ Paper ☐ Electronic ☐ RON

Entry 4
- **DATE:**
- **TIME:**
- **NAME:** ☐ Signer ☐ Witness
- **IDENTITY VERIFIED:** ☐ D.L. ☐ Passport ☐ Credible Witness ☐ Other
- **WILLINGNESS & COMPETENCE:** ☐ Expressed willingness ☐ Mentally alert ☐ Indicated understanding
- **FORMAT:** ☐ Paper ☐ Electronic ☐ RON

DOCUMENT(S) SIGNED

Document	Type		SIGNER			
☐ Borrower's Aff	Acknowledgment	Jurat	1	2	3	4
☐ Compliance Agrmt	Acknowledgment	Jurat	1	2	3	4
☐ Correction Agrmt	Acknowledgment	Jurat	1	2	3	4
☐ Debts/Leins Aff	Acknowledgment	Jurat	1	2	3	4
☐ Deed of Trust	Acknowledgment	Jurat	1	2	3	4
☐ Distrib of Proceeds	Acknowledgment	Jurat	1	2	3	4
☐ E&O Agrmt	Acknowledgment	Jurat	1	2	3	4
☐ Grant Deed	Acknowledgment	Jurat	1	2	3	4
☐ Marital Stat Aff	Acknowledgment	Jurat	1	2	3	4
☐ Mortgage	Acknowledgment	Jurat	1	2	3	4
☐ Occupancy/Fin Aff	Acknowledgment	Jurat	1	2	3	4
☐ Owner's Aff	Acknowledgment	Jurat	1	2	3	4
☐ Payoff Aff	Acknowledgment	Jurat	1	2	3	4
☐ Quit-Claim Deed	Acknowledgment	Jurat	1	2	3	4
☐ Sig/Name Aff	Acknowledgment	Jurat	1	2	3	4
☐ Survey Aff	Acknowledgment	Jurat	1	2	3	4
☐ Warranty Deed	Acknowledgment	Jurat	1	2	3	4

Document	Type						SIGNER			
☐ Minor Medical Consent	Acknowledgment	Jurat	Copy	Oath	SW		1	2	3	4
☐ Minor Passport Consent	Acknowledgment	Jurat	Copy	Oath	SW		1	2	3	4
☐ Minor Travel Consent	Acknowledgment	Jurat	Copy	Oath	SW		1	2	3	4
☐ Vehicle Duplicate Title	Acknowledgment	Jurat	Copy	Oath	SW		1	2	3	4
☐ Vehicle Lein Release	Acknowledgment	Jurat	Copy	Oath	SW		1	2	3	4
☐ Vehicle Odom/Vin Ver	Acknowledgment	Jurat	Copy	Oath	SW		1	2	3	4
☐ Vehicle Title Transfer	Acknowledgment	Jurat	Copy	Oath	SW		1	2	3	4
☐ Adv Health Care Dir	Acknowledgment	Jurat	Copy	Oath	SW		1	2	3	4
☐ Assign of Digital Assets	Acknowledgment	Jurat	Copy	Oath	SW		1	2	3	4
☐ Assign of Personal Prop	Acknowledgment	Jurat	Copy	Oath	SW		1	2	3	4
☐ HIPAA Release	Acknowledgment	Jurat	Copy	Oath	SW		1	2	3	4
☐ Living Trust	Acknowledgment	Jurat	Copy	Oath	SW		1	2	3	4
☐ Last Will & Testament	Acknowledgment	Jurat	Copy	Oath	SW		1	2	3	4
☐ POA	Acknowledgment	Jurat	Copy	Oath	SW		1	2	3	4
☐ Trust Certification	Acknowledgment	Jurat	Copy	Oath	SW		1	2	3	4

SIGNING ADDRESS	OTHERS IN ATTENDANCE	CLIENT / SIGNING SERVICE	FEE
		LENDER / LOAN NUMBER	

NOTES

	ADDRESS	PHONE	SIGNATURE	INITIAL IF OATH/AFF TAKEN	RIGHT THUMB PRINT
1		EMAIL			
2	ADDRESS	PHONE	SIGNATURE	INITIAL IF OATH/AFF TAKEN	RIGHT THUMB PRINT
		EMAIL			
3	ADDRESS	PHONE	SIGNATURE	INITIAL IF OATH/AFF TAKEN	RIGHT THUMB PRINT
		EMAIL			
4	ADDRESS	PHONE	SIGNATURE	INITIAL IF OATH/AFF TAKEN	RIGHT THUMB PRINT
		EMAIL			

Notary Journal Entry Form

Entries 1–4

#	DATE / TIME	NAME	IDENTITY VERIFIED	WILLINGNESS & COMPETENCE	FORMAT
1	DATE ____ / TIME ____	☐ Signer ☐ Witness	☐ D.L. ☐ Passport ☐ Credible Witness ☐ Other	☐ Expressed willingness ☐ Mentally alert ☐ Indicated understanding	☐ Paper ☐ Electronic ☐ RON
2	DATE ____ / TIME ____	☐ Signer ☐ Witness	☐ D.L. ☐ Passport ☐ Credible Witness ☐ Other	☐ Expressed willingness ☐ Mentally alert ☐ Indicated understanding	☐ Paper ☐ Electronic ☐ RON
3	DATE ____ / TIME ____	☐ Signer ☐ Witness	☐ D.L. ☐ Passport ☐ Credible Witness ☐ Other	☐ Expressed willingness ☐ Mentally alert ☐ Indicated understanding	☐ Paper ☐ Electronic ☐ RON
4	DATE ____ / TIME ____	☐ Signer ☐ Witness	☐ D.L. ☐ Passport ☐ Credible Witness ☐ Other	☐ Expressed willingness ☐ Mentally alert ☐ Indicated understanding	☐ Paper ☐ Electronic ☐ RON

DOCUMENT(S) SIGNED

Document	Type	SIGNER 1	2	3	4
☐ Borrower's Aff	Acknowledgment / Jurat	1	2	3	4
☐ Compliance Agrmt	Acknowledgment / Jurat	1	2	3	4
☐ Correction Agrmt	Acknowledgment / Jurat	1	2	3	4
☐ Debts/Leins Aff	Acknowledgment / Jurat	1	2	3	4
☐ Deed of Trust	Acknowledgment / Jurat	1	2	3	4
☐ Distrib of Proceeds	Acknowledgment / Jurat	1	2	3	4
☐ E&O Agrmt	Acknowledgment / Jurat	1	2	3	4
☐ Grant Deed	Acknowledgment / Jurat	1	2	3	4
☐ Marital Stat Aff	Acknowledgment / Jurat	1	2	3	4
☐ Mortgage	Acknowledgment / Jurat	1	2	3	4
☐ Occupancy/Fin Aff	Acknowledgment / Jurat	1	2	3	4
☐ Owner's Aff	Acknowledgment / Jurat	1	2	3	4
☐ Payoff Aff	Acknowledgment / Jurat	1	2	3	4
☐ Quit-Claim Deed	Acknowledgment / Jurat	1	2	3	4
☐ Sig/Name Aff	Acknowledgment / Jurat	1	2	3	4
☐ Survey Aff	Acknowledgment / Jurat	1	2	3	4
☐ Warranty Deed	Acknowledgment / Jurat	1	2	3	4

Document	Type	SIGNER 1	2	3	4
☐ Minor Medical Consent	Acknowledgment / Jurat	1	2	3	4
☐ Minor Passport Consent	Acknowledgment / Jurat	1	2	3	4
☐ Minor Travel Consent	Acknowledgment / Jurat	1	2	3	4
☐ Vehicle Duplicate Title	Acknowledgment / Jurat	1	2	3	4
☐ Vehicle Lein Release	Acknowledgment / Jurat	1	2	3	4
☐ Vehicle Odom/Vin Ver	Acknowledgment / Jurat	1	2	3	4
☐ Vehicle Title Transfer	Acknowledgment / Jurat	1	2	3	4
☐ Adv Health Care Dir	Acknowledgment / Jurat	1	2	3	4
☐ Assign of Digital Assets	Acknowledgment / Jurat	1	2	3	4
☐ Assign of Personal Prop	Acknowledgment / Jurat	1	2	3	4
☐ HIPAA Release	Acknowledgment / Jurat	1	2	3	4
☐ Living Trust	Acknowledgment / Jurat	1	2	3	4
☐ Last Will & Testament	Acknowledgment / Jurat	1	2	3	4
☐ POA	Acknowledgment / Jurat	1	2	3	4
☐ Trust Certification	Acknowledgment / Jurat	1	2	3	4

Additional columns (top right list): Acknowledgment — Jurat — Copy — Oath — SW, SIGNER 1 2 3 4

SIGNING ADDRESS	OTHERS IN ATTENDANCE	CLIENT / SIGNING SERVICE	FEE
		LENDER / LOAN NUMBER	

NOTES

#	ADDRESS	PHONE	EMAIL	SIGNATURE	INITIAL IF OATH/AFF TAKEN	RIGHT THUMB PRINT
1						
2						
3						
4						

Signer Records

1
	DATE			
1	TIME			

NAME: ☐ Signer ☐ Witness

WILLINGNESS & COMPETENCE: ☐ Expressed willingness ☐ Mentally alert ☐ Indicated understanding

IDENTITY VERIFIED: ☐ D.L. ☐ Passport ☐ Credible Witness ☐ Other

FORMAT: ☐ Paper ☐ Electronic ☐ RON

2
DATE / TIME

NAME: ☐ Signer ☐ Witness

WILLINGNESS & COMPETENCE: ☐ Expressed willingness ☐ Mentally alert ☐ Indicated understanding

IDENTITY VERIFIED: ☐ D.L. ☐ Passport ☐ Credible Witness ☐ Other

FORMAT: ☐ Paper ☐ Electronic ☐ RON

3
DATE / TIME

NAME: ☐ Signer ☐ Witness

WILLINGNESS & COMPETENCE: ☐ Expressed willingness ☐ Mentally alert ☐ Indicated understanding

IDENTITY VERIFIED: ☐ D.L. ☐ Passport ☐ Credible Witness ☐ Other

FORMAT: ☐ Paper ☐ Electronic ☐ RON

4
DATE / TIME

NAME: ☐ Signer ☐ Witness

WILLINGNESS & COMPETENCE: ☐ Expressed willingness ☐ Mentally alert ☐ Indicated understanding

IDENTITY VERIFIED: ☐ D.L. ☐ Passport ☐ Credible Witness ☐ Other

FORMAT: ☐ Paper ☐ Electronic ☐ RON

DOCUMENT(S) SIGNED

Document	Type		SIGNER 1 2 3 4
☐ Borrower's Aff	Acknowledgment	Jurat _____	1 2 3 4
☐ Compliance Agrmt	Acknowledgment	Jurat _____	1 2 3 4
☐ Correction Agrmt	Acknowledgment	Jurat _____	1 2 3 4
☐ Debts/Leins Aff	Acknowledgment	Jurat _____	1 2 3 4
☐ Deed of Trust	Acknowledgment	Jurat _____	1 2 3 4
☐ Distrib of Proceeds	Acknowledgment	Jurat _____	1 2 3 4
☐ E&O Agrmt	Acknowledgment	Jurat _____	1 2 3 4
☐ Grant Deed	Acknowledgment	Jurat _____	1 2 3 4
☐ Marital Stat Aff	Acknowledgment	Jurat _____	1 2 3 4
☐ Mortgage	Acknowledgment	Jurat _____	1 2 3 4
☐ Occupancy/Fin Aff	Acknowledgment	Jurat _____	1 2 3 4
☐ Owner's Aff	Acknowledgment	Jurat _____	1 2 3 4
☐ Payoff Aff	Acknowledgment	Jurat _____	1 2 3 4
☐ Quit-Claim Deed	Acknowledgment	Jurat _____	1 2 3 4
☐ Sig/Name Aff	Acknowledgment	Jurat _____	1 2 3 4
☐ Survey Aff	Acknowledgment	Jurat _____	1 2 3 4
☐ Warranty Deed	Acknowledgment	Jurat _____	1 2 3 4

Document	Type				SIGNER 1 2 3 4
☐ Minor Medical Consent	Acknowledgment	Jurat	Copy	Oath SW	1 2 3 4
☐ Minor Passport Consent	Acknowledgment	Jurat	Copy	Oath SW	1 2 3 4
☐ Minor Travel Consent	Acknowledgment	Jurat	Copy	Oath SW	1 2 3 4
☐ Vehicle Duplicate Title	Acknowledgment	Jurat	Copy	Oath SW	1 2 3 4
☐ Vehicle Lein Release	Acknowledgment	Jurat	Copy	Oath SW	1 2 3 4
☐ Vehicle Odom/Vin Ver	Acknowledgment	Jurat	Copy	Oath SW	1 2 3 4
☐ Vehicle Title Transfer	Acknowledgment	Jurat	Copy	Oath SW	1 2 3 4
☐ Adv Health Care Dir	Acknowledgment	Jurat	Copy	Oath SW	1 2 3 4
☐ Assign of Digital Assets	Acknowledgment	Jurat	Copy	Oath SW	1 2 3 4
☐ Assign of Personal Prop	Acknowledgment	Jurat	Copy	Oath SW	1 2 3 4
☐ HIPAA Release	Acknowledgment	Jurat	Copy	Oath SW	1 2 3 4
☐ Living Trust _____	Acknowledgment	Jurat	Copy	Oath SW	1 2 3 4
☐ Last Will & Testament	Acknowledgment	Jurat	Copy	Oath SW	1 2 3 4
☐ POA _____	Acknowledgment	Jurat	Copy	Oath SW	1 2 3 4
☐ Trust Certification	Acknowledgment	Jurat	Copy	Oath SW	1 2 3 4

SIGNING ADDRESS	OTHERS IN ATTENDANCE	CLIENT / SIGNING SERVICE	FEE
		LENDER / LOAN NUMBER	

NOTES

_____

#	ADDRESS	PHONE	EMAIL	SIGNATURE	INITIAL IF OATH/AFF TAKEN	RIGHT THUMB PRINT
1						
2						
3						
4						

#	Date / Time	Name	Identity Verified	Willingness & Competence	Format
1	DATE TIME	NAME ❑ Signer ❑ Witness	IDENTITY VERIFIED ❑ D.L. ❑ Passport ❑ Credible Witness ❑ Other	WILLINGNESS & COMPETENCE ❑ Expressed willingness ❑ Mentally alert ❑ Indicated understanding	FORMAT ❑ Paper ❑ Electronic ❑ RON
2	DATE TIME	NAME ❑ Signer ❑ Witness	IDENTITY VERIFIED ❑ D.L. ❑ Passport ❑ Credible Witness ❑ Other	WILLINGNESS & COMPETENCE ❑ Expressed willingness ❑ Mentally alert ❑ Indicated understanding	FORMAT ❑ Paper ❑ Electronic ❑ RON
3	DATE TIME	NAME ❑ Signer ❑ Witness	IDENTITY VERIFIED ❑ D.L. ❑ Passport ❑ Credible Witness ❑ Other	WILLINGNESS & COMPETENCE ❑ Expressed willingness ❑ Mentally alert ❑ Indicated understanding	FORMAT ❑ Paper ❑ Electronic ❑ RON
4	DATE TIME	NAME ❑ Signer ❑ Witness	IDENTITY VERIFIED ❑ D.L. ❑ Passport ❑ Credible Witness ❑ Other	WILLINGNESS & COMPETENCE ❑ Expressed willingness ❑ Mentally alert ❑ Indicated understanding	FORMAT ❑ Paper ❑ Electronic ❑ RON

DOCUMENT(S) SIGNED

Document	Type	Signer	Document	Type	Signer	Other
❑ Borrower's Aff	Acknowledgment Jurat ______	1 2 3 4	❑ Minor Medical Consent	Acknowledgment Jurat ______	1 2 3 4	❑ ______
❑ Compliance Agrmt	Acknowledgment Jurat ______	1 2 3 4	❑ Minor Passport Consent	Acknowledgment Jurat ______	1 2 3 4	Acknowledgment Jurat Copy Oath SW 1 2 3 4
❑ Correction Agrmt	Acknowledgment Jurat ______	1 2 3 4	❑ Minor Travel Consent	Acknowledgment Jurat ______	1 2 3 4	
❑ Debts/Leins Aff	Acknowledgment Jurat ______	1 2 3 4				❑ ______
❑ Deed of Trust	Acknowledgment Jurat ______	1 2 3 4	❑ Vehicle Duplicate Title	Acknowledgment Jurat ______	1 2 3 4	Acknowledgment Jurat Copy Oath SW 1 2 3 4
❑ Distrib of Proceeds	Acknowledgment Jurat ______	1 2 3 4	❑ Vehicle Lein Release	Acknowledgment Jurat ______	1 2 3 4	
❑ E&O Agrmt	Acknowledgment Jurat ______	1 2 3 4	❑ Vehicle Odom/Vin Ver	Acknowledgment Jurat ______	1 2 3 4	❑ ______
❑ Grant Deed	Acknowledgment Jurat ______	1 2 3 4	❑ Vehicle Title Transfer	Acknowledgment Jurat ______	1 2 3 4	Acknowledgment Jurat Copy Oath SW 1 2 3 4
❑ Marital Stat Aff	Acknowledgment Jurat ______	1 2 3 4				
❑ Mortgage	Acknowledgment Jurat ______	1 2 3 4	❑ Adv Health Care Dir	Acknowledgment Jurat ______	1 2 3 4	❑ ______
❑ Occupancy/Fin Aff	Acknowledgment Jurat ______	1 2 3 4	❑ Assign of Digital Assets	Acknowledgment Jurat ______	1 2 3 4	Acknowledgment Jurat Copy Oath SW 1 2 3 4
❑ Owner's Aff	Acknowledgment Jurat ______	1 2 3 4	❑ Assign of Personal Prop	Acknowledgment Jurat ______	1 2 3 4	
❑ Payoff Aff	Acknowledgment Jurat ______	1 2 3 4	❑ HIPAA Release	Acknowledgment Jurat ______	1 2 3 4	❑ ______
❑ Quit-Claim Deed	Acknowledgment Jurat ______	1 2 3 4	❑ Living Trust ______	Acknowledgment Jurat ______	1 2 3 4	Acknowledgment Jurat Copy Oath SW 1 2 3 4
❑ Sig/Name Aff	Acknowledgment Jurat ______	1 2 3 4	❑ Last Will & Testament	Acknowledgment Jurat ______	1 2 3 4	
❑ Survey Aff	Acknowledgment Jurat ______	1 2 3 4	❑ POA ______	Acknowledgment Jurat ______	1 2 3 4	❑ ______
❑ Warranty Deed	Acknowledgment Jurat ______	1 2 3 4	❑ Trust Certification	Acknowledgment Jurat ______	1 2 3 4	Acknowledgment Jurat Copy Oath SW 1 2 3 4

SIGNING ADDRESS	OTHERS IN ATTENDANCE	CLIENT / SIGNING SERVICE	FEE
		LENDER / LOAN NUMBER	

NOTES

	ADDRESS	PHONE	EMAIL	SIGNATURE	INITIAL IF OATH/AFF TAKEN	RIGHT THUMB PRINT
1						
2						
3						
4						

Notary Journal Entry Form

Entries 1–4

#	DATE / TIME	NAME	IDENTITY VERIFIED	WILLINGNESS & COMPETENCE	FORMAT
1	DATE _____ / TIME _____	☐ Signer ☐ Witness	☐ D.L. ☐ Passport ☐ Credible Witness ☐ Other	☐ Expressed willingness ☐ Mentally alert ☐ Indicated understanding	☐ Paper ☐ Electronic ☐ RON
2	DATE _____ / TIME _____	☐ Signer ☐ Witness	☐ D.L. ☐ Passport ☐ Credible Witness ☐ Other	☐ Expressed willingness ☐ Mentally alert ☐ Indicated understanding	☐ Paper ☐ Electronic ☐ RON
3	DATE _____ / TIME _____	☐ Signer ☐ Witness	☐ D.L. ☐ Passport ☐ Credible Witness ☐ Other	☐ Expressed willingness ☐ Mentally alert ☐ Indicated understanding	☐ Paper ☐ Electronic ☐ RON
4	DATE _____ / TIME _____	☐ Signer ☐ Witness	☐ D.L. ☐ Passport ☐ Credible Witness ☐ Other	☐ Expressed willingness ☐ Mentally alert ☐ Indicated understanding	☐ Paper ☐ Electronic ☐ RON

DOCUMENT(S) SIGNED

Document		SIGNER 1 2 3 4
☐ Borrower's Aff	Acknowledgment Jurat _____	1 2 3 4
☐ Compliance Agrmt	Acknowledgment Jurat _____	1 2 3 4
☐ Correction Agrmt	Acknowledgment Jurat _____	1 2 3 4
☐ Debts/Leins Aff	Acknowledgment Jurat _____	1 2 3 4
☐ Deed of Trust	Acknowledgment Jurat _____	1 2 3 4
☐ Distrib of Proceeds	Acknowledgment Jurat _____	1 2 3 4
☐ E&O Agrmt	Acknowledgment Jurat _____	1 2 3 4
☐ Grant Deed	Acknowledgment Jurat _____	1 2 3 4
☐ Marital Stat Aff	Acknowledgment Jurat _____	1 2 3 4
☐ Mortgage	Acknowledgment Jurat _____	1 2 3 4
☐ Occupancy/Fin Aff	Acknowledgment Jurat _____	1 2 3 4
☐ Owner's Aff	Acknowledgment Jurat _____	1 2 3 4
☐ Payoff Aff	Acknowledgment Jurat _____	1 2 3 4
☐ Quit-Claim Deed	Acknowledgment Jurat _____	1 2 3 4
☐ Sig/Name Aff	Acknowledgment Jurat _____	1 2 3 4
☐ Survey Aff	Acknowledgment Jurat _____	1 2 3 4
☐ Warranty Deed	Acknowledgment Jurat _____	1 2 3 4

Document		SIGNER 1 2 3 4
☐ Minor Medical Consent	Acknowledgment Jurat _____	1 2 3 4
☐ Minor Passport Consent	Acknowledgment Jurat _____	1 2 3 4
☐ Minor Travel Consent	Acknowledgment Jurat _____	1 2 3 4
☐ Vehicle Duplicate Title	Acknowledgment Jurat _____	1 2 3 4
☐ Vehicle Lein Release	Acknowledgment Jurat _____	1 2 3 4
☐ Vehicle Odom/Vin Ver	Acknowledgment Jurat _____	1 2 3 4
☐ Vehicle Title Transfer	Acknowledgment Jurat _____	1 2 3 4
☐ Adv Health Care Dir	Acknowledgment Jurat _____	1 2 3 4
☐ Assign of Digital Assets	Acknowledgment Jurat _____	1 2 3 4
☐ Assign of Personal Prop	Acknowledgment Jurat _____	1 2 3 4
☐ HIPAA Release	Acknowledgment Jurat _____	1 2 3 4
☐ Living Trust _____	Acknowledgment Jurat _____	1 2 3 4
☐ Last Will & Testament	Acknowledgment Jurat _____	1 2 3 4
☐ POA _____	Acknowledgment Jurat _____	1 2 3 4
☐ Trust Certification	Acknowledgment Jurat _____	1 2 3 4

Legend (right side): Acknowledgment · Jurat · Copy · Oath · SW — 1 2 3 4

SIGNING ADDRESS	OTHERS IN ATTENDANCE	CLIENT / SIGNING SERVICE	FEE
		LENDER / LOAN NUMBER	

NOTES

	ADDRESS	PHONE	SIGNATURE	INITIAL IF OATH/AFF TAKEN	RIGHT THUMB PRINT
1		EMAIL			
2	ADDRESS	PHONE	SIGNATURE	INITIAL IF OATH/AFF TAKEN	RIGHT THUMB PRINT
		EMAIL			
3	ADDRESS	PHONE	SIGNATURE	INITIAL IF OATH/AFF TAKEN	RIGHT THUMB PRINT
		EMAIL			
4	ADDRESS	PHONE	SIGNATURE	INITIAL IF OATH/AFF TAKEN	RIGHT THUMB PRINT
		EMAIL			

Notary Journal Entries

#	DATE / TIME	NAME (☐ Signer ☐ Witness)	IDENTITY VERIFIED	WILLINGNESS & COMPETENCE	FORMAT
1	DATE ___ TIME ___		☐ D.L. ☐ Passport ☐ Credible Witness ☐ Other	☐ Expressed willingness ☐ Mentally alert ☐ Indicated understanding	☐ Paper ☐ Electronic ☐ RON
2	DATE ___ TIME ___		☐ D.L. ☐ Passport ☐ Credible Witness ☐ Other	☐ Expressed willingness ☐ Mentally alert ☐ Indicated understanding	☐ Paper ☐ Electronic ☐ RON
3	DATE ___ TIME ___		☐ D.L. ☐ Passport ☐ Credible Witness ☐ Other	☐ Expressed willingness ☐ Mentally alert ☐ Indicated understanding	☐ Paper ☐ Electronic ☐ RON
4	DATE ___ TIME ___		☐ D.L. ☐ Passport ☐ Credible Witness ☐ Other	☐ Expressed willingness ☐ Mentally alert ☐ Indicated understanding	☐ Paper ☐ Electronic ☐ RON

DOCUMENT(S) SIGNED

☐ Document	Notarial Act	SIGNER
☐ Borrower's Aff	Acknowledgment Jurat	1 2 3 4
☐ Compliance Agrmt	Acknowledgment Jurat	1 2 3 4
☐ Correction Agrmt	Acknowledgment Jurat	1 2 3 4
☐ Debts/Leins Aff	Acknowledgment Jurat	1 2 3 4
☐ Deed of Trust	Acknowledgment Jurat	1 2 3 4
☐ Distrib of Proceeds	Acknowledgment Jurat	1 2 3 4
☐ E&O Agrmt	Acknowledgment Jurat	1 2 3 4
☐ Grant Deed	Acknowledgment Jurat	1 2 3 4
☐ Marital Stat Aff	Acknowledgment Jurat	1 2 3 4
☐ Mortgage	Acknowledgment Jurat	1 2 3 4
☐ Occupancy/Fin Aff	Acknowledgment Jurat	1 2 3 4
☐ Owner's Aff	Acknowledgment Jurat	1 2 3 4
☐ Payoff Aff	Acknowledgment Jurat	1 2 3 4
☐ Quit-Claim Deed	Acknowledgment Jurat	1 2 3 4
☐ Sig/Name Aff	Acknowledgment Jurat	1 2 3 4
☐ Survey Aff	Acknowledgment Jurat	1 2 3 4
☐ Warranty Deed	Acknowledgment Jurat	1 2 3 4
☐ Minor Medical Consent	Acknowledgment Jurat	1 2 3 4
☐ Minor Passport Consent	Acknowledgment Jurat Copy Oath SW	1 2 3 4
☐ Minor Travel Consent	Acknowledgment Jurat	1 2 3 4
☐ Vehicle Duplicate Title	Acknowledgment Jurat Copy Oath SW	1 2 3 4
☐ Vehicle Lein Release	Acknowledgment Jurat	1 2 3 4
☐ Vehicle Odom/Vin Ver	Acknowledgment Jurat	1 2 3 4
☐ Vehicle Title Transfer	Acknowledgment Jurat Copy Oath SW	1 2 3 4
☐ Adv Health Care Dir	Acknowledgment Jurat	1 2 3 4
☐ Assign of Digital Assets	Acknowledgment Jurat Copy Oath SW	1 2 3 4
☐ Assign of Personal Prop	Acknowledgment Jurat	1 2 3 4
☐ HIPAA Release	Acknowledgment Jurat	1 2 3 4
☐ Living Trust	Acknowledgment Jurat Copy Oath SW	1 2 3 4
☐ Last Will & Testament	Acknowledgment Jurat	1 2 3 4
☐ POA ___	Acknowledgment Jurat	1 2 3 4
☐ Trust Certification	Acknowledgment Jurat Copy Oath SW	1 2 3 4

SIGNING ADDRESS	OTHERS IN ATTENDANCE	CLIENT / SIGNING SERVICE	FEE
		LENDER / LOAN NUMBER	

NOTES

	ADDRESS	PHONE	SIGNATURE	INITIAL IF OATH/AFF TAKEN	RIGHT THUMB PRINT
1		EMAIL			
2	ADDRESS	PHONE	SIGNATURE	INITIAL IF OATH/AFF TAKEN	RIGHT THUMB PRINT
		EMAIL			
3	ADDRESS	PHONE	SIGNATURE	INITIAL IF OATH/AFF TAKEN	RIGHT THUMB PRINT
		EMAIL			
4	ADDRESS	PHONE	SIGNATURE	INITIAL IF OATH/AFF TAKEN	RIGHT THUMB PRINT
		EMAIL			

Notary Journal Entries

Entry 1
DATE	
TIME	

NAME: ☐ Signer ☐ Witness

IDENTITY VERIFIED: ☐ D.L. ☐ Passport ☐ Credible Witness ☐ Other

WILLINGNESS & COMPETENCE: ☐ Expressed willingness ☐ Mentally alert ☐ Indicated understanding

FORMAT: ☐ Paper ☐ Electronic ☐ RON

Entry 2
DATE	
TIME	

NAME: ☐ Signer ☐ Witness

IDENTITY VERIFIED: ☐ D.L. ☐ Passport ☐ Credible Witness ☐ Other

WILLINGNESS & COMPETENCE: ☐ Expressed willingness ☐ Mentally alert ☐ Indicated understanding

FORMAT: ☐ Paper ☐ Electronic ☐ RON

Entry 3
DATE	
TIME	

NAME: ☐ Signer ☐ Witness

IDENTITY VERIFIED: ☐ D.L. ☐ Passport ☐ Credible Witness ☐ Other

WILLINGNESS & COMPETENCE: ☐ Expressed willingness ☐ Mentally alert ☐ Indicated understanding

FORMAT: ☐ Paper ☐ Electronic ☐ RON

Entry 4
DATE	
TIME	

NAME: ☐ Signer ☐ Witness

IDENTITY VERIFIED: ☐ D.L. ☐ Passport ☐ Credible Witness ☐ Other

WILLINGNESS & COMPETENCE: ☐ Expressed willingness ☐ Mentally alert ☐ Indicated understanding

FORMAT: ☐ Paper ☐ Electronic ☐ RON

DOCUMENT(S) SIGNED

Document			SIGNER 1	2	3	4
☐ Borrower's Aff	Acknowledgment	Jurat	1	2	3	4
☐ Compliance Agrmt	Acknowledgment	Jurat	1	2	3	4
☐ Correction Agrmt	Acknowledgment	Jurat	1	2	3	4
☐ Debts/Leins Aff	Acknowledgment	Jurat	1	2	3	4
☐ Deed of Trust	Acknowledgment	Jurat	1	2	3	4
☐ Distrib of Proceeds	Acknowledgment	Jurat	1	2	3	4
☐ E&O Agrmt	Acknowledgment	Jurat	1	2	3	4
☐ Grant Deed	Acknowledgment	Jurat	1	2	3	4
☐ Marital Stat Aff	Acknowledgment	Jurat	1	2	3	4
☐ Mortgage	Acknowledgment	Jurat	1	2	3	4
☐ Occupancy/Fin Aff	Acknowledgment	Jurat	1	2	3	4
☐ Owner's Aff	Acknowledgment	Jurat	1	2	3	4
☐ Payoff Aff	Acknowledgment	Jurat	1	2	3	4
☐ Quit-Claim Deed	Acknowledgment	Jurat	1	2	3	4
☐ Sig/Name Aff	Acknowledgment	Jurat	1	2	3	4
☐ Survey Aff	Acknowledgment	Jurat	1	2	3	4
☐ Warranty Deed	Acknowledgment	Jurat	1	2	3	4

Document						SIGNER 1	2	3	4
☐ Minor Medical Consent	Acknowledgment	Jurat				1	2	3	4
☐ Minor Passport Consent	Acknowledgment	Jurat				1	2	3	4
☐ Minor Travel Consent	Acknowledgment	Jurat				1	2	3	4
☐ Vehicle Duplicate Title	Acknowledgment	Jurat				1	2	3	4
☐ Vehicle Lein Release	Acknowledgment	Jurat				1	2	3	4
☐ Vehicle Odom/Vin Ver	Acknowledgment	Jurat				1	2	3	4
☐ Vehicle Title Transfer	Acknowledgment	Jurat				1	2	3	4
☐ Adv Health Care Dir	Acknowledgment	Jurat				1	2	3	4
☐ Assign of Digital Assets	Acknowledgment	Jurat				1	2	3	4
☐ Assign of Personal Prop	Acknowledgment	Jurat				1	2	3	4
☐ HIPAA Release	Acknowledgment	Jurat				1	2	3	4
☐ Living Trust	Acknowledgment	Jurat				1	2	3	4
☐ Last Will & Testament	Acknowledgment	Jurat				1	2	3	4
☐ POA	Acknowledgment	Jurat				1	2	3	4
☐ Trust Certification	Acknowledgment	Jurat	Copy	Oath	SW	1	2	3	4

SIGNING ADDRESS	OTHERS IN ATTENDANCE	CLIENT / SIGNING SERVICE	FEE
		LENDER / LOAN NUMBER	

NOTES

_____
_____
_____
_____
_____
_____
_____
_____
_____
_____
_____

	ADDRESS	PHONE	EMAIL	SIGNATURE	INITIAL IF OATH/AFF TAKEN	RIGHT THUMB PRINT
1						
2						
3						
4						

#	DATE / TIME	NAME	IDENTITY VERIFIED	WILLINGNESS & COMPETENCE	FORMAT
1	DATE _____ TIME _____	☐ Signer ☐ Witness	☐ D.L. ☐ Passport ☐ Credible Witness ☐ Other	☐ Expressed willingness ☐ Mentally alert ☐ Indicated understanding	☐ Paper ☐ Electronic ☐ RON
2	DATE _____ TIME _____	☐ Signer ☐ Witness	☐ D.L. ☐ Passport ☐ Credible Witness ☐ Other	☐ Expressed willingness ☐ Mentally alert ☐ Indicated understanding	☐ Paper ☐ Electronic ☐ RON
3	DATE _____ TIME _____	☐ Signer ☐ Witness	☐ D.L. ☐ Passport ☐ Credible Witness ☐ Other	☐ Expressed willingness ☐ Mentally alert ☐ Indicated understanding	☐ Paper ☐ Electronic ☐ RON
4	DATE _____ TIME _____	☐ Signer ☐ Witness	☐ D.L. ☐ Passport ☐ Credible Witness ☐ Other	☐ Expressed willingness ☐ Mentally alert ☐ Indicated understanding	☐ Paper ☐ Electronic ☐ RON

DOCUMENT(S) SIGNED

Document	Type	SIGNER
☐ Borrower's Aff	Acknowledgment Jurat	1 2 3 4
☐ Compliance Agrmt	Acknowledgment Jurat	1 2 3 4
☐ Correction Agrmt	Acknowledgment Jurat	1 2 3 4
☐ Debts/Leins Aff	Acknowledgment Jurat	1 2 3 4
☐ Deed of Trust	Acknowledgment Jurat	1 2 3 4
☐ Distrib of Proceeds	Acknowledgment Jurat	1 2 3 4
☐ E&O Agrmt	Acknowledgment Jurat	1 2 3 4
☐ Grant Deed	Acknowledgment Jurat	1 2 3 4
☐ Marital Stat Aff	Acknowledgment Jurat	1 2 3 4
☐ Mortgage	Acknowledgment Jurat	1 2 3 4
☐ Occupancy/Fin Aff	Acknowledgment Jurat	1 2 3 4
☐ Owner's Aff	Acknowledgment Jurat	1 2 3 4
☐ Payoff Aff	Acknowledgment Jurat	1 2 3 4
☐ Quit-Claim Deed	Acknowledgment Jurat	1 2 3 4
☐ Sig/Name Aff	Acknowledgment Jurat	1 2 3 4
☐ Survey Aff	Acknowledgment Jurat	1 2 3 4
☐ Warranty Deed	Acknowledgment Jurat	1 2 3 4
☐ Minor Medical Consent	Acknowledgment Jurat	1 2 3 4
☐ Minor Passport Consent	Acknowledgment Jurat	1 2 3 4
☐ Minor Travel Consent	Acknowledgment Jurat	1 2 3 4
☐ Vehicle Duplicate Title	Acknowledgment Jurat	1 2 3 4
☐ Vehicle Lein Release	Acknowledgment Jurat	1 2 3 4
☐ Vehicle Odom/Vin Ver	Acknowledgment Jurat	1 2 3 4
☐ Vehicle Title Transfer	Acknowledgment Jurat	1 2 3 4
☐ Adv Health Care Dir	Acknowledgment Jurat	1 2 3 4
☐ Assign of Digital Assets	Acknowledgment Jurat	1 2 3 4
☐ Assign of Personal Prop	Acknowledgment Jurat	1 2 3 4
☐ HIPAA Release	Acknowledgment Jurat	1 2 3 4
☐ Living Trust	Acknowledgment Jurat	1 2 3 4
☐ Last Will & Testament	Acknowledgment Jurat	1 2 3 4
☐ POA _____	Acknowledgment Jurat	1 2 3 4
☐ Trust Certification	Acknowledgment Jurat	1 2 3 4

Additional (right margin) options:

	Type	Number
☐	Acknowledgment Jurat Copy Oath SW	1 2 3 4
☐	Acknowledgment Jurat Copy Oath SW	1 2 3 4
☐	Acknowledgment Jurat Copy Oath SW	1 2 3 4
☐	Acknowledgment Jurat Copy Oath SW	1 2 3 4
☐	Acknowledgment Jurat Copy Oath SW	1 2 3 4

Signing Address	Others in Attendance	Client / Signing Service Lender / Loan Number	Fee

Notes

1	Address	Phone Email	Signature	Initial if oath/aff taken	Right Thumb Print
2	Address	Phone Email	Signature	Initial if oath/aff taken	Right Thumb Print
3	Address	Phone Email	Signature	Initial if oath/aff taken	Right Thumb Print
4	Address	Phone Email	Signature	Initial if oath/aff taken	Right Thumb Print

Notary Journal Entries

#	DATE / TIME	NAME	IDENTITY VERIFIED	WILLINGNESS & COMPETENCE	FORMAT
1	DATE _____ TIME _____	☐ Signer ☐ Witness	☐ D.L. ☐ Passport ☐ Credible Witness ☐ Other	☐ Expressed willingness ☐ Mentally alert ☐ Indicated understanding	☐ Paper ☐ Electronic ☐ RON
2	DATE _____ TIME _____	☐ Signer ☐ Witness	☐ D.L. ☐ Passport ☐ Credible Witness ☐ Other	☐ Expressed willingness ☐ Mentally alert ☐ Indicated understanding	☐ Paper ☐ Electronic ☐ RON
3	DATE _____ TIME _____	☐ Signer ☐ Witness	☐ D.L. ☐ Passport ☐ Credible Witness ☐ Other	☐ Expressed willingness ☐ Mentally alert ☐ Indicated understanding	☐ Paper ☐ Electronic ☐ RON
4	DATE _____ TIME _____	☐ Signer ☐ Witness	☐ D.L. ☐ Passport ☐ Credible Witness ☐ Other	☐ Expressed willingness ☐ Mentally alert ☐ Indicated understanding	☐ Paper ☐ Electronic ☐ RON

DOCUMENT(S) SIGNED

Document	Type		SIGNER 1 2 3 4
☐ Borrower's Aff	Acknowledgment	Jurat	1 2 3 4
☐ Compliance Agrmt	Acknowledgment	Jurat	1 2 3 4
☐ Correction Agrmt	Acknowledgment	Jurat	1 2 3 4
☐ Debs/Leins Aff	Acknowledgment	Jurat	1 2 3 4
☐ Deed of Trust	Acknowledgment	Jurat	1 2 3 4
☐ Distrib of Proceeds	Acknowledgment	Jurat	1 2 3 4
☐ E&O Agrmt	Acknowledgment	Jurat	1 2 3 4
☐ Grant Deed	Acknowledgment	Jurat	1 2 3 4
☐ Marital Stat Aff	Acknowledgment	Jurat	1 2 3 4
☐ Mortgage	Acknowledgment	Jurat	1 2 3 4
☐ Occupancy/Fin Aff	Acknowledgment	Jurat	1 2 3 4
☐ Owner's Aff	Acknowledgment	Jurat	1 2 3 4
☐ Payoff Aff	Acknowledgment	Jurat	1 2 3 4
☐ Quit-Claim Deed	Acknowledgment	Jurat	1 2 3 4
☐ Sig/Name Aff	Acknowledgment	Jurat	1 2 3 4
☐ Survey Aff	Acknowledgment	Jurat	1 2 3 4
☐ Warranty Deed	Acknowledgment	Jurat	1 2 3 4

Document	Type					SIGNER 1 2 3 4
☐ Minor Medical Consent	Acknowledgment	Jurat				1 2 3 4
☐ Minor Passport Consent	Acknowledgment	Jurat	Copy	Oath	SW	1 2 3 4
☐ Minor Travel Consent	Acknowledgment	Jurat				1 2 3 4
☐ Vehicle Duplicate Title	Acknowledgment	Jurat	Copy	Oath	SW	1 2 3 4
☐ Vehicle Lein Release	Acknowledgment	Jurat				1 2 3 4
☐ Vehicle Odom/Vin Ver	Acknowledgment	Jurat	Copy	Oath	SW	1 2 3 4
☐ Vehicle Title Transfer	Acknowledgment	Jurat				1 2 3 4
☐ Adv Health Care Dir	Acknowledgment	Jurat	Copy	Oath	SW	1 2 3 4
☐ Assign of Digital Assets	Acknowledgment	Jurat				1 2 3 4
☐ Assign of Personal Prop	Acknowledgment	Jurat	Copy	Oath	SW	1 2 3 4
☐ HIPAA Release	Acknowledgment	Jurat				1 2 3 4
☐ Living Trust _____	Acknowledgment	Jurat	Copy	Oath	SW	1 2 3 4
☐ Last Will & Testament	Acknowledgment	Jurat				1 2 3 4
☐ POA _____	Acknowledgment	Jurat				1 2 3 4
☐ Trust Certification	Acknowledgment	Jurat	Copy	Oath	SW	1 2 3 4

SIGNING ADDRESS	OTHERS IN ATTENDANCE	CLIENT / SIGNING SERVICE	FEE
		LENDER / LOAN NUMBER	

NOTES

	ADDRESS	PHONE / EMAIL	SIGNATURE	INITIAL IF OATH/AFF TAKEN	RIGHT THUMB PRINT
1		PHONE / EMAIL			
2		PHONE / EMAIL			
3		PHONE / EMAIL			
4		PHONE / EMAIL			

1	DATE TIME	NAME ❑ Signer ❑ Witness	IDENTITY VERIFIED ❑ D.L. ❑ Passport ❑ Credible Witness ❑ Other	WILLINGNESS & COMPETENCE ❑ Expressed willingness ❑ Mentally alert ❑ Indicated understanding	FORMAT ❑ Paper ❑ Electronic ❑ RON
2	DATE TIME	NAME ❑ Signer ❑ Witness	IDENTITY VERIFIED ❑ D.L. ❑ Passport ❑ Credible Witness ❑ Other	WILLINGNESS & COMPETENCE ❑ Expressed willingness ❑ Mentally alert ❑ Indicated understanding	FORMAT ❑ Paper ❑ Electronic ❑ RON
3	DATE TIME	NAME ❑ Signer ❑ Witness	IDENTITY VERIFIED ❑ D.L. ❑ Passport ❑ Credible Witness ❑ Other	WILLINGNESS & COMPETENCE ❑ Expressed willingness ❑ Mentally alert ❑ Indicated understanding	FORMAT ❑ Paper ❑ Electronic ❑ RON
4	DATE TIME	NAME ❑ Signer ❑ Witness	IDENTITY VERIFIED ❑ D.L. ❑ Passport ❑ Credible Witness ❑ Other	WILLINGNESS & COMPETENCE ❑ Expressed willingness ❑ Mentally alert ❑ Indicated understanding	FORMAT ❑ Paper ❑ Electronic ❑ RON

DOCUMENT(S) SIGNED

Document			Signer	Document			Signer		
❑ Borrower's Aff	Acknowledgment	Jurat ____	1 2 3 4	❑ Minor Medical Consent	Acknowledgment	Jurat ____	1 2 3 4	❑ ____	
❑ Compliance Agrmt	Acknowledgment	Jurat ____	1 2 3 4	❑ Minor Passport Consent	Acknowledgment	Jurat ____	1 2 3 4	Acknowledgment Jurat Copy Oath SW	1 2 3 4
❑ Correction Agrmt	Acknowledgment	Jurat ____	1 2 3 4	❑ Minor Travel Consent	Acknowledgment	Jurat ____	1 2 3 4		
❑ Debts/Leins Aff	Acknowledgment	Jurat ____	1 2 3 4					❑ ____	
❑ Deed of Trust	Acknowledgment	Jurat ____	1 2 3 4	❑ Vehicle Duplicate Title	Acknowledgment	Jurat ____	1 2 3 4	Acknowledgment Jurat Copy Oath SW	1 2 3 4
❑ Distrib of Proceeds	Acknowledgment	Jurat ____	1 2 3 4	❑ Vehicle Lein Release	Acknowledgment	Jurat ____	1 2 3 4		
❑ E&O Agrmt	Acknowledgment	Jurat ____	1 2 3 4	❑ Vehicle Odom/Vin Ver	Acknowledgment	Jurat ____	1 2 3 4	❑ ____	
❑ Grant Deed	Acknowledgment	Jurat ____	1 2 3 4	❑ Vehicle Title Transfer	Acknowledgment	Jurat ____	1 2 3 4	Acknowledgment Jurat Copy Oath SW	1 2 3 4
❑ Marital Stat Aff	Acknowledgment	Jurat ____	1 2 3 4						
❑ Mortgage	Acknowledgment	Jurat ____	1 2 3 4	❑ Adv Health Care Dir	Acknowledgment	Jurat ____	1 2 3 4	❑ ____	
❑ Occupancy/Fin Aff	Acknowledgment	Jurat ____	1 2 3 4	❑ Assign of Digital Assets	Acknowledgment	Jurat ____	1 2 3 4	Acknowledgment Jurat Copy Oath SW	1 2 3 4
❑ Owner's Aff	Acknowledgment	Jurat ____	1 2 3 4	❑ Assign of Personal Prop	Acknowledgment	Jurat ____	1 2 3 4		
❑ Payoff Aff	Acknowledgment	Jurat ____	1 2 3 4	❑ HIPAA Release	Acknowledgment	Jurat ____	1 2 3 4	❑ ____	
❑ Quit-Claim Deed	Acknowledgment	Jurat ____	1 2 3 4	❑ Living Trust ____	Acknowledgment	Jurat ____	1 2 3 4	Acknowledgment Jurat Copy Oath SW	1 2 3 4
❑ Sig/Name Aff	Acknowledgment	Jurat ____	1 2 3 4	❑ Last Will & Testament	Acknowledgment	Jurat ____	1 2 3 4		
❑ Survey Aff	Acknowledgment	Jurat ____	1 2 3 4	❑ POA ____	Acknowledgment	Jurat ____	1 2 3 4	❑ ____	
❑ Warranty Deed	Acknowledgment	Jurat ____	1 2 3 4	❑ Trust Certification	Acknowledgment	Jurat ____	1 2 3 4	Acknowledgment Jurat Copy Oath SW	1 2 3 4

SIGNING ADDRESS	OTHERS IN ATTENDANCE	CLIENT / SIGNING SERVICE	FEE
		LENDER / LOAN NUMBER	

NOTES

	ADDRESS	PHONE	SIGNATURE	INITIAL IF OATH/AFF TAKEN	RIGHT THUMB PRINT
1		EMAIL			
2	ADDRESS	PHONE	SIGNATURE	INITIAL IF OATH/AFF TAKEN	RIGHT THUMB PRINT
		EMAIL			
3	ADDRESS	PHONE	SIGNATURE	INITIAL IF OATH/AFF TAKEN	RIGHT THUMB PRINT
		EMAIL			
4	ADDRESS	PHONE	SIGNATURE	INITIAL IF OATH/AFF TAKEN	RIGHT THUMB PRINT
		EMAIL			

Notary Journal Entries

#	DATE / TIME	NAME	IDENTITY VERIFIED	WILLINGNESS & COMPETENCE	FORMAT
1	DATE ___ / TIME ___	☐ Signer ☐ Witness	☐ D.L. ☐ Passport ☐ Credible Witness ☐ Other	☐ Expressed willingness ☐ Mentally alert ☐ Indicated understanding	☐ Paper ☐ Electronic ☐ RON
2	DATE ___ / TIME ___	☐ Signer ☐ Witness	☐ D.L. ☐ Passport ☐ Credible Witness ☐ Other	☐ Expressed willingness ☐ Mentally alert ☐ Indicated understanding	☐ Paper ☐ Electronic ☐ RON
3	DATE ___ / TIME ___	☐ Signer ☐ Witness	☐ D.L. ☐ Passport ☐ Credible Witness ☐ Other	☐ Expressed willingness ☐ Mentally alert ☐ Indicated understanding	☐ Paper ☐ Electronic ☐ RON
4	DATE ___ / TIME ___	☐ Signer ☐ Witness	☐ D.L. ☐ Passport ☐ Credible Witness ☐ Other	☐ Expressed willingness ☐ Mentally alert ☐ Indicated understanding	☐ Paper ☐ Electronic ☐ RON

DOCUMENT(S) SIGNED

Document	Acknowledgment	Jurat	SIGNER 1	2	3	4
☐ Borrower's Aff	Acknowledgment	Jurat	1	2	3	4
☐ Compliance Agrmt	Acknowledgment	Jurat	1	2	3	4
☐ Correction Agrmt	Acknowledgment	Jurat	1	2	3	4
☐ Debts/Leins Aff	Acknowledgment	Jurat	1	2	3	4
☐ Deed of Trust	Acknowledgment	Jurat	1	2	3	4
☐ Distrib of Proceeds	Acknowledgment	Jurat	1	2	3	4
☐ E&O Agrmt	Acknowledgment	Jurat	1	2	3	4
☐ Grant Deed	Acknowledgment	Jurat	1	2	3	4
☐ Marital Stat Aff	Acknowledgment	Jurat	1	2	3	4
☐ Mortgage	Acknowledgment	Jurat	1	2	3	4
☐ Occupancy/Fin Aff	Acknowledgment	Jurat	1	2	3	4
☐ Owner's Aff	Acknowledgment	Jurat	1	2	3	4
☐ Payoff Aff	Acknowledgment	Jurat	1	2	3	4
☐ Quit-Claim Deed	Acknowledgment	Jurat	1	2	3	4
☐ Sig/Name Aff	Acknowledgment	Jurat	1	2	3	4
☐ Survey Aff	Acknowledgment	Jurat	1	2	3	4
☐ Warranty Deed	Acknowledgment	Jurat	1	2	3	4
☐ Minor Medical Consent	Acknowledgment	Jurat	1	2	3	4
☐ Minor Passport Consent	Acknowledgment	Jurat	1	2	3	4
☐ Minor Travel Consent	Acknowledgment	Jurat	1	2	3	4
☐ Vehicle Duplicate Title	Acknowledgment	Jurat	1	2	3	4
☐ Vehicle Lein Release	Acknowledgment	Jurat	1	2	3	4
☐ Vehicle Odom/Vin Ver	Acknowledgment	Jurat	1	2	3	4
☐ Vehicle Title Transfer	Acknowledgment	Jurat	1	2	3	4
☐ Adv Health Care Dir	Acknowledgment	Jurat	1	2	3	4
☐ Assign of Digital Assets	Acknowledgment	Jurat	1	2	3	4
☐ Assign of Personal Prop	Acknowledgment	Jurat	1	2	3	4
☐ HIPAA Release	Acknowledgment	Jurat	1	2	3	4
☐ Living Trust ___	Acknowledgment	Jurat	1	2	3	4
☐ Last Will & Testament	Acknowledgment	Jurat	1	2	3	4
☐ POA ___	Acknowledgment	Jurat	1	2	3	4
☐ Trust Certification	Acknowledgment	Jurat	1	2	3	4

SIGNING ADDRESS	OTHERS IN ATTENDANCE	CLIENT / SIGNING SERVICE	FEE
		LENDER / LOAN NUMBER	

NOTES

#	ADDRESS		PHONE	EMAIL	SIGNATURE	INITIAL IF OATH/AFF TAKEN	RIGHT THUMB PRINT
1							
2							
3							
4							

Notary Journal Entry

Entries 1–4

#	DATE	TIME	NAME	IDENTITY VERIFIED	WILLINGNESS & COMPETENCE	FORMAT
1			☐ Signer ☐ Witness	☐ D.L. ☐ Passport ☐ Credible Witness ☐ Other	☐ Expressed willingness ☐ Mentally alert ☐ Indicated understanding	☐ Paper ☐ Electronic ☐ RON
2			☐ Signer ☐ Witness	☐ D.L. ☐ Passport ☐ Credible Witness ☐ Other	☐ Expressed willingness ☐ Mentally alert ☐ Indicated understanding	☐ Paper ☐ Electronic ☐ RON
3			☐ Signer ☐ Witness	☐ D.L. ☐ Passport ☐ Credible Witness ☐ Other	☐ Expressed willingness ☐ Mentally alert ☐ Indicated understanding	☐ Paper ☐ Electronic ☐ RON
4			☐ Signer ☐ Witness	☐ D.L. ☐ Passport ☐ Credible Witness ☐ Other	☐ Expressed willingness ☐ Mentally alert ☐ Indicated understanding	☐ Paper ☐ Electronic ☐ RON

DOCUMENT(S) SIGNED

Document	Type	SIGNER
☐ Borrower's Aff	Acknowledgment Jurat	1 2 3 4
☐ Compliance Agrmt	Acknowledgment Jurat	1 2 3 4
☐ Correction Agrmt	Acknowledgment Jurat	1 2 3 4
☐ Debts/Leins Aff	Acknowledgment Jurat	1 2 3 4
☐ Deed of Trust	Acknowledgment Jurat	1 2 3 4
☐ Distrib of Proceeds	Acknowledgment Jurat	1 2 3 4
☐ E&O Agrmt	Acknowledgment Jurat	1 2 3 4
☐ Grant Deed	Acknowledgment Jurat	1 2 3 4
☐ Marital Stat Aff	Acknowledgment Jurat	1 2 3 4
☐ Mortgage	Acknowledgment Jurat	1 2 3 4
☐ Occupancy/Fin Aff	Acknowledgment Jurat	1 2 3 4
☐ Owner's Aff	Acknowledgment Jurat	1 2 3 4
☐ Payoff Aff	Acknowledgment Jurat	1 2 3 4
☐ Quit-Claim Deed	Acknowledgment Jurat	1 2 3 4
☐ Sig/Name Aff	Acknowledgment Jurat	1 2 3 4
☐ Survey Aff	Acknowledgment Jurat	1 2 3 4
☐ Warranty Deed	Acknowledgment Jurat	1 2 3 4
☐ Minor Medical Consent	Acknowledgment Jurat	1 2 3 4
☐ Minor Passport Consent	Acknowledgment Jurat Copy Oath SW	1 2 3 4
☐ Minor Travel Consent	Acknowledgment Jurat	1 2 3 4
☐ Vehicle Duplicate Title	Acknowledgment Jurat Copy Oath SW	1 2 3 4
☐ Vehicle Lein Release	Acknowledgment Jurat	1 2 3 4
☐ Vehicle Odom/Vin Ver	Acknowledgment Jurat	1 2 3 4
☐ Vehicle Title Transfer	Acknowledgment Jurat Copy Oath SW	1 2 3 4
☐ Adv Health Care Dir	Acknowledgment Jurat	1 2 3 4
☐ Assign of Digital Assets	Acknowledgment Jurat Copy Oath SW	1 2 3 4
☐ Assign of Personal Prop	Acknowledgment Jurat	1 2 3 4
☐ HIPAA Release	Acknowledgment Jurat	1 2 3 4
☐ Living Trust	Acknowledgment Jurat Copy Oath SW	1 2 3 4
☐ Last Will & Testament	Acknowledgment Jurat	1 2 3 4
☐ POA	Acknowledgment Jurat	1 2 3 4
☐ Trust Certification	Acknowledgment Jurat Copy Oath SW	1 2 3 4

SIGNING ADDRESS	OTHERS IN ATTENDANCE	CLIENT / SIGNING SERVICE	FEE
		LENDER / LOAN NUMBER	

NOTES

#	ADDRESS	PHONE	EMAIL	SIGNATURE	INITIAL IF OATH/AFF TAKEN	RIGHT THUMB PRINT
1						
2						
3						
4						

Notary Record — Signers

#	DATE / TIME	NAME	IDENTITY VERIFIED	WILLINGNESS & COMPETENCE	FORMAT
1	DATE ___ TIME ___	☐ Signer ☐ Witness	☐ D.L. ☐ Passport ☐ Credible Witness ☐ Other	☐ Expressed willingness ☐ Mentally alert ☐ Indicated understanding	☐ Paper ☐ Electronic ☐ RON
2	DATE ___ TIME ___	☐ Signer ☐ Witness	☐ D.L. ☐ Passport ☐ Credible Witness ☐ Other	☐ Expressed willingness ☐ Mentally alert ☐ Indicated understanding	☐ Paper ☐ Electronic ☐ RON
3	DATE ___ TIME ___	☐ Signer ☐ Witness	☐ D.L. ☐ Passport ☐ Credible Witness ☐ Other	☐ Expressed willingness ☐ Mentally alert ☐ Indicated understanding	☐ Paper ☐ Electronic ☐ RON
4	DATE ___ TIME ___	☐ Signer ☐ Witness	☐ D.L. ☐ Passport ☐ Credible Witness ☐ Other	☐ Expressed willingness ☐ Mentally alert ☐ Indicated understanding	☐ Paper ☐ Electronic ☐ RON

DOCUMENT(S) SIGNED

Document	Type		SIGNER 1 2 3 4
☐ Borrower's Aff	Acknowledgment	Jurat	1 2 3 4
☐ Compliance Agrmt	Acknowledgment	Jurat	1 2 3 4
☐ Correction Agrmt	Acknowledgment	Jurat	1 2 3 4
☐ Debts/Leins Aff	Acknowledgment	Jurat	1 2 3 4
☐ Deed of Trust	Acknowledgment	Jurat	1 2 3 4
☐ Distrib of Proceeds	Acknowledgment	Jurat	1 2 3 4
☐ E&O Agrmt	Acknowledgment	Jurat	1 2 3 4
☐ Grant Deed	Acknowledgment	Jurat	1 2 3 4
☐ Marital Stat Aff	Acknowledgment	Jurat	1 2 3 4
☐ Mortgage	Acknowledgment	Jurat	1 2 3 4
☐ Occupancy/Fin Aff	Acknowledgment	Jurat	1 2 3 4
☐ Owner's Aff	Acknowledgment	Jurat	1 2 3 4
☐ Payoff Aff	Acknowledgment	Jurat	1 2 3 4
☐ Quit-Claim Deed	Acknowledgment	Jurat	1 2 3 4
☐ Sig/Name Aff	Acknowledgment	Jurat	1 2 3 4
☐ Survey Aff	Acknowledgment	Jurat	1 2 3 4
☐ Warranty Deed	Acknowledgment	Jurat	1 2 3 4

Document	Type		SIGNER 1 2 3 4
☐ Minor Medical Consent	Acknowledgment	Jurat	1 2 3 4
☐ Minor Passport Consent	Acknowledgment	Jurat	1 2 3 4
☐ Minor Travel Consent	Acknowledgment	Jurat	1 2 3 4
☐ Vehicle Duplicate Title	Acknowledgment	Jurat	1 2 3 4
☐ Vehicle Lein Release	Acknowledgment	Jurat	1 2 3 4
☐ Vehicle Odom/Vin Ver	Acknowledgment	Jurat	1 2 3 4
☐ Vehicle Title Transfer	Acknowledgment	Jurat	1 2 3 4
☐ Adv Health Care Dir	Acknowledgment	Jurat	1 2 3 4
☐ Assign of Digital Assets	Acknowledgment	Jurat	1 2 3 4
☐ Assign of Personal Prop	Acknowledgment	Jurat	1 2 3 4
☐ HIPAA Release	Acknowledgment	Jurat	1 2 3 4
☐ Living Trust ___	Acknowledgment	Jurat	1 2 3 4
☐ Last Will & Testament	Acknowledgment	Jurat	1 2 3 4
☐ POA	Acknowledgment	Jurat	1 2 3 4
☐ Trust Certification	Acknowledgment	Jurat	1 2 3 4

(Right column additional types: ☐ Acknowledgment Jurat Copy Oath SW — 1 2 3 4)

SIGNING ADDRESS	OTHERS IN ATTENDANCE	CLIENT / SIGNING SERVICE	FEE
		LENDER / LOAN NUMBER	

NOTES

#	ADDRESS	PHONE / EMAIL	SIGNATURE	INITIAL IF OATH/AFF TAKEN	RIGHT THUMB PRINT
1		PHONE / EMAIL			
2		PHONE / EMAIL			
3		PHONE / EMAIL			
4		PHONE / EMAIL			

Notary Journal Entry

#	DATE / TIME	NAME	IDENTITY VERIFIED	WILLINGNESS & COMPETENCE	FORMAT
1	DATE _____ TIME _____	☐ Signer ☐ Witness	☐ D.L. ☐ Passport ☐ Credible Witness ☐ Other	☐ Expressed willingness ☐ Mentally alert ☐ Indicated understanding	☐ Paper ☐ Electronic ☐ RON
2	DATE _____ TIME _____	☐ Signer ☐ Witness	☐ D.L. ☐ Passport ☐ Credible Witness ☐ Other	☐ Expressed willingness ☐ Mentally alert ☐ Indicated understanding	☐ Paper ☐ Electronic ☐ RON
3	DATE _____ TIME _____	☐ Signer ☐ Witness	☐ D.L. ☐ Passport ☐ Credible Witness ☐ Other	☐ Expressed willingness ☐ Mentally alert ☐ Indicated understanding	☐ Paper ☐ Electronic ☐ RON
4	DATE _____ TIME _____	☐ Signer ☐ Witness	☐ D.L. ☐ Passport ☐ Credible Witness ☐ Other	☐ Expressed willingness ☐ Mentally alert ☐ Indicated understanding	☐ Paper ☐ Electronic ☐ RON

DOCUMENT(S) SIGNED

Document	Type	SIGNER
☐ Borrower's Aff	Acknowledgment Jurat	1 2 3 4
☐ Compliance Agrmt	Acknowledgment Jurat	1 2 3 4
☐ Correction Agrmt	Acknowledgment Jurat	1 2 3 4
☐ Debts/Leins Aff	Acknowledgment Jurat	1 2 3 4
☐ Deed of Trust	Acknowledgment Jurat	1 2 3 4
☐ Distrib of Proceeds	Acknowledgment Jurat	1 2 3 4
☐ E&O Agrmt	Acknowledgment Jurat	1 2 3 4
☐ Grant Deed	Acknowledgment Jurat	1 2 3 4
☐ Marital Stat Aff	Acknowledgment Jurat	1 2 3 4
☐ Mortgage	Acknowledgment Jurat	1 2 3 4
☐ Occupancy/Fin Aff	Acknowledgment Jurat	1 2 3 4
☐ Owner's Aff	Acknowledgment Jurat	1 2 3 4
☐ Payoff Aff	Acknowledgment Jurat	1 2 3 4
☐ Quit-Claim Deed	Acknowledgment Jurat	1 2 3 4
☐ Sig/Name Aff	Acknowledgment Jurat	1 2 3 4
☐ Survey Aff	Acknowledgment Jurat	1 2 3 4
☐ Warranty Deed	Acknowledgment Jurat	1 2 3 4

Document	Type	SIGNER
☐ Minor Medical Consent	Acknowledgment Jurat Copy Oath SW	1 2 3 4
☐ Minor Passport Consent	Acknowledgment Jurat Copy Oath SW	1 2 3 4
☐ Minor Travel Consent	Acknowledgment Jurat Copy Oath SW	1 2 3 4
☐ Vehicle Duplicate Title	Acknowledgment Jurat Copy Oath SW	1 2 3 4
☐ Vehicle Lein Release	Acknowledgment Jurat Copy Oath SW	1 2 3 4
☐ Vehicle Odom/Vin Ver	Acknowledgment Jurat Copy Oath SW	1 2 3 4
☐ Vehicle Title Transfer	Acknowledgment Jurat Copy Oath SW	1 2 3 4
☐ Adv Health Care Dir	Acknowledgment Jurat Copy Oath SW	1 2 3 4
☐ Assign of Digital Assets	Acknowledgment Jurat Copy Oath SW	1 2 3 4
☐ Assign of Personal Prop	Acknowledgment Jurat Copy Oath SW	1 2 3 4
☐ HIPAA Release	Acknowledgment Jurat Copy Oath SW	1 2 3 4
☐ Living Trust	Acknowledgment Jurat Copy Oath SW	1 2 3 4
☐ Last Will & Testament	Acknowledgment Jurat Copy Oath SW	1 2 3 4
☐ POA	Acknowledgment Jurat Copy Oath SW	1 2 3 4
☐ Trust Certification	Acknowledgment Jurat Copy Oath SW	1 2 3 4

SIGNING ADDRESS	OTHERS IN ATTENDANCE	CLIENT / SIGNING SERVICE	FEE
		LENDER / LOAN NUMBER	

NOTES

#	ADDRESS	PHONE	EMAIL	SIGNATURE	INITIAL IF OATH/AFF TAKEN	RIGHT THUMB PRINT
1						
2						
3						
4						

1	DATE TIME	NAME ❑ Signer ❑ Witness	IDENTITY VERIFIED ❑ D.L. ❑ Passport ❑ Credible Witness ❑ Other	WILLINGNESS & COMPETENCE ❑ Expressed willingness ❑ Mentally alert ❑ Indicated understanding	FORMAT ❑ Paper ❑ Electronic ❑ RON
2	DATE TIME	NAME ❑ Signer ❑ Witness	IDENTITY VERIFIED ❑ D.L. ❑ Passport ❑ Credible Witness ❑ Other	WILLINGNESS & COMPETENCE ❑ Expressed willingness ❑ Mentally alert ❑ Indicated understanding	FORMAT ❑ Paper ❑ Electronic ❑ RON
3	DATE TIME	NAME ❑ Signer ❑ Witness	IDENTITY VERIFIED ❑ D.L. ❑ Passport ❑ Credible Witness ❑ Other	WILLINGNESS & COMPETENCE ❑ Expressed willingness ❑ Mentally alert ❑ Indicated understanding	FORMAT ❑ Paper ❑ Electronic ❑ RON
4	DATE TIME	NAME ❑ Signer ❑ Witness	IDENTITY VERIFIED ❑ D.L. ❑ Passport ❑ Credible Witness ❑ Other	WILLINGNESS & COMPETENCE ❑ Expressed willingness ❑ Mentally alert ❑ Indicated understanding	FORMAT ❑ Paper ❑ Electronic ❑ RON

DOCUMENT(S) SIGNED

Document			Signer
❑ Borrower's Aff	Acknowledgment	Jurat ______	1 2 3 4
❑ Compliance Agrmt	Acknowledgment	Jurat ______	1 2 3 4
❑ Correction Agrmt	Acknowledgment	Jurat ______	1 2 3 4
❑ Debts/Leins Aff	Acknowledgment	Jurat ______	1 2 3 4
❑ Deed of Trust	Acknowledgment	Jurat ______	1 2 3 4
❑ Distrib of Proceeds	Acknowledgment	Jurat ______	1 2 3 4
❑ E&O Agrmt	Acknowledgment	Jurat ______	1 2 3 4
❑ Grant Deed	Acknowledgment	Jurat ______	1 2 3 4
❑ Marital Stat Aff	Acknowledgment	Jurat ______	1 2 3 4
❑ Mortgage	Acknowledgment	Jurat ______	1 2 3 4
❑ Occupancy/Fin Aff	Acknowledgment	Jurat ______	1 2 3 4
❑ Owner's Aff	Acknowledgment	Jurat ______	1 2 3 4
❑ Payoff Aff	Acknowledgment	Jurat ______	1 2 3 4
❑ Quit-Claim Deed	Acknowledgment	Jurat ______	1 2 3 4
❑ Sig/Name Aff	Acknowledgment	Jurat ______	1 2 3 4
❑ Survey Aff	Acknowledgment	Jurat ______	1 2 3 4
❑ Warranty Deed	Acknowledgment	Jurat ______	1 2 3 4

Document			Signer
❑ Minor Medical Consent	Acknowledgment	Jurat ______	1 2 3 4
❑ Minor Passport Consent	Acknowledgment	Jurat ______	1 2 3 4
❑ Minor Travel Consent	Acknowledgment	Jurat ______	1 2 3 4
❑ Vehicle Duplicate Title	Acknowledgment	Jurat ______	1 2 3 4
❑ Vehicle Lein Release	Acknowledgment	Jurat ______	1 2 3 4
❑ Vehicle Odom/Vin Ver	Acknowledgment	Jurat ______	1 2 3 4
❑ Vehicle Title Transfer	Acknowledgment	Jurat ______	1 2 3 4
❑ Adv Health Care Dir	Acknowledgment	Jurat ______	1 2 3 4
❑ Assign of Digital Assets	Acknowledgment	Jurat ______	1 2 3 4
❑ Assign of Personal Prop	Acknowledgment	Jurat ______	1 2 3 4
❑ HIPAA Release	Acknowledgment	Jurat ______	1 2 3 4
❑ Living Trust ______	Acknowledgment	Jurat ______	1 2 3 4
❑ Last Will & Testament	Acknowledgment	Jurat ______	1 2 3 4
❑ POA ______	Acknowledgment	Jurat ______	1 2 3 4
❑ Trust Certification	Acknowledgment	Jurat ______	1 2 3 4

❑ ______	Acknowledgment Jurat Copy Oath SW 1 2 3 4
❑ ______	Acknowledgment Jurat Copy Oath SW 1 2 3 4
❑ ______	Acknowledgment Jurat Copy Oath SW 1 2 3 4
❑ ______	Acknowledgment Jurat Copy Oath SW 1 2 3 4
❑ ______	Acknowledgment Jurat Copy Oath SW 1 2 3 4
❑ ______	Acknowledgment Jurat Copy Oath SW 1 2 3 4

SIGNING ADDRESS	OTHERS IN ATTENDANCE	CLIENT / SIGNING SERVICE	FEE
		LENDER / LOAN NUMBER	

NOTES

#						
1	ADDRESS	PHONE	EMAIL	SIGNATURE	INITIAL IF OATH/AFF TAKEN	RIGHT THUMB PRINT
2	ADDRESS	PHONE	EMAIL	SIGNATURE	INITIAL IF OATH/AFF TAKEN	RIGHT THUMB PRINT
3	ADDRESS	PHONE	EMAIL	SIGNATURE	INITIAL IF OATH/AFF TAKEN	RIGHT THUMB PRINT
4	ADDRESS	PHONE	EMAIL	SIGNATURE	INITIAL IF OATH/AFF TAKEN	RIGHT THUMB PRINT